Frank J. Ambrosio
Monroe Community College

Jim C. DeLoach
DeVry Institute of Technology—Atlanta

Gregory L. Moss
Purdue University

LAB MANUAL

Troubleshooting and Design

to accompany

DIGITAL SYSTEMS
Principles and Applications

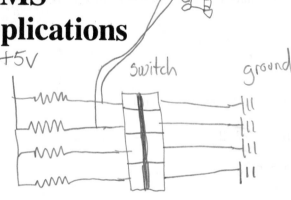

Sixth Edition

Ronald J. Tocci
Monroe Community College

Prentice Hall
Upper Saddle River, New Jersey **Columbus, Ohio**

© 1995 by Prentice-Hall, Inc.
Simon & Schuster/A Viacom Company
Upper Saddle River, New Jersey 07458

The data sheets included in this book have been reprinted with the permission of the following companies:

All materials reproduced courtesy of Analog Devices, Inc.
All materials reproduced courtesy of Fairchild-A Schlumberger Company.
All materials reproduced by permission of Intel Corporation. Intel Corporation assumes no responsibility for errors which may appear in this document nor does it make a commitmemnt to update the information contained herein.
All materials reprinted with permission of National Semiconductor Corp.
All materials reproduced courtesy of Texas Instruments, Incorporated.

Printed in the United States of America

10 9 8 7 6 5 4 3 2 1

ISBN: 0-13-727454-8

Prentice-Hall International (UK) Limited, *London*
Prentice-Hall of Australia Pty. Limited, *Sydney*
Prentice-Hall of Canada, Inc., *Toronto*
Prentice-Hall Hispanoamericana, S. A., *Mexico*
Prentice-Hall of India Private Limited, *New Delhi*
Prentice-Hall of Japan, Inc., *Tokyo*
Simon & Schuster Asia Pte. Ltd., *Singapore*
Editora Prentice-Hall do Brasil, Ltda., *Rio de Janeiro*

EQUIPMENT LIST

Laboratory Equipment

Digital breadboarding system
Power supply (5v, 500ma)
Logic probe
Digital voltmeter
Oscilloscope (dual-trace minimum, preferably 4-trace)
Frequency counter
Signal generator
PLD (or universal) programmer
Personal computer (IBM or compatible)

Digital Integrated Circuits

2	74LS00	Quad 2-input NAND
1	74HC00	Quad 2-input NAND (CMOS)
2	74LS02	Quad 2-input NOR
2	74LS04	Hex INVERTERS
2	74LS08	Quad 2-input AND
2	74LS10	Triple 3-input NAND
1	74LS14	Hex Schmitt-trigger INVERTERS
2	74LS20	Dual 4-input NAND
1	74LS27	Triple 3-input NOR
1	74LS32	Quad 2-input OR
2	74LS47	BCD-to-7-segment DECODER/DRIVER
1	74LS75	4-bit bistable LATCH
1	74LS83A	4-bit binary FULL ADDER (or 74LS283)
1	74LS85	4-bit MAGNITUDE COMPARATOR
1	74LS86A	Quad 2-input EXCLUSIVE-OR
1	74LS90	Decade COUNTER
1	74LS93	4-bit binary COUNTER
2	74LS95B	4-bit, parallel-access SHIFT REGISTER
2	74LS112A	Dual JK, negative-edge triggered FLIP-FLOPS
1	74LS138	3-line-to-8-line DECODER/DEMULTIPLEXER
2	74LS148	8-line-to-3-line priority ENCODER
1	74150	1-of-16 MULTIPLEXER

1	74LS151	1-of-8 MULTIPLEXER
1	74LS160A	Synchronous decade COUNTER
1	74LS164	8-bit, serial-in, parallel-out SHIFT REGISTER
1	74LS166A	8-bit, parallel-in, serial-out SHIFT REGISTER
1	74LS190	Synchronous up/down decade COUNTER
1	74LS191	Synchronous up/down binary COUNTER
1	74LS193	Synchronous, 4-bit, up/down binary COUNTER
1	74LS221	Dual MONOSTABLE MULTIVIBRATOR
1	74LS244	Octal 3-state BUFFER
1	74S260	Dual 5-input NOR
1	74LS373	Octal D-type LATCH (PIPO REGISTER)
1	74LS393	Dual 4-bit binary COUNTER
2	2114	Static RAM (1K x 4)
1	GAL16V8	Electrically Erasable Programmable Logic Device

Linear Integrated Circuits

1	NE555	Timer
1	AD557	8-bit digital-to-analog converter
1	ADC0804	8-bit analog-to-digital converter

Miscellaneous Components

MAN72 (or equivalent) common-anode, 7-segment LED display (2 parts)
Resistors (1/4 watt):

330 Ω (10 parts)	1KΩ (10 parts)	3.3KΩ
10KΩ (2 parts)	27KΩ	33KΩ
47KΩ	68KΩ	82KΩ

Capacitors:

10 µf	0.01 µf (3 parts)	0.001 µf
0.0047 µf	150 pf	

Potentiometers:

10KΩ	50KΩ

Grayhill 84BB1-003 (or equivalent) Keypad (4 x 4 matrix) -- optional
SPST switches, pushbuttons, and LEDs -- optional

Software

CUPL by Logical Devices, Inc.
CSIM by Logical Devices, Inc.
EZ EDIT by Logical Devices, Inc. (or other text editor)

Experiment 1

Name _Daniel Wood_

Mike
Marc

NC

PRELIMINARY CONCEPTS

OBJECTIVES

1. To observe differences between analog and digital devices.
2. To learn binary-to-decimal conversions.
3. To learn decimal-to-binary conversions.
4. To investigate basic pulse characteristics.

TEXT REFERENCES

Read sections 1.1 through 1.6 and section 2.5. Also read Appendix A of this manual.

EQUIPMENT NEEDED

Components
74147 IC;
7404 IC;
7442 IC;
4 toggle switches;
4 LED monitors;
1 k-ohm resistors (9).

Instruments
volt-ohm-milliameter (VOM);
digital multimeter (DMM);
pulse or square wave generator (SWG);
triggered oscilloscope;
0–5 volt DC power supply.

DISCUSSION

In this experiment, you will discover the major difference between analog and digital quantities by using both an analog and a digital measuring device to measure the output voltage of a power supply. Keep in mind that analog measuring devices display their measurements continuously on a scaled meter, which can be difficult to read with precision. On the other hand, digital devices display their measurements in steps using digits and therefore are capable of being read with much greater precision.

You will also observe how decimal quantities are represented in binary and, conversely, how binary numbers are represented by a decimal number by constructing special circuits called decimal-to-binary encoders and binary-to-decimal decoders. If this is your first experience working with integrated circuits (ICs), you should not be intimidated by your lack of knowledge of what is inside the IC. Concentrate on the experiment at hand, that is, to show that each decimal digit (0–9) has a unique binary representation, and that these same binary numbers have a unique decimal representation.

Finally, you will discover some of the characteristics of pulses and learn how to use an oscilloscope to measure these characteristics.

PROCEDURE

a) *Analog vs. digital:* Turn on the power supply and set it to +5 volts. Set the VOM to measure +5 volts DC, and connect the VOM probes to the output of the power supply, being careful to observe correct polarity. Note the smooth swing of the VOM needle as it swings from zero toward +5 volts. Note also that the amount of deflection of the needle is determined by, and therefore proportional to, the voltage at the VOM's probes. Record the value indicated by the VOM: +4.98 volts .

Now set the DMM to measure +5 volts DC, and touch the probes to the output of the power supply, being careful to observe correct polarity. Note that the readout displays its measurement in one or more values before it settles near +5 volts. In other words, it displays increasing values in a number of steps. Finally, note that voltage is represented by digits. Record the readout value: +5 volts .

b) *Decimal-to-binary:* In this step, a 74147 IC and a 7404 IC will be combined to convert decimal digits to binary coded decimal (BCD). Refer to the data sheet for the 74147 and 7404, and draw the pin layout diagram for each:

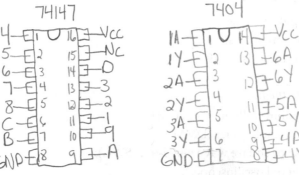

Use the 74147 and 7404 and connect the circuit in Figure 1-1 according to the procedure outlined in Appendix A. There are nine inputs to this circuit (I_1–I_9), each representing a decimal digit (1–9, respectively) and each connected through a spdt

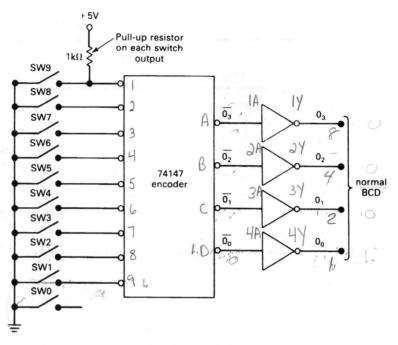

Figure 1-1

switch to either ground (input activated) or V_{cc} (input-deactivated, or normal). If nine spdt input switches are not available, leave all input connections open, then connect a single wire to ground. You will use this wire to activate each input as is called for below by touching the wire to the appropriate input pin on the 74147.

The BCD output of this circuit will be monitored by connecting an LED monitor, DMM, or VOM to the outputs of the circuit labelled 0_0–0_3. If LED monitors are used to monitor the output, you will interpret a lighted LED as a binary 1 and an unlighted LED as a binary 0. If a DMM or VOM is used, interpret each output as follows:

$$0 \text{ to} + 0.8 \text{ volt} = \text{binary } 0$$

$$+2 \text{ to} + 5 \text{ volts} = \text{binary } 1$$

The Least Significant Bit (LSB) of the output is 0_0; the Most Significant Bit (MSB) is 0_3. The output of this circuit is normally 0000 when none of the 74147 inputs are activated. Turn on the power supply and check to see that this is the case. If so, then proceed with the experiment; otherwise, turn off the power supply, check your circuit wiring, correct any faults, and repeat this step.

Once you have have verified that the circuit is initially working correctly, activate each of the inputs, one at a time, and record the BCD output observed in Table 1-1 on page 4.

c) *Binary-to-decimal*: Refer to the data sheet for the 7442 IC, and draw the pin layout diagram:

Table 1-1

Input Activated	Decimal Digit	BCD Output			
		0_0	0_1	0_2	0_3
None	0	0	0	0	0
I_1	1	0	0	0	1
I_2	2	0	0	1	0
I_3	3	0	0	1	1
I_4	4	0	1	0	0
I_5	5	0	1	0	1
I_6	6	0	1	1	0
I_7	7	0	1	1	1
I_8	8	1	0	0	0
I_9	9	1	0	0	1

Turn the power supply off, and disassemble the circuit used in step b. Use the 7442, and connect the circuit in Figure 1-2, which is a circuit for converting BCD to decimal. Connect a separate spdt switch to each of the inputs A, B, C, and D of the 7442 so that each can be switched to ground (binary 0) or V_{CC} (binary 1). Input A is LSB, and input D is MSB. To monitor the outputs, connect an LED monitor, DMM, or VOM to each 7442 output 0_0–0_9, representing decimal digits 0–9, respectively. One (and only one) output will be activated (indicated by an unlighted LED or a reading of near 0 volts DC) for each combination of input switch conditions. Use the binary equivalences given in step b above to interpret the input and output levels of the 7442.

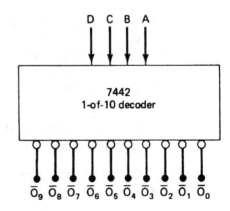

Figure 1-2

Set all of the input switches to the ground position (all inputs binary 0). Monitor the O_0 output (pin 1 of the 7442): it should be activated. Now check all of the other outputs O_1–O_9 (pins 2–7 and 9–11, respectively), and verify that they are all inactive (all LED monitors connected to these outputs should be lighted or show voltage readings 2.4 V). If this is not the case, recheck the input switches. If the switches are all set to ground position, turn the power supply off and recheck your circuit wiring. If a fault is found, correct it, and repeat this step. If you have problems getting the right results, call your instructor.

Refer to Table 1-2, and toggle the input switches so that each BCD number from 0001 to 1001 is entered into the 7442, recording the output conditions for each BCD number in the table.

d) *Pulse characteristics*: Set up an oscilloscope as follows:

DC vertical input at 1 volt/division
Horizontal sweep rate at 1 millisecond/division

Table 1-2

| BCD Input | | | | 7442 Output Conditions | | | | | | | | | | Decimal |
D	C	B	A	O_0	O_1	O_2	O_3	O_4	O_5	O_6	O_7	O_8	O_9	Digit
0	0	0	0	0	1	1	1	1	1	1	1	1	1	0
0	0	0	1	1	0	1	1	1	1	1	0	0	1	1
0	0	1	0	1	1	0	1	1	1	1	1	1	0	2
0	0	1	1	1	1	1	0	1	1	1	1	1	1	3
0	1	0	0	1	1	1	1	0	1	1	1	1	1	4
0	1	0	1	1	1	1	1	1	0	1	1	1	1	5
0	1	1	0	1	1	1	1	1	1	0	1	1	1	6
0	1	1	1	1	1	1	1	1	1	1	0	1	1	7
1	0	0	0	1	1	1	1	1	1	1	1	0	1	8
1	0	0	1	1	1	1	1	1	1	1	1	1	0	9

Auto triggering
Negative trigger slope

Set up a pulse, function, or square wave generator to 200 Hz. The output of the generator should be TTL compatible (i.e., LOW level of pulse should be 0 to +0.8 volt and HIGH level of pulse should be +2.0 to +5.0 volts). Connect the output of the generator to both the vertical and external trigger inputs of the scope. Adjust the generator frequency until the oscilloscope display shows two repetitions of the generated pulse. Sketch the display on Timing Diagram 1-1.

Adjust the vertical position control so that the leading edge of a positive-going pulse intersects a convenient vertical graticule at 2.5 volts (50% point). Measure the distance between this point and the 50% point of the trailing

[Handwritten margin note: You monitored $\overline{O_1}$, $\overline{O_8}$, $\overline{O_7}$, etc. instead of O_9, O_8, O_7, etc. The 1's in the Table should be 0's, and the 0's should be 1's. However, this is OK.]

Timing Diagram 1-1

edge along the horizontal graticule. Record your result: _____. Multiply the distance observed by the setting on the horizontal sweep control. Record your calculation: _____. The calculated result is the *pulse duration* (t_p). Now measure the distance between the leading edges of two consecutive pulses, and convert the distance into time by multiplying by the horizontal sweep setting. Record your computation: _____. This measurement is called the *period* (T) of the waveform. The duty cycle of the waveform can now be calculated using the formula:

$$\text{Duty Cycle} = \frac{(t_p)}{T} \times 100\%$$

Record your computation for the duty cycle: _____.

Set the pulse generator to 1 kHz, and adjust the oscilloscope to display the leading edge of a positive-going pulse. Use the highest horizontal speed possible (magnified, if available). Adjust the oscilloscope's positioning controls so that the 0.5 V (10%) point of the pulse intersects a convenient vertical graticule. Estimate the distance between this point and a vertical line passing through both the 4.5 V (90%) point of the pulse and the main horizontal graticule. Multiply your measurement by the horizontal sweep speed, and record your computation: _____. This is the pulse's *rise time* (t_r). Repeat this procedure on the trailing edge of the pulse. Record your measurement: _____. This is the *fall time* of the pulse (t_f).

One more important pulse characteristic is *propagation delay*. This measurement will be performed in a future experiment.

e) *Review*: This concludes the exercises on preliminary concepts of digital systems. To test your understanding of the principles covered by this experiment, complete the following statements:

1. Based on your observations [analog, digital] voltmeters are the easiest to read because voltage is represented by _____. [Analog, Digital] representations are continuous (smooth) while [analog, digital] representations are discrete (in steps).

2. In this experiment, a binary 0 is represented by _____ volts. An LED monitor is [unlighted, lighted] when indicating a binary 0.

3. In this experiment, a binary 1 is represented by _____ volts. An LED monitor is [unlighted, lighted] when indicating a binary 1.

4. When input I_5 of the 74147 IC is activated, the outputs of the IC will indicate a binary _____.

5. A 7442 IC has a BCD input of 0110. Its output will indicate a decimal ____.

6. For a series of pulses, T = 8 microseconds and t_p = 3 microseconds. The duty cycle of the waveform is ____%.

Experiment 3

Name _____

TROUBLESHOOTING OR, AND, AND NOT GATES

OBJECTIVES

1. To test the operation of a logic probe.
2. To test the operation of a logic pulser.
3. To troubleshoot OR, AND, and NOT gates with pulser and probe.

TEXT REFERENCES

Read sections 4.9 through 4.13 and Appendix A of this manual.

EQUIPMENT NEEDED

Components
7404 IC;
7408 IC;
7432 IC;
4 toggle switches.

Instruments
DMM or VOM;
0–5 volt DC power supply;
oscilloscope;
logic probe;
logic pulser.

DISCUSSION

Most digital systems incorporate numerous IC logic gates into their circuitry. IC gates are very reliable, but like all electronic devices they fail, and when they do fail, they must be isolated and replaced. Troubleshooting gates and their faults is essential to learning how to troubleshoot a digital system. The techniques employed at the gate level can be used to troubleshoot larger devices.

In this experiment, you will learn to use a logic probe and a logic pulser together to "discover" some typical gate faults. These two tools are probably the most popular of all digital test equipment. They are easy to use, small, and lightweight. They get their power from the power supply of the device being serviced. Figure 3-1 shows a Model LP700 logic probe, and Figure 3-2 shows a Model LP600 logic pulser, both manufactured by Elenco Electronics, Inc. Descriptions of these devices can be found in Appendix A of this manual.

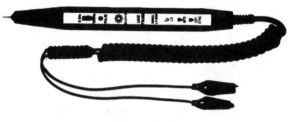

Figure 3-1

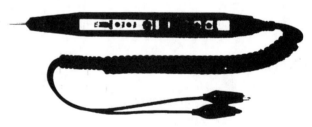

Figure 3-2

LOGIC PROBES

A logic probe is a small, hand-held instrument used to indicate the logic level at a point in a digital circuit. It is capable of indicating a logic 0, logic 1, and a level floating between logic 0 and 1. In many cases it is capable of detecting the presence of high speed pulses. Figure 3-3 shows a typical application of the logic probe, that is, static testing a logic gate by monitoring its output while the gate's inputs are switched through their various combinations.

LOGIC PULSERS

A logic pulser generates digital pulses. Like the logic probe, the pulser uses the logic power supply to get its own power. The tip of the pulser is placed on a circuit

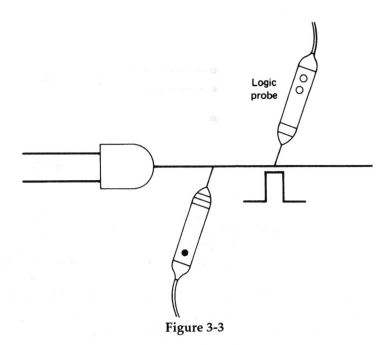

Figure 3-3

node where an injected pulse is desired. The pulser senses the logic state of the node and generates a pulse that will attempt to drive the node to the opposite state. This is a valuable aid in troubleshooting, since it permits the triggering of gates and other devices without removing them from their circuits.

PROCEDURE

a) *Testing the logic probe:* First, make sure the lab power supply is OFF, then set the TTL/CMOS switch to TTL, and connect the logic probe power leads to the logic power supply of the device under test. For this experiment, we will be troubleshooting TTL IC gates, so the logic power supply will be our 0–5 volt DC lab power supply. Make sure to connect the red clip to +5 volts and the black clip to power supply ground. Turn the lab power supply ON. If your probe has a single LED to indicate logic levels, as in the case of the LP700, the LED should be blinking to indicate that the level at the probe tip is floating. (If your probe has two LEDs to represent the two logic levels, both should be out.) If you have a DMM available, connect its leads between the logic power ground and the probe tip. The DMM should read a value between 1.3 and 1.5 volts. This value is called by various names—"indeterminate," "bad," "invalid," and "floating." All refer to the fact that if a voltage value falls into a range of greater than 0.8 volts and less than 2.0 volts, the value cannot represent a logic 0 or a logic 1. These values all have a tolerance of 20%.

Refer now to Figure 3-4. Turn the power supply off and connect a 1 k-ohm linear potentiometer and DMM to the power supply as shown. Set the potentiometer so that the DMM reads 0 volts. Touch the probe to the center tap, and turn the power supply ON. Its LED(s) should indicate logic 0. Now slowly turn the potentiometer away from ground and toward V_{cc}. When the LED(s) indicate a floating level, you have reached the top end of the range for logic 0. Now slowly continue to turn the potentiometer toward V_{cc}, this time until the LED(s) indicate a logic 1. This is the bottom end of the range for logic 1.

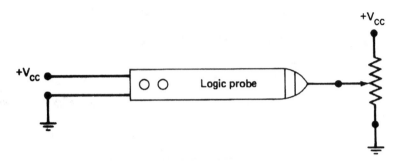

Figure 3-4

b) *Testing the logic pulser*: Install a 7404 IC, a 7408 IC, and a 7432 IC on the circuit board. Connect V_{cc} and ground to each IC. For this part of the experiment, we will use only the 7404 and 7408. Refer to Figure 3-5. Connect one vertical input of the oscilloscope to the output of one of the 7404 inverters. Select a horizontal graticule near the bottom of the oscilloscope display, and adjust the trace of the oscilloscope to that graticule. This marking will be your LOW reference.

Connect the black power connector of the pulser to the logic power supply ground and the red to V_{cc}. Place the pulser tip on the inverter output that is being observed. Adjust the oscilloscope timing until a stable pulse is displayed. You should note that the pulse is a positive-going pulse.

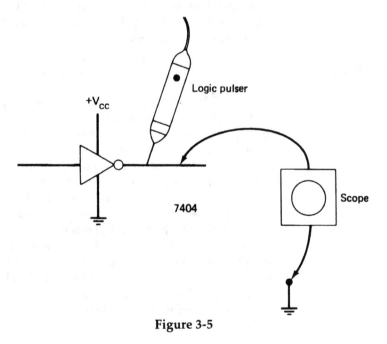

Figure 3-5

Refer now to Figure 3-6. Place the oscilloscope input on the output of one 7408 AND gate. Adjust the oscilloscope trace to a suitable horizontal graticule near the top of the screen. This will be your HIGH reference. Touch the pulser tip to the AND output being observed, and adjust the oscilloscope timing until a stable pulse is displayed. You should note that the pulse is negative-going. This confirms that the pulser will attempt to drive a node to its opposite state.

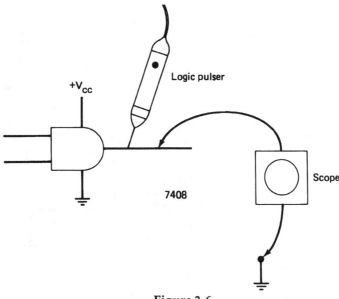

Figure 3-6

Finally, refer to Figure 3-7. Connect the oscilloscope input to V_{cc}. Adjust the oscilloscope trace to a convenient HIGH reference graticule. Touch the pulser tip to V_{cc}. You should note that the pulser cannot drive V_{cc} to a logic 0. Now connect the oscilloscope input to ground, and adjust the oscilloscope trace to a convenient LOW reference graticule. Touch the pulser to ground, and note that it cannot drive ground to a logic 1.

c) *Using the logic probe and logic pulser to troubleshoot gates:* In what follows, the probe-pulser combination will be used to aid in locating certain types of faults of IC gates. We will not look at every possible type of fault, but we can simulate most of the common ones and develop a procedure for testing for them. The faults will be shaded in the figures.

A word of caution: some of the fault simulations call for shorting gate inputs together and outputs together. **Never** short inputs together that are all connected to your trainer's data switches. **Never** short a trainer data switch directly to ground or to V_{cc}. **Never** short any gate output to ground or to V_{cc}. **Do** exercise care in following the instructions below and elsewhere in this manual. Do not substitute LS-TTL for TTL ICs in this exercise, since shorting LS-TTL outputs together for more than one second is not recommended. Voltages at shorted LS-TTL outputs cannot be measured with any consistency.

OR Gates

1) Refer to Figure 3-8, and wire a 7432 OR gate as shown. Recall that when all inputs to an OR gate are the same, the output is the same as the inputs. Touch the probe tip to one of the inputs and the pulser to the other input. You should observe that the pulsing on one of the inputs is detected by the probe on the other. Normally, unless the two inputs are purposely wired together, you should not observe this condition.

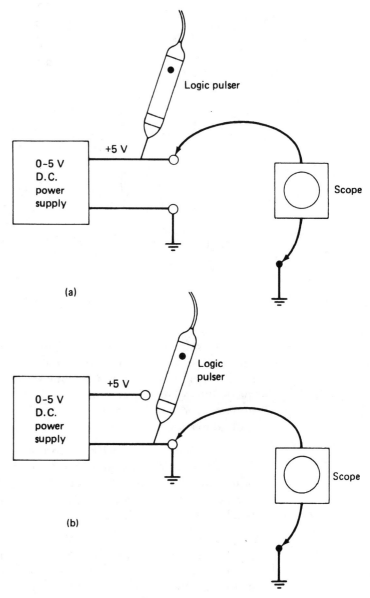

(a)

(b)

Figure 3-7

2) Refer to Figure 3-9, and wire a 7432 OR gate as shown. Connect point A to a data switch, but leave points B and C disconnected. Place the probe tip on point C, and observe that the output is HIGH. Toggle the data switch, and observe that it has no effect on the output. Now place the probe tip on point D. You should observe that the level there is floating. This tells you that either the input (point D) has an external open or an internal open. To verify that the open is external, place the pulser tip to point D and the probe tip to point C. Set the data switch at A to LOW. You should observe that the probe now indicates a pulsing condition. If the open had been internal, you would still see a HIGH at point C.

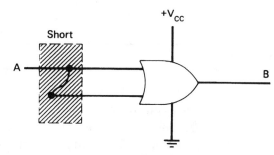

Figure 3-8

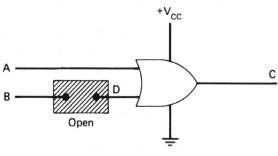

Figure 3-9

3) Refer to Figure 3-10, and wire three 7432 OR gates as shown. Note that a short between the outputs of gate 3 and gate 2 has been wired purposely. Connect data switches to inputs A, B, C, and D. Set switches A and B to LOW and switches C and D to HIGH. Place the tip of the logic probe on output E. You should observe that the level there is LOW. The HIGH output of gate 2 has no effect on the output of gate 1. This is because one of gate 1's inputs is LOW, and the LOW output of gate 3 is pulling the level at the other input of gate 1 down to LOW. Now toggle switch B several times while observing the output at E with the logic probe. You should observe that the output at E toggles also.

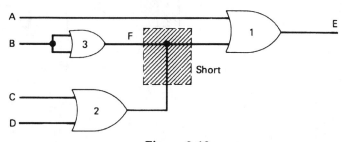

Figure 3-10

Set switches C and D to LOW. Now toggle switch B several times, again monitoring output E with the logic probe. You should observe that the logic probe indicates a constant LOW. Why?

_____

_____

_____

Place the tip of your probe on point F, and toggle switch B several times. You should observe that switch B has no effect on point F. Measure the voltage at point F with the DMM. The voltage at that point should be near the midrange value for a LOW, which is 0.4 V. A typical reading would be about 0.38 V. Remove the short between the outputs of gate 2 and gate 3, and measure the voltage at point F. It should now measure less than 0.4 V, typically 0.15 V. Set switch B to HIGH and measure the voltage at point F with the DMM. Record this voltage: _____.

Finally, replace the short between the outputs of gate 2 and gate 3. Place the tip of the logic probe on the output of gate 1 and the tip of the logic pulser on point F. You should note that the logic probe indicates a pulsing output at E. Thus, the logic pulser can overcome a LOW produced by the output of a gate.

4) Refer to Figures 3-11 and 3-12. You will not wire these circuits. In step 3 above, when the output of gate 2 was HIGH, it had no effect on the output of gate 3. Switch B could be toggled, producing a toggling output at E if switch A was set to 0. A short to V_{cc} at point F could not be overcome by the output of gate 3. So point F would be stuck HIGH. Measuring the actual voltage level at point F can help you determine whether or not a circuit node is shorted to V_{cc}, since the outputs of TTL gates are normally lower than V_{cc}. A logic pulser cannot overcome a short to V_{cc}.

If point F measures 0 V, then it is likely that point F is shorted to ground. Also, a logic pulser cannot overcome this type of short.

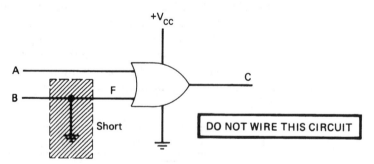

Figure 3-11

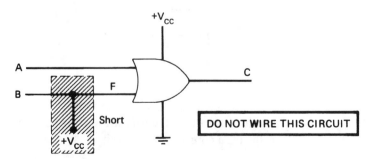

Figure 3-12

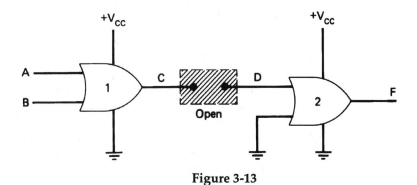

Figure 3-13

5) Refer to Figure 3-13, and wire two 7432 OR gates as shown. Leave points A and B disconnected. We will assume that gate 2 is functioning normally. Place your probe tip on point D. It should indicate a floating level. This is symptomatic of an open in the output circuit of gate 1. The question is whether it is an external or internal open. Place the probe on the output pin of gate 1. If it is HIGH, then there is an external open somewhere between the IC and point C. If the output pin is floating, then an internal open in gate 1's output circuit could be the cause.

AND Gates

1) Refer to Figure 3-14, and wire a 7408 AND gate as shown. Recall that when all inputs to an AND gate are the same, the output is the same as the inputs. Touch the probe tip to one of the inputs and the pulser to the other input. You should observe that the pulsing on one of the inputs is detected by the probe on the other.

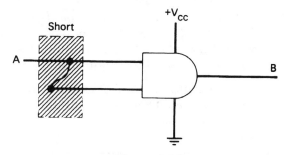

Figure 3-14

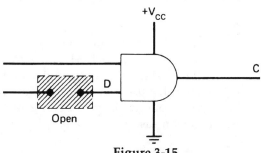

Figure 3-15

Normally, unless the two inputs are purposely wired together, you should not observe this condition.

  2) Refer to Figure 3-15, and wire a 7408 AND gate as shown. Connect point A to a data switch, but leave points B and C disconnected. Place the probe tip on point C, and observe that the output is HIGH. Toggle the data switch, and observe that the output acts normally. Now place the probe tip on point D. You should observe that the level there is floating. This tells you that either the input (point D) has an external open or an internal open. To verify that the open is external, place the pulser tip on point D and the probe tip on point C. Set the data switch at A to HIGH. You should observe that the probe now indicates a pulsing condition. If the open had been internal, you would still see a HIGH at point C.

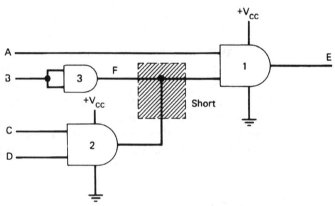

Figure 3-16

  3) Refer to Figure 3-16, and wire three 7408 AND gates as shown. Note that a short between the outputs of gate 3 and gate 2 has been wired purposely. Connect data switches to inputs A, B, C, and D. Set switch A to HIGH and B to LOW and switches C and D to HIGH. Place the tip of the logic probe to output E. You should observe that the level there is LOW. The HIGH output of gate 2 has no effect on the output of gate 1. This is because one of gate 1's inputs is HIGH, and the LOW output of gate 3 is pulling the level at the other input of gate 1 down to LOW. Now toggle switch B several times while observing the output at E with the logic probe. You should observe that the output at E toggles also.

  Set switches C and D to LOW. Now toggle switch B several times, again monitoring output E with the logic probe. You should observe that the logic probe indicates a constant LOW. Why?

_____

_____

_____

  Place the tip of your probe on point F, and toggle switch B several times. You should observe that switch B has no effect on point F. Measure the voltage at point F with the DMM. The voltage at that point should be near the midrange value for a LOW, which is 0.4 V. A typical reading would be about 0.39 V. Remove the short between the outputs of gate 2 and gate 3, and measure the voltage at point F. It should now measure considerably less than 0.4 V, typically 0.10 V. Set switch B to

HIGH and measure the voltage at point F with the DMM. Record this voltage: _____.

Finally, replace the short between the outputs of gate 2 and gate 3. Place the tip of the logic probe on the output of gate 1 and the tip of the logic pulser on point F. You should note that the logic probe indicates a pulsing output at E. Thus, the logic pulser can overcome a LOW produced by the output of a gate.

4) Refer to Figures 3-17 and 3-18. You will not wire these circuits. In step 3 above, when the output of gate 2 was HIGH, it had no effect on the output of gate 3. Switch B could be toggled, producing a toggling output at E. A short to V_{cc} at point F could not be overcome by the output of gate 3, so point F would be stuck HIGH. Measuring the actual voltage level at point F can help you determine whether or not a circuit node is shorted to V_{cc}, since the outputs of TTL gates are normally lower than V_{cc}. A logic pulser cannot overcome a short to V_{cc}.

If point F measures 0 V, then it is likely that point F is shorted to ground. A logic pulser cannot overcome this type of short either.

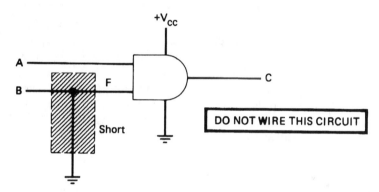

Figure 3-17

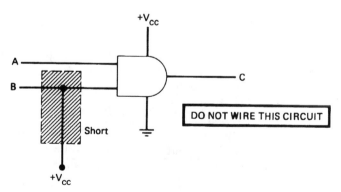

Figure 3-18

5) Refer to Figure 3-19, and wire two 7408 AND gates as shown. Leave points A and B disconnected. We will assume that gate 2 is functioning normally. Place your probe tip on point D. It should indicate a floating level. This is symptomatic of an open in the output circuit of gate 1. The question is whether it is an external or internal open. Place the probe on the output pin of gate 1. If it is HIGH, then there is an external open somewhere between the IC and point C. If the output pin is floating, then an internal open in gate 1's output circuit could be the cause.

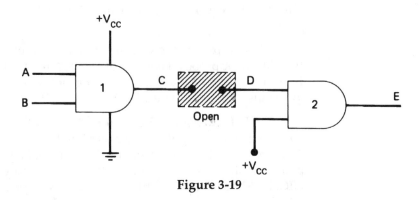

Figure 3-19

NOT Gates

1) Refer to Figure 3-20, and wire a 7404 NOT gate as shown. Connect point A to a data switch, but leave points B and C disconnected. Place the probe tip on point C, and observe that the output is LOW. Toggle the data switch, and observe that it has no effect on the output. Now place the probe tip on point C. You should observe that the level there is floating. This tells you that the input (point C) has either an external open or an internal open. To verify that the open is external, place the pulser tip to point C and the probe tip on point B. You should observe that the probe now indicates a pulsing condition. If the open had been internal, you would still see a LOW at point B.

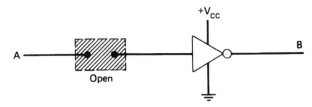

Figure 3-20

2) Refer to Figure 3-21, and wire two 7404 NOT gates as shown. Note that a short between the outputs of the two inverters has been wired purposely. Connect data switches to inputs A and C. Set switch A to HIGH and C to LOW. Place the tip of the logic probe on output B. You should observe that the level there is LOW. The HIGH output of gate 2 has no effect on the output of gate 1. This is because the LOW output of gate 1 is pulling the level of the output of gate 2 down to LOW. Now toggle switch A several times while observing the output at B with the logic probe. You should observe that the output at B toggles also.

Set switch C to HIGH. Now toggle switch A several times, again monitoring output B with the logic probe. You should observe that the logic probe indicates a constant LOW. Why?

_____

_____

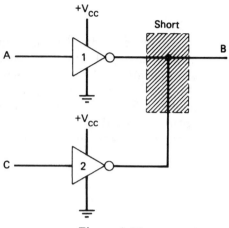

Figure 3-21

Measure the voltage at point B with the DMM. The voltage at that point should be near the midrange value for a LOW, which is 0.4 V. A typical reading would be about 0.39 V. Remove the short between the outputs of gate 1 and gate 2, and measure the voltage at point B. It should now measure considerably less than 0.4 V, typically 0.10 V. Set switch A to LOW and measure the voltage at point B with the DMM. Record this voltage: _____.

Finally, replace the short between the outputs of gate 2 and gate 3. Place the tips of the logic probe and the logic pulser on point C. You should note that the logic probe indicates a pulsing output at E. Thus, the logic pulser can overcome a LOW produced by the output of a gate.

3) Refer to Figures 3-22 and 3-23. Do not wire these circuits. As with the AND and OR gates above, shorts to V_{cc} and ground can be found by making a voltage measurement at the point that is stuck. You should never measure exactly V_{cc} or ground unless there is a short to one or the other.

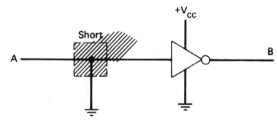

Figure 3-22

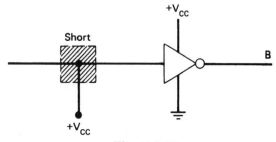

Figure 3-23

Summary

In the preceding exercises, you have learned several techniques for isolating problems in digital systems. These techniques can help you to isolate the problems to a small area in the system. Many times, you will hit it lucky and isolate one or more defective ICs in sockets by using these techniques. Other times, you will isolate several defective ICs that must be desoldered, removed, tested, and then replaced. Since digital systems can contain hundreds of ICs (and thousands of gates!), these techniques are extremely important in the field.

Name *Daniel Woods*

Mike Gbomene.

Marc Melanson

100

LOGIC GATES I: OR, AND, AND NOT

OBJECTIVES

1. To investigate the behavior of the OR gate.
2. To investigate the behavior of the AND gate.
3. To investigate the behavior of the NOT gate (inverter).

TEXT REFERENCES

Read sections 3.1 through 3.5.

EQUIPMENT NEEDED

Components
7404 IC;
7411 IC;
7432 IC;
4 toggle switches;
1 LED monitor.

Instruments
VOM;
0–5 volt DC power supply;
logic probe (optional).

DISCUSSION

In general, logic circuits have one or more inputs and only one output. The circuits respond to various input combinations, and a truth table shows this relationship between a circuit's input combinations and its output. The truth table for a particular circuit explains how the circuit behaves under normal conditions. Familiarization with a logic circuit's truth table is essential to the technologist or technician before he or she can design with or troubleshoot the circuit.

In this experiment, three logic circuits are covered: the OR, AND, and NOT gates. The OR operation can be summarized as follows:

1) When any input is 1, the output is also 1.
2) When all inputs are 0, the output is also 0.

The AND operation can be summarized similarly:

1) When any input is 0, the output is also 0.
2) When all inputs are 1, the output is also 1.

Finally, the NOT operation is said to be complementary. In other words:

1) If the input is 0, the output is 1.
2) If the input is 1, the output is 0.

You should recall that the logic levels, 0 and 1, have voltage assignments. For TTL circuits, a logic 0 can be anywhere from 0 V to +0.8 V, and a logic 1 is in the range of +2.0 V to +5.0 V.

PROCEDURE

a) *The OR gate*: Refer to the data sheet for the 7432 IC and draw its pin layout diagram:

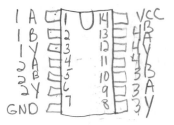

A	B	x = A + B
0	0	0
0	1	1
1	0	1
1	1	1

(a)

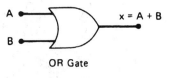

OR Gate

(b)

Figure 2-1

b) Figure 2-1 shows the logic symbol and truth table for the OR logic gate. The 7432 contains four of these gates. Wire one of them as follows:

1) V_{cc} to +5 volts; GND to power ground.
2) Inputs A and B to separate toggle switches.
3) The output to the VOM.

Table 2-1

Data Switches A B	VOM (Volts)	Logic Level (0/1)
0 0	0 ✓	0
0 1	5 ✓	1
1 0	5 ✓	1
1 1	5 ✓	1

c) You will now verify the OR operation by setting inputs A and B to each set of logic values listed in the truth table of Figure 2-1, recording the output voltage observed, and converting the output voltage to a logic level. Use

$$0 \text{ V–0.8 V} = 0 \text{ and } 2 \text{ V–5 V} = 1$$

for the conversions and record your observations in Table 2-1.

d) Disconnect the VOM from the circuit, and use an LED monitor to observe the output. Repeat step c using the conversion rule LED OFF (unlighted) = 0 and LED ON (lighted) = 1.

e) Disconnect one of the inputs, and set the remaining one to 0. Is the output level 0 or 1? Based on your observation and knowledge of the OR operation, what level does the unconnected input act like? __High__.

f) *The AND gate:* Refer to the data sheet for the 7411 IC, and draw its pin diagram:

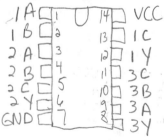

g) Figure 2-2 shows the logic symbol and truth table for the three input AND logic gate. The 7411 contains three 3-input AND gates. Wire one of the AND gates as follows:

1) V_{cc} to +5 V and GND to power ground.
2) Inputs A, B, and C to toggle switches.
3) Output to an LED monitor.

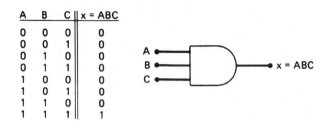

A	B	C	x = ABC
0	0	0	0
0	0	1	0
0	1	0	0
0	1	1	0
1	0	0	0
1	0	1	0
1	1	0	0
1	1	1	1

Figure 2-2

Table 2-2

Data Switches			Output LED Monitor (On/Off)	Output Logic Level (0/1)
A	B	C		
0	0	0	OFF	0
0	0	1	OFF	0
0	1	0	OFF	0
0	1	1	OFF	0
1	0	0	OFF	0
1	0	1	OFF	0
1	1	0	OFF	0
1	1	1	ON	1

h) You will now verify the AND operation by setting toggle switches A, B, and C to each set of input values of the truth table in Figure 2-2 and recording the output level observed on the LED monitor using Table 2-2.

i) Disconnect input A from the toggle switch, and set inputs B and C to 1. Note the logic level indicated by the LED monitor. Based on your observation, what logic level does the unconnected input act like? _High_

j) *The NOT gate:* Mount a 7404 IC on the circuit board. Refer to the data sheet for the 7404, and draw its pin layout diagram:

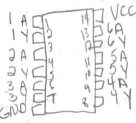

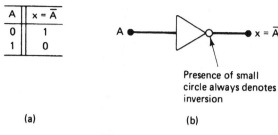

A	x = Ā
0	1
1	0

Presence of small
circle always denotes
inversion

(a)   (b)

Figure 2-3

Table 2-3

Data Switch A	Output LED Monitor (On/Off)	Output Logic Level (0/1)	
0	ON	1	
1	OFF	0	✓

k) Figure 2-3 shows the logic symbol and truth table for the NOT gate, also commonly called an inverter. The 7404 IC contains six inverters. Connect one of the inverters as follows:

1) V_{cc} to +5 V and GND to power ground.
2) Input A to a toggle switch.
3) Output to an LED monitor.

l) You will now verify the NOT operation given by the truth table in Figure 2-3 and record your observations in Table 2-3.

m) *Review:* This concludes the investigation of basic logic gate operation. To test your understanding of the logic gates, complete the following statements:

1. The output of an OR gate is LOW only when __inputs are 0__.
2. The output of an AND gate is __low__ whenever any input is LOW.
3. The output of an inverter is always __inverse to__ the input.
4. Using the results obtained in step h, one could conclude that to use a three-input AND gate as a two-input gate, one input should be connected to [V_{cc}/GND].
5. If an OR gate input were accidentally shorted to V_{cc}, the output of the gate would always be __High__, no matter what level the other input level might be.

Experiment 5

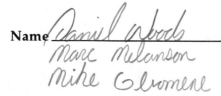

Name *Daniel Wood*
Marc Melanson
Mike Glromere

LOGIC GATES II: NOR AND NAND

OBJECTIVES

1. To investigate the behavior of the NOR gate.
2. To investigate the behavior of the NAND gate.

TEXT REFERENCE

Read section 3.9.

EQUIPMENT NEEDED

Components
7400 IC;
7402 IC;
7404 IC;
7408 IC;
7432 IC;
4 toggle switches;
1 LED monitor.

Instruments
0–5 volt DC power supply;
pulse or square wave generator;
oscilloscope.

DISCUSSION

In Experiment 2, you learned the characteristics of three of the fundamental logic gates: the AND, OR, and NOT. You will now be introduced to two of the remaining logic gates: the NAND and NOR. The NAND and NOR gates are nothing more than inverted AND and OR gates, respectively. That is important, but not the most important thing. The fact that a NAND or a NOR can be used to create all other gates is important, because this fact has made them more popular in use than the others.

PROCEDURE

a) *The NOR gate:* Figure 5-1 shows the logic symbol for a two-input NOR gate and its truth table. Examine the truth table, and familiarize yourself with the NOR operation.

b) Refer to the data sheet for a 7402 IC, and draw the pin layout diagram:

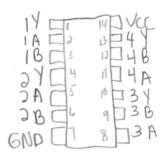

c) Mount a 7402 on the circuit board. Connect V_{cc} to +5 V and GND to power ground. Connect toggle switches to inputs A and B of one of the 7402 NOR gates. Observe the output of the gate with an LED monitor.

d) Set the toggle switches to each input combination listed in Table 5-1, observe and record the output state of the LED monitor in the table.

Table 5-1

Data Switch A B	Output LED Monitor (On/Off)	Output Logic Level (0/1)
0 0	ON	1
0 1	OFF	0
1 0	OFF	0
1 1	OFF	0

Verify that your results agree with the truth table in Figure 5-1.

e) Disconnect input B from the toggle switch. Set toggle switch A alternately to 0 and 1, and observe the effect on the output. Based on your observations, the disconnected NOR input acts like a High input level.

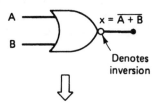

		OR	NOR
A	B	$A + B$	$\overline{A + B}$
0	0	0	1
0	1	1	0
1	0	1	0
1	1	1	0

Denotes inversion

Figure 5-1

f) Connect a pulse generator set to 1 kHz to input B. Disconnect the LED monitor from the NOR output, and connect one of the vertical inputs of the oscilloscope in its place. Connect the other vertical input to the output of the pulse generator, and trigger on this channel. Set input A alternately to 0 and 1, and observe the effect on the output. Sketch the waveform displayed on the oscilloscope for both settings of switch A using Timing Diagrams 5-1 and 5-2.

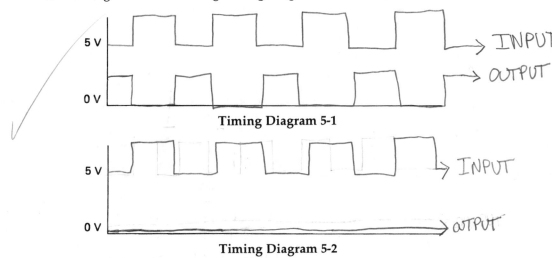

Timing Diagram 5-1

Timing Diagram 5-2

g) *NOR equivalent:* Disconnect the toggle switches from the NOR gate but do NOT remove the 7402 from the board. Mount a 7432 IC and a 7404 IC on the circuit board. Connect V_{cc} to +5 V and GND to power ground for each IC. Connect toggle switches to inputs A and B of one of the 7432 OR gates. Connect the OR gate output to a 7404 inverter as illustrated in Figure 5-2. Observe the output of the inverter with an LED monitor.

$x = \overline{A + B}$

Figure 5-2

h) Repeat step d. Do not record the output values, but do verify that your results are the same as those recorded for the NOR gate.

i) *The NAND gate*: Figure 5-3 shows the logic symbol, truth table, and an equivalent circuit for a two-input NAND gate. Examine the truth table and familiarize yourself with the NAND operation.

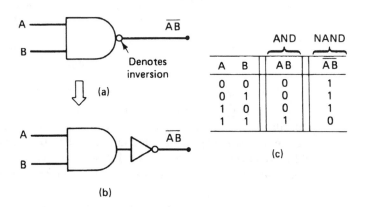

		AND	NAND
A	B	$\overline{AB}$ represented as AB	$\overline{AB}$
0	0	0	1
0	1	0	1
1	0	0	1
1	1	1	0

(c)

Figure 5-3

j) Refer to the data sheet for a 7400 IC and draw its pin layout diagram:

k) Mount a 7400 IC on the circuit board. Connect V_{cc} to +5 V and GND to power ground. Connect toggle switches to inputs A and B of one of the NAND gates and an LED monitor to its output.

l) Set switches A and B to each input combination listed in Table 5-2, and record your observations of the output monitor in the table.

Verify that your results agree with the truth table in Figure 5-3.

Table 5-2

Data Switch A B	Output LED Monitor (On/Off)	Output Logic Level (0/1)
0 0	ON	1
0 1	ON	1
1 0	ON	1
1 1	OFF	0

m) Disconnect the toggle switch from input B of the NAND gate. What will the state of output x be when A = 0? _1_. When A = 1? _0_. Verify your results.

n) Connect the pulse generator to input B and set the generator to 1 kHz.

Remove the output connection to the LED monitor, and connect one of the vertical inputs of the oscilloscope in its place. Connect the output of the pulse generator to the other vertical input of the oscilloscope, and trigger internally using this channel.

o) Set input A alternately to 0 and 1, and observe the effect on the output. Draw the waveforms displayed on the oscilloscope for each setting of A using Timing Diagrams 5-3 and 5-4.

this output waveform should be inverted

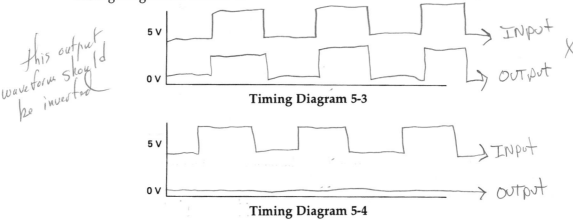

Timing Diagram 5-3

Timing Diagram 5-4

p) *NAND equivalent:* Connect a 7408 AND gate and a 7404 inverter so that the wiring agrees with the alternate NAND circuit of Figure 5-3. Connect toggle switches to inputs A and B of the AND gate and an LED monitor to the output of the inverter.

q) Verify that the alternate circuit does perform the NAND operation.

r) *Review:* This concludes the investigation of the NOR and NAND logic gates. To test your understanding of these gates, complete the following statements:

1. A difference between the NOR and NAND operations is that a _High_ at any one NOR input results in a LOW output, while a _Low_ at any one NAND input results in a HIGH output.

2. A gate is said to be *enabled* if a signal at one of its inputs is permitted to pass to the output of the gate. The signal may be inverted or noninverted, depending on the gate's function. For a two-input NOR gate to be enabled, one of its inputs must be _Low_ ; the signal at the other input will be [inverted, noninverted] at the output. For a two-input NAND to be enabled, one input must be _High_; the signal at the other input will be [inverted, noninverted] at the output.

3. A gate is said to be *inhibited* if the gate's output remains at a constant level regardless of any signals applied at its inputs. To inhibit a NOR gate, a _High_ must be applied to one of its inputs. For a NAND gate to be an inhibitor, one input must be _Low_.

4. The NOR operation can be performed by a(n) _OR_ gate whose output is _inverted_.

5. The NAND operation can be performed by a(n) _AND_ gate whose output is _inverted_ .

Experiment 4

Name *Daniel Woods*

Marc Melanson

Mike Gibomene

BASIC COMBINATORIAL CIRCUITS

OBJECTIVES

1. To investigate the behavior of simple logic circuits constructed from a logic diagram containing AND and OR gates.
2. To investigate the use of parentheses in Boolean expressions.
3. To demonstrate the use of a logic probe in evaluating a logic circuit.
4. To implement a logic circuit from a Boolean expression.
5. To practice troubleshooting on a simple combinatorial circuit using a logic probe.

TEXT REFERENCES

Read sections 3.6 through 3.8. Also review Appendix A of this manual.

EQUIPMENT NEEDED

Components
7404 IC;
7411 IC;
7432 IC;
1 LED monitor;
4 toggle switches.

Instruments
0–5 volt DC power supply;
logic probe.

DISCUSSION

In Experiment 2, you learned the characteristics of three of the fundamental logic gates: the AND, OR, and NOT. In Experiment 3, you learned how to recognize and troubleshoot some of their faults. In this experiment, you will combine these gates into logic circuits, investigate their behavior, and troubleshoot them. In future experiments, we will see that these so-called combinatorial circuits are often manufactured as ICs and become part of digital systems, so this experiment will help to prepare us for dealing with these larger ICs when we encounter them.

PROCEDURE

a) *AND/OR combinations*: Construct the circuit of Figure 4-1. Connect toggle switches to circuit inputs A, B, and C. Monitor the output x of the circuit with an LED monitor. For each input combination in Table 4-1, observe the output state of the LED monitor and record the state.

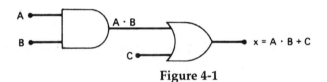

Figure 4-1

Table 4-1

Toggle Switches			Output LED Monitor (On/Off)	Output Logic Level (0/1)
A	B	C		
0	0	0	OFF	0
0	0	1	ON	1
0	1	0	OFF	0
0	1	1	ON	1
1	0	0	OFF	0
1	0	1	ON	1
1	1	0	ON	1
1	1	1	ON	1

b) Connect the circuit of Figure 4-2. Connect toggle switches to inputs A, B, and C, and observe the output of the circuit with an LED monitor. For each input combination in Table 4-2, observe the output state of the LED monitor, and record the state in the table.

You should have obtained different results for Tables 4-1 and 4-2. This demonstrates experimentally that the two Boolean expressions AB + C and (A + B)C are not the same. Recall that the AND operation must be performed before the OR in an expression containing both operations EXCEPT when parentheses are used. When parentheses are used, the operation (or expression) inside the parentheses is performed first. In the expression (A + B)C, the parentheses encloses the output of the OR gate used as an input to an AND gate. Parentheses are not

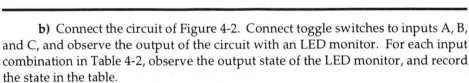

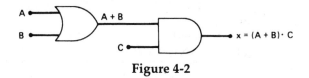

Figure 4-2

Table 4-2

Toggle Switches			Output LED Monitor	Output Logic Level
A	B	C	(On/Off)	(0/1)
0	0	0	OFF	0
0	0	1	OFF	0
0	1	0	OFF	0
0	1	1	ON	1
1	0	0	OFF	0
1	0	1	ON	1
1	1	0	OFF	0
1	1	1	ON	1

necessary in the expression A + BC, but if they were, the expression would be A + (BC). In this case, the parentheses enclose the output of an AND gate that is used as one input to an OR gate.

c) *Circuits with inverters:* In this step, you will construct a circuit containing all of the basic logic gates covered thus far. You will then use a logic probe to evaluate the circuit at each gate output for all input combinations.

Draw a logic diagram for the expression

$$x = \overline{ABC(A + D)}$$

in the space provided below.

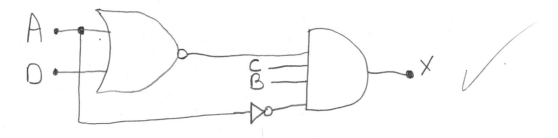

Complete Table 4-3 using the evaluation procedure given in section 3.7 of the text.

Table 4-3

Toggle Switches				Outputs		
A	B	C	D	$\overline{ABC}$	$\overline{A+D}$	$\overline{ABC(A+D)}$
0	0	0	0			
0	0	0	1			
0	0	1	0			
0	0	1	1			
0	1	0	0			
0	1	0	1			
0	1	1	0			
0	1	1	1			
1	0	0	0			
1	0	0	1			
1	0	1	0			
1	0	1	1			
1	1	0	0			
1	1	0	1			
1	1	1	0			
1	1	1	1			

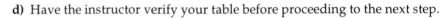

d) Have the instructor verify your table before proceeding to the next step.

e) Review the operating instructions for your logic probe.

Construct the circuit you drew in step c. Connect toggle switches to circuit inputs A, B, C, and D. Next verify with the logic probe all output entries you made earlier. Write the values you obtain with the probe next to the values in the table. If you note any differences, you have probably wired the circuit incorrectly. If so, find and correct the wiring error(s) before proceeding with the next step.

f) *Troubleshooting:* Have the instructor or lab assistant introduce a fault into your circuit, then troubleshoot the circuit by repeating the circuit evaluation performed in step e with the logic probe. Use Table 4-4 to record your test results. If you spot the fault visually, ignore it. Use your test results to try and isolate the fault. When you think you have correctly isolated the fault, have the instructor or lab assistant verify it.

Repeat this step as many times as your schedule will permit by having your lab partner or another student introduce a fault while you are not looking.

g) *Review:* In Experiment 2, you learned how to test the operation of logic gates. In this experiment, you expanded your capabilities to include the construction and testing of simple logic circuits composed of the basic logic gate. You verified that parentheses are required in a Boolean expression whenever the expression could be interpreted incorrectly, and that a logic circuit can be constructed directly from a Boolean expression. You also practiced troubleshooting a simple combinatorial circuit. To test your understanding of the principles covered in this experiment, complete the following statements:

1. In the expression ABC + DE, the AND operation is performed first and the OR operation is performed last.

Table 4-4

Toggle Switches				Outputs		
A	B	C	D	$\overline{ABC}$	$\overline{A+D}$	$\overline{ABC}(\overline{A+D})$
0	0	0	0			
0	0	0	1			
0	0	1	0			
0	0	1	1			
0	1	0	0			
0	1	0	1			
0	1	1	0			
0	1	1	1			
1	0	0	0			
1	0	0	1			
1	0	1	0			
1	0	1	1			
1	1	0	0			
1	1	0	1			
1	1	1	0			
1	1	1	1			

2. In the expression (A + C)BD, the expression inside the parentheses is one input to a _2_ -input _OR_ gate. *(A+C), B, and D are inputs (3 of them)*

3. The correct operation of a combinatorial circuit is given in a _truth table_.

4. Tracing logic levels through a logic circuit is equivalent to _solve_ a Boolean expression for given input values.

5. If the circuit used in step f were to be completely contained in one IC, you would evaluate the _output expression_ of the IC.

6. The troubleshooting technique employed in step f is referred to as [(static) dynamic] testing.

7. Draw a logic diagram for the expression (AC + B$\overline{C}$) + A$\overline{B}$C.

AC + B$\overline{C}$ + A$\overline{B}$C

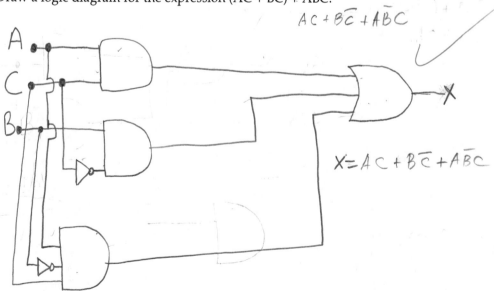

$X = AC + B\overline{C} + A\overline{B}C$

Daniel Wood
Mike Gbomeme
Marc Milsansome

UNIT 5

COMBINATIONAL CIRCUIT DESIGN: SOP EXPRESSIONS AND KARNAUGH MAPPING

Objectives

- To write standard sum-of-product (SOP) logic expressions for functions defined in given truth tables.
- To implement SOP logic expressions using standard AND/OR and NAND/NAND circuit configurations.
- To write simplified SOP logic expressions using Karnaugh mapping techniques.
- To design a combinational logic circuit that will perform a stated task by first defining the logic function with a truth table and then determining the simplified circuit solution using Karnaugh mapping.

Suggested Parts					
74LS00	74LS04	74LS08	74LS10	74LS20	74LS32
74LS393					

Combinational Circuit Design

SOP Expressions

The most commonly used format for writing a logic expression is a standard form called sum-of-product (SOP). SOP expressions can be quickly written from a truth table and they are easily implemented using a two-level (not counting inverters that may be needed) gate network. Conversely, these standard circuits that are used to implement SOP functions can be quickly analyzed just by inspection. A sum-of-product expression consists of two or more product (AND) terms that are ORed together. The SOP expression is obtained from a truth table by writing down all of the product terms (also called minterms) whose outputs are high for the desired function and then ORing them together. The resultant SOP expression can be directly implemented with either AND/OR or NAND/NAND circuit designs.

Karnaugh Mapping

The basic procedure for combinational logic circuit design is to develop first the truth table that defines the desired function and then from the table, write a simplified SOP expression. The expression can be simplified using various techniques (such as Boolean algebra, Karnaugh mapping, etc.). Karnaugh mapping is a simple and fast procedure for reducing SOP logic expressions and thereby also reducing the implemented circuit's complexity and cost. In Karnaugh mapping, the function is defined graphically. The relationships between the function's inputs and the output are plotted in a Karnaugh map (K-map). This will be the same information that would be listed in the truth table for the function. The input variables must be labeled on the K-map in a very systematic fashion. If the K-map is not properly labeled, the function cannot be correctly simplified and the resulting design will be wrong. With K-mapping, the function reduction is accomplished by forming appropriate groupings of 1s in the output. Then identify the common input variables for the group and write the indicated product term. Karnaugh mapping can best be applied to functions with 5 or fewer input variables.

Example 5-1

Design a combinational circuit that will indicate the majority result of 3 individuals voting.

First, define the problem in a truth table as shown in Table 5-1.

A	B	C	V
0	0	0	0
0	0	1	0
0	1	0	0
0	1	1	1
1	0	0	0
1	0	1	1
1	1	0	1
1	1	1	1

Table 5-1 Truth table for example 5-1

The unsimplified SOP expression for example 5-1 would be:

$$V = \bar{A}\,B\,C + A\,\bar{B}\,C + A\,B\,\bar{C} + A\,B\,C$$

The Karnaugh map for this function is plotted in Fig. 5-1.

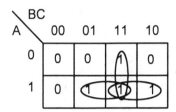

Fig. 5-1 Karnaugh map for example 5-1

The simplified SOP expression for this function would be:

$$V = B\,C + A\,C + A\,B$$

The simplified SOP expression can be easily implemented with a NAND/NAND circuit arrangement using 2 chips (7400 and 7410). The circuit schematic for this solution is given in Fig. 5-2.

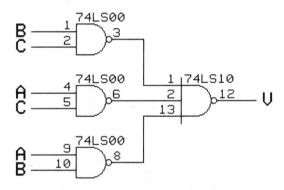

Fig. 5-2 Schematic for simplified SOP solution to example 5-1

Example 5-2

Design a simplified logic circuit to implement the function W defined in the truth table given in Table 5-2.

A	B	C	D	W
0	0	0	0	0
0	0	0	1	1
0	0	1	0	1
0	0	1	1	1
0	1	0	0	0
0	1	0	1	0
0	1	1	0	0
0	1	1	1	0
1	0	0	0	1
1	0	0	1	1
1	0	1	0	0
1	0	1	1	0
1	1	0	0	0
1	1	0	1	0
1	1	1	0	0
1	1	1	1	0

Table 5-2 Truth table for example 5-2

The output produced for the function W is plotted in a Karnaugh map in Fig. 5-3. Then appropriate groups of 1s are identified in the K-map to create the SOP expression for W. The two simplified expressions given in Fig. 5-3 can be obtained with K-mapping. The groupings of 1s shown in the K-map are represented by the first equation. The two solutions each require the same number of gates or chips and so either simplified SOP expression can be implemented. See Fig. 5-4a and b for the two solution schematics.

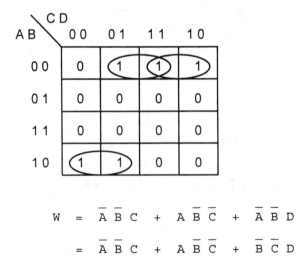

$$W = \overline{A}\,\overline{B}\,C + A\,\overline{B}\,\overline{C} + \overline{A}\,\overline{B}\,D$$

$$= \overline{A}\,\overline{B}\,C + A\,\overline{B}\,\overline{C} + \overline{B}\,\overline{C}\,D$$

Fig. 5-3 Karnaugh map and simplified expressions for example 5-2

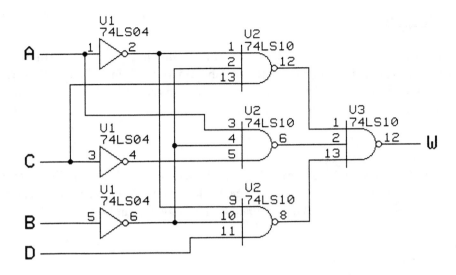

Fig. 5-4a Schematics for simplified SOP solutions to example 5-2

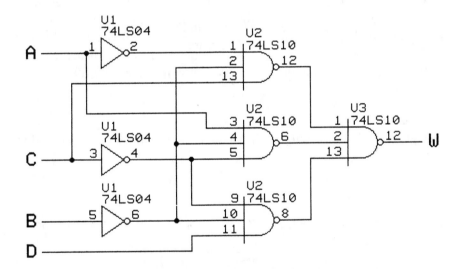

Fig. 5-4b Schematics for simplified SOP solutions to example 5-2

Laboratory Projects

Design logic circuits to perform each of the following functions. Define the problem with a truth table and then use K-mapping to write the simplified SOP expression. Draw and label the schematics to implement your simplified designs. Construct, test, and verify the operation of your design.

5.1   Two-input multiplexer
Design a circuit whose output (Y) is equivalent to one of two possible data inputs (A or B). A control input (S) selects either the data on the A input (if S is low) or the data on the B input (if S is high) to be routed to the single output line.

5.2   Three-bit equality detector
Design a 3-bit equality detector circuit that will output a low whenever the 3 input bits are all at the same logic level.

5.3   Elevator control
Design an elevator control system for a large building that has 5 elevators. Four of the elevators are turned on all of the time, while the fifth is activated only if a majority of the other 4 are being used (to save energy). The control system will have an input for each of the 4 primary elevators to indicate that that elevator is being used (with a logic "1"). A high output from the control system will activate the fifth elevator for its use.

5.4   Greater than 9 detector
Design a circuit whose output will be high if the 4-bit data input is a value greater than 9.

5.5   Window detector
Design a circuit whose output will be low for all 4-bit input combinations that meet the following criteria:
$$4 \; < \; I \; < \; 11$$
where I represents the 4-bit input value.

5.6   Two-bit comparator
Design a comparator circuit to compare two 2-bit numbers (A1 A0 and B1 B0). The circuit will have two output signals: GE and LT. GE will be high to indicate that the 2-bit A value is equal to or greater than the 2-bit B value. LT will be high if A < B.

5.7   Alarm circuit
Design an alarm circuit to be used in a process control system. Temperature (T), pressure (P), flow (F), and level (L) of a fluid are each monitored by separate sensor circuits that produce a <u>high</u> logic output signal when the following indicated <u>physical</u> conditions exist:

> high fluid temperature
> high fluid pressure
> low fluid flow rate
> low fluid level

The alarm circuit output (A) should be <u>high</u> if any of the following <u>physical</u> conditions exist in the system:

(1) the pressure is high when the flow is low
(2) the temperature is high when either the pressure is high or the level is low

Be sure to identify the correct physical conditions for the alarm in the logic truth table.

5.8   Prime number detector
Design a 4-bit prime number detector circuit. The 4-bit input will allow the binary numbers for 0 through 15 to be applied to the circuit. The output should be high only if prime numbers (1, 2, 3, 5, 7, 11, 13) are being input to the detector circuit.

5.9   Multiplier circuit
Design a multiplier circuit that will output the product of any 3-bit input number (0 through 7) multiplied by the constant 3. Note that this circuit will have several output bits and that each output will have to be mapped <u>separately</u>. Each output bit represents a circuit that must be constructed.

5.10   Digital switcher

Design a digital signal switching circuit that has two outputs (X and Y). For each of the two outputs, the circuit can select from two different signal sources (inputs A or B). The two input signals will be obtained from a binary counter chip, the 74LS393, as shown in the diagram below. The 74LS393 is being used as a 2-bit counter in this application. Use a low frequency such as 1 Hz for the CLOCK input to the counter. Do not forget to ground the CLR control on the 74LS393 or the counter will stay at zero and not count. The input signal selection is controlled by the signals C and D. The two control signals will be obtained from two logic switches. The circuit function is described in the following truth table. Test your design using lights to monitor X and Y. If a dual-trace oscilloscope is available, increase the CLOCK frequency to approximately 1 KHz and monitor the two output signals (X and Y) on the scope. Hint: Expand the function table to show the 16 combinations that are possible with the four inputs D, C, B, and A and K-map for each of the functions X and Y.

D	C	X	Y
0	0	A	B
0	1	A	A
1	0	B	B
1	1	B	A

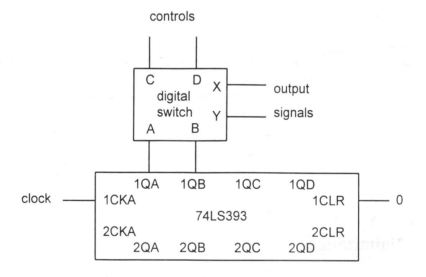

Daniel Woods
Marc Melansen
Mike Glomene

UNIT 6

CIRCUIT MINIMIZATION WITH BOOLEAN ALGEBRA

Objectives

- To simplify logic circuits using Boolean algebra techniques.
- To determine the minimum number of logic chips needed to implement a logic function.

Suggested Parts				
74LS00	74LS02	74LS04	74LS10	74S260

Logic Circuit Minimization

The various laws and theorems of Boolean algebra can be systematically applied to logic expressions in order to manipulate and/or simplify the expressions. Of course, extreme care must be exercised to correctly apply the laws and theorems or the resultant expression will not be equivalent to the original function. There are often many alternative Boolean algebra techniques that can be applied in the process of logic circuit simplification.

While a given logic expression is manipulated into different equivalent expression forms, the corresponding circuit implementations of each expression can be analyzed to determine the quantity of chips necessary for the circuit construction. The design that uses the minimum number of available chips may be selected as an optimum design choice (based on the amount of board space required by the circuit, the cost of the needed parts, etc.). This process generally requires some trial and error in order to determine the minimum chip solution.

Example 6-1

Redesign the circuit in Fig. 6-1 so that its function may be implemented with a minimum number of chips.

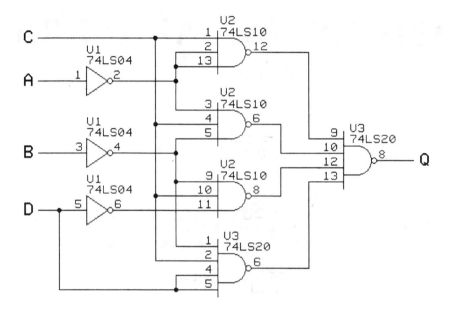

Fig. 6-1 Logic circuit for example 6-1

First, determine the original circuit's logic expression and then, using Boolean algebra techniques, reduce the expression to an equivalent simplified form. Determine the necessary chips for implementation of the simplified expression. Continue manipulating the expression and selecting appropriate chips for implementation until a minimal design is found.

$$Q = \overline{\overline{\overline{A} \, C} \cdot \overline{\overline{A} \, \overline{B} \, C} \cdot \overline{B \, C \, \overline{D}} \cdot \overline{B \, C \, \overline{D} \cdot D}}$$
original circuit expression
(uses 3 chips: 7404, 7410, 7420)

$$Q = \overline{A}\,C + \overline{A}\,\overline{B}\,C + \overline{B}\,C\,\overline{D} + \overline{B}\,C\,D$$

$$Q = \overline{A}\,C + \overline{A}\,\overline{B}\,C + \overline{B}\,C\,\overline{D} + \overline{B}\,C\,D$$

$$Q = \overline{A}\,C\,(1 + \overline{B}) + \overline{B}\,C\,(\overline{D} + D)$$

$$Q = \overline{A}\,C + \overline{B}\,C \qquad \Leftarrow \text{ possible solution?}$$
$$\text{(uses 3 chips: 7404, 7408, 7432)}$$

$$Q = \overline{A}\,C + \overline{B}\,C$$
try another alternative route

$$Q = \overline{\overline{A}\,C} \;\; \overline{\overline{B}\,C} \qquad \Leftarrow \text{ possible solution?}$$
$$\text{(uses 2 chips: 7400 \& 7404)}$$

$$Q = \overline{A}\,C + \overline{B}\,C$$
try another route from here

$$Q = C\,(\overline{A} + \overline{B}) \qquad \Leftarrow \text{ possible solution?}$$
$$\text{(uses 3 chips: 7404, 7408, 7432)}$$

$$Q = C\;\overline{\overline{A}\,\overline{B}} \qquad \Leftarrow \text{ possible solution?}$$
$$\text{(uses 2 chips: 7404 \& 7408)}$$

$$Q = C\;\overline{A\,B} \qquad \Leftarrow \text{ possible solution?}$$
$$\text{(uses 1 chip: 7400)} \quad \therefore \quad \textbf{\underline{best solution}!}$$

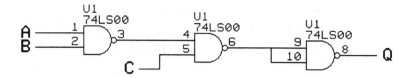

Fig. 6-2 Minimized circuit solution

Laboratory Projects

Redesign each of the following logic circuits so that a minimum number of available chips will be used to implement the logic functions of each circuit. Compare the number of chips required for the original circuits with your new equivalent designs. Construct and test each of your simplified designs.

6.1 Circuit 1

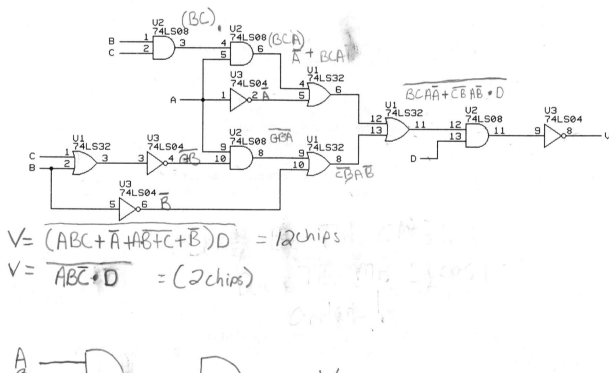

$$V = (ABC + \bar{A} + A\bar{B} + C + \bar{B})D = 12 \text{ chips}$$
$$V = \overline{AB\bar{C} \cdot D} = (2 \text{ chips})$$

6.2   Circuit 2

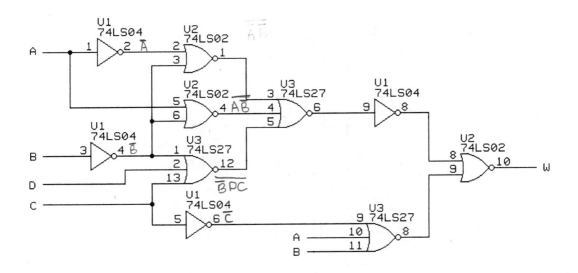

6.3   Circuit 3

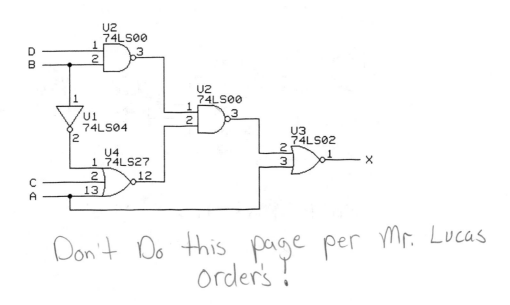

Don't Do this page per Mr. Lucas
Order's!

6.4   Circuit 4

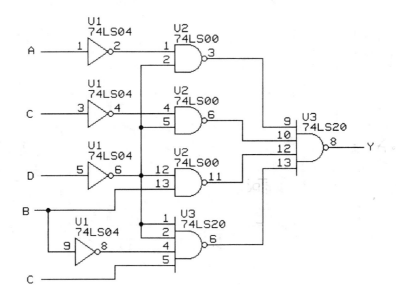

6.5   Circuit 5

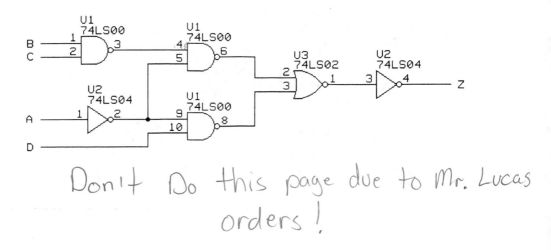

Don't Do this page due to Mr. Lucas orders!

UNIT 7

COMBINATIONAL CIRCUIT DESIGN USING PROGRAMMABLE LOGIC DEVICES

Objectives

- To implement combinational logic circuits using programmable logic devices (PLDs).
- To create PLD logic description files that define combinational circuit designs using Boolean expressions and truth tables.
- To use logic compiler software to create JEDEC files for programming PLDs.

Suggested Part
GAL16V8

Programmable Logic Devices

With programmable logic devices (PLDs), logic circuit designers can go from a conceptual design to customized functional parts in a matter of minutes. A PLD is a digital IC that is capable of being programmed to provide a specific logical function. The PLD family of devices consists of a variety of device architectures and configurations. The most common PLDs are based on the familiar AND/OR logic gate array in which the specific inputs to each AND gate are programmed to achieve the desired function. Sets of available AND gates in the PLD are internally connected to different OR gates to produce the needed outputs. The programmable AND/OR gate configuration is used to implement sum-of-product functions and, since the SOP form can be used to express any Boolean function, PLD designs are limited only by the number of terms available in the arrays. Many different PLD part numbers are available that provide a wide variety of choices in the number of inputs and outputs that are available, the number of product terms that can be handled, the output assertion level, the ability for outputs to be tristated, and the ability to produce registered outputs. The programmable flexibility of PLD devices typically allows circuit designers to replace many different standard SSI/MSI chips with a single PLD package. PLD devices are available for either one-time-only programming (commonly referred to as PALs) or are erasable and reprogrammable (EPLDs and EEPLDs).

The Lattice Semiconductor GAL16V8 is an example of an electrically erasable PLD. The GAL16V8 is quite versatile. This device can be programmed for a maximum of 8 outputs or a maximum of 16 inputs (although not that many of each simultaneously). Each of the outputs can accommodate up to 8 product terms. The GAL (generic array logic) chip has a flexible output structure called an output logic macrocell. The output logic macrocell (OLMC) allows a number of options to be programmed into the device. Each of the outputs can be programmed to be active high or active low, to be combinational or registered, and to be tristated or normal.

The GAL16V8 is a CMOS device and, as such, should be handled carefully. CMOS devices can be easily damaged by static electricity. Some recommended precautions for handling CMOS devices include storing the chip in conductive foam when not in a circuit, wearing an anti-static wrist strap, turning off the power when inserting or removing the chip, and connecting all unused IC pins to either ground or Vcc when the chip is inserted in a circuit.

Implementing a logic circuit with a PLD consists of developing the appropriate design information (Boolean equations, truth tables, or state machine description) that is then entered into a (computer) logic description file using a text editor (or a word processor program). A logic compiler is then used by the computer to transform the circuit description into a standard output form called a JEDEC file. The JEDEC file is then downloaded to a PLD programmer that is used to program the design into the PLD. The PLD is then ready to be used in your application. Design changes can be implemented simply by altering the logic description file with the text editor, re-compiling the logic description file, and then reprogramming the same PLD (if it is electrically erasable like the GALs). The old EEPLD configuration is erased automatically by the programmer hardware when it is reprogrammed.

Logic Compiler Operation

CUPL (from Logical Devices, Inc.) is an example of a very powerful logic compiler program. The compiler's operational procedures are made easy to use with a menuing program called MCUPL. Desired options are selected from the menu by pressing the first letter of the listed function or by moving the highlight bar with the up and down cursor keys to the option and then pressing ENTER. The highlighted menu choices are described in the Message Center window. File viewing/editing and compiling of the design file can be accomplished from within MCUPL's menu. The fundamental MAIN MENU choices are:

> Edit Design Entry
> Compile CUPL file
> Look at DOC file
> Review error LST file
> Quit

The editor operation from the menu permits the user to work with existing files or create new files. To create the PLD design files, it is actually easier and much faster to prepare a master template file that contains the general information found in all CUPL logic description files and can be edited from MCUPL's menu (and saved with a new filename for the current design project).

The purpose of the logic compiler is to translate the design's logic description file information into a standard output file format called a JEDEC file (filename.JED), which is then used to program the PLD device for the desired function. A design logic description file will be compiled by choosing "Compile CUPL file" from the MAIN MENU. Next, select the desired PLD file from the on-screen list. A list of CUPL compiler options will then appear. Choose the needed option flags and press F5 when finished. A selected option flag will be marked with an asterisk and the letter representing the option will be included in the flag list at the bottom of the screen. The basic compiler options include:

> Listing file
> Xpanded product terms
> Minimization Levels

The "Listing file" option will cause the compiler to output an error listing file (filename.LST), which will be saved on disk. The error listing file is a copy of the logic description file that is annotated with any error messages produced by the compiler. The "Xpanded product terms" option will output a documentation file (filename.DOC), which is also saved on disk. This file contains the SOP equations generated by the compiler and a symbol table of all variables used in the logic description file. CUPL provides five different choices of minimization algorithms for the user to select. The default level is 1. The most thorough but slowest is level 2. These "Minimization Levels" are:

0	No minimization	3	Presto minimization
1	Quick minimization (default)	4	Expresso minimization
2	Quine-McCluskey minimization		

```
┌─────────────────────────────────────────────────────────────────────┐
│           PLD DESIGN PROCEDURES USING CUPL                            │
│                                                                       │
│   (1)   Determine the design solution                                 │
│   (2)   Formulate the logic description using appropriate design entry│
│         format (Boolean expressions, truth tables, or state machine   │
│         description)                                                  │
│   (3)   Choose the target PLD device                                  │
│   (4)   Make desired pin assignments                                  │
│   (5)   Create CUPL logic description file                            │
│   (6)   Run CUPL to compile logic description file and produce JEDEC  │
│         file                                                          │
│   (7)   Program target device with JEDEC file using a PLD programmer  │
└─────────────────────────────────────────────────────────────────────┘
```

Fig. 7-1 Summary PLD design procedure

CUPL Logic Description File

The CUPL logic description file contains the data that describes the desired PLD logic design. CUPL assumes that the logic description file is named with the extension ".PLD". A text editor is used to create this logic description file. An editor called EZ EDIT is included with CUPL, but any editor can be linked to the compiler through the configuration file called MCUPL.CFG. The essential logic description file information includes:

> HEADER INFORMATION
> PIN ASSIGNMENTS
> LOGIC DESCRIPTION

The header information section is normally placed at the beginning of the logic description file. Each statement in the header section will begin with a keyword, followed by any valid ASCII characters, and end with a semicolon. The header consists of the keywords and appropriate data shown in Fig. 7-2.

The pin assignment statements are used to assign input and output variable names to desired pin numbers on the PLD. These assignments generally have a great deal of flexibility but must be made in accordance with the architectural capabilities of the target PLD device.

The logic description section of the PLD logic description file provides the functional definition of the logic circuit design. The circuit design can be described with a combination of three formats: state machine description (for sequential circuits), truth table, or Boolean equation.

```
NAME           logic description filename [8 characters max]
PARTNO         part number for design [not PLD part number]
REVISION       file revision number used to track design updates
               [start with 01 and increment each time file is altered]
DATE           date of last file changes
DESIGNER       designer's name
COMPANY        company's name [for documentation]
ASSEMBLY       PC board name where PLD will be used
LOCATION       schematic identifier for PLD location
DEVICE         default device type [can be overridden to select alternate
               device during compilation of logic description file]
FORMAT         instructs compiler to produce correct format output file
               automatically for programming PLD
               [use j (lower case) to produce JEDEC output file]
```

Fig. 7-2 CUPL header information

In addition, other types of information will typically be included to make the design file easier to interpret and to develop. This includes:

COMMENTS
DECLARATIONS AND INTERMEDIATE VARIABLE DEFINITIONS

The PLD design logic description file should be annotated with comments for clarity. The logic of the design will be much more understandable with appropriate comments. Comments will be ignored by the logic compiler.

Bits may be grouped together and intermediate variables can be defined to make writing the logic description for a design much easier and clearer. This information is placed in the declarations and intermediate variable definitions section of the design logic description file.

The fundamental language elements for CUPL logic description files are summarized in Fig. 7-3a and b.

CUPL LANGUAGE ELEMENTS

Variables:
- Specify device pins, internal nodes, constants, input signals, output signals, intermediate signals.
- Start with a numeric digit, alphabet character, or underscore.
- Must include at least one alphabet character.
- Are case sensitive.
- Cannot have spaces within the variable name.
- May be up to 31 characters long.
- Cannot contain any reserved symbols.
- Cannot be the same as a reserved keyword.
- Can be indexed variables -- variable names that end in a decimal number between 0 and 31.

Reserved words:

APPEND	ELSE	JUMP	PRESENT
ASSEMBLY	FIELD	MACRO	REV
ASSY	FLD	MIN	REVISION
COMPANY	FORMAT	NAME	SEQUENCE
CONDITION	FUNCTION	NODE	SEQUENCED
DATE	FUSE	OUT	SEQUENCEJK
DEFAULT	IF	PARTNO	SEQUENCERS
DESIGNER	LOC	PIN	SEQUENCET
DEVICE	LOCATION	PINNODE	TABLE

Reserved symbols:

&	#	(	)	-	@	*
+	[	]	/	^	:	.
/*	*/	=	!	;	,	..
$	'					

Numbers:

Values may be from 0 to $2^{32}-1$.

Default base for numbers is hexadecimal except for device pin numbers and indexed variables, which are decimal.

Binary, octal, and hexadecimal can have don't care values (X) and numerical values.

Base	Prefix (use upper- or lower-case)
binary	**'b'**
octal	**'o'**
decimal	**'d'**
hexadecimal	**'h'**

Fig. 7-3a Summary of CUPL language elements

```
                    CUPL LANGUAGE ELEMENTS

Logical operators
     &    =    Logical AND
     #    =    Logical OR
     $    =    Logical XOR
     !    =    Logical NEGATION
Comment indicators
     /*   =    Start comment
     */   =    End comment
Intermediate variables
     You can arbitrarily create and define a symbolic name as follows:
              MEMREQ = MEMW # MEMR;
     where MEMREQ does not appear as a pin variable name.  MEMREQ can
     then be used in expressions for other variables.  The value
     "MEMW # MEMR" will be substituted wherever MEMREQ is used.
List notations
     You can represent groups of variables in a shorthand list notation
     by using the following formats:
              [var1, var2, ..., varN] as in [MEMR,MEMW,IOR,IOW]
                                or
              [varN..0] as in [A7..0], which is equivalent to
              [A7,A6,A5,A4,A3,A2,A1,A0]
Bit fields
     A bit field is a declaration of a group of bits that is
     represented by a single symbolic name.  Bit fields are declared as
     follows:
              FIELD IOADR = [A7..0];
     where IOADR can then be used in expressions instead of [A7..0].
Equality operator
     The equality operator symbol is a colon ":".  This operator
     compares bit equality between a set of variables (or a bit field)
     and a constant value or a list of constant values.  For example,
     if IOADR represents a set of eight bits or variables, then:
              IOADR:C3
     would be true if the bit field named IOADR were equal to the hex
     value C3.  Also:
              IOADR:[10..3F]
     would be true if IOADR were in the range of hex values 10 through
     3F.
```

Fig. 7-3b Summary of CUPL language elements

Example 7-1

Design a logic circuit that will detect various input conditions for a 4-bit input value (DCBA). The output GT9 will be high if the input value is greater than 9. Another output, LT4, will be low if the input value is less than 4. The output signal RNG will be high if the input is greater than 6 and less than 11. And the output signal TEN will be low if the input is equal to 10.

The first step is to define the problem in a truth table as shown in Table 7-1 and then determine appropriate signal assertion levels and logic expressions. Signals may be asserted either as active-high or active-low signals. To develop the PLD design using a high level compiler such as CUPL, the active level of the signals are determined separately from the logic expression that determines the signal activation. The active level of the signal is independent (and can be easily changed) of the expression that describes activation. The logic expression determines when the function is to be asserted while the active level given in the pin assignment determines the voltage level of the signal when it is asserted.

D C B A	GT9	LT4	RNG	TEN
0 0 0 0	0	0	0	1
0 0 0 1	0	0	0	1
0 0 1 0	0	0	0	1
0 0 1 1	0	0	0	1
0 1 0 0	0	1	0	1
0 1 0 1	0	1	0	1
0 1 1 0	0	1	0	1
0 1 1 1	0	1	1	1
1 0 0 0	0	1	1	1
1 0 0 1	0	1	1	1
1 0 1 0	1	1	1	0
1 0 1 1	1	1	0	1
1 1 0 0	1	1	0	1
1 1 0 1	1	1	0	1
1 1 1 0	1	1	0	1
1 1 1 1	1	1	0	1

Function	Active-level for output	Logic equation to produce active output
GT9	high	$D\,B + D\,C$
LT4	low	$\overline{D}\ \overline{C}$
RNG	high	$D\,\overline{C}\,\overline{B} + D\,\overline{C}\,\overline{A} + \overline{D}\,C\,B\,A$
TEN	low	$D\,\overline{C}\,B\,\overline{A}$

Table 7-1 Truth table and equations for PLD example 7-1

The CUPL logic description file shown in Fig. 7-4 has been created using a text editor for this PLD design. The logic description file has been named LAB-EX1.PLD. Appropriate design information has been provided in the header section, which is given first in the file. Note that a specific device (GAL16V8) has been selected and that a

JEDEC output file is requested to be produced by the logic compiler. Comments have been included in the logic description file to help document the design. Applicable input and output pins have been selected and declared in the logic description file. Note that the active output level is also indicated by the presence or absence of the negation symbol "!" in the output pin assignment statements. The logic equation section provides the necessary logic expression that describes when each of the outputs is to be asserted. Every statement line ends with a semicolon ";". Comment lines do not end with semicolons.

```
Name          LAB-EX1;
Partno        L105-1;
Date          06/30/93;
Revision      01;
Designer      Greg Moss;
Company       Digi-Lab, Inc.;
Assembly      Example Board;
Location      U101;
Device        G16V8A;
Format        j;

      /******************************************/
      /* example circuit design using a PLD    */
      /* circuit detects various input values  */
      /*    and produces multiple outputs      */
      /******************************************/

              /**   Input pins  **/
Pin  1  =   D;
Pin  2  =   C;
Pin  3  =   B;
Pin  4  =   A;

              /**   Output pins  **/
Pin 12  =   GT9;   /* GT9 hi output if DCBA > 9   */
Pin 13  =  !LT4;   /* LT9 low output if DCBA < 4  */
Pin 14  =   RNG;   /* RNG hi out if 6 < DCBA < 11 */
Pin 15  =  !TEN;   /* TEN low output if DCBA = 10 */

              /**  Logic Equations  **/
GT9  =  D & B  #  D & C;
LT4  =  !D & !C;
RNG  =  D & !C & (!B # !A)  #  !D & C & B & A;
TEN  =  D & !C & B & !A;
```

Fig. 7-4 CUPL logic description file for example 7-1

```
******************************************************************
                            LAB-EX1
******************************************************************

CUPL            4.0a Serial# XX-XXX-XXXX
Device          g16v8as   Library DLIB-h-26-1
Created         Wed Jun 30 15:12:55 1993
Name            LAB-EX1
Partno          L105-1
Revision        01
Date            06/30/93
Designer        Greg Moss
Company         Digi-Lab, Inc.
Assembly        Example Board
Location        U101


================================================================
                     Expanded Product Terms
================================================================

GT9 =>
    B & D
  # C & D

LT4 =>
    !C & !D

RNG =>
    !A & !C & D
  # !B & !C & D
  # A & B & C & !D

TEN =>
    !A & B & !C & D


================================================================
                         Symbol Table
================================================================

Pin Variable                                 Pterms   Max     Min
Pol    Name          Ext     Pin     Type    Used     Pterms  Level
--- --------         ---     ---     ----    ------   ------  ----

       A                      4       V       -        -       -
       B                      3       V       -        -       -
       C                      2       V       -        -       -
       D                      1       V       -        -       -
       GT9                   12       V       2        8       1
  !    LT4                   13       V       1        8       1
       RNG                   14       V       3        8       1
  !    TEN                   15       V       1        8       1

LEGEND   F : field     D : default variable    M : extended node
         N : node      I : intermediate variable  T : function
         V : variable  X : extended variable   U : undefined
```

Fig. 7-5 CUPL Xpanded product terms ".DOC" file for example 7-1

The documentation file shown in Fig. 7-5 was produced by CUPL and automatically saved on the disk by setting the "X" compiler flag. The JEDEC file for a GAL16V8 was created by the compiler with the "DEVICE" and "FORMAT" statements in the header. The ".JED" file is then downloaded to a PLD programmer to program a GAL16V8, which has been inserted in the programmer's socket.

Another possible solution to Example 7-1 is shown in Fig. 7-6. In this logic description file the set of input variables (D, C, B, A) is assigned the name INPUTS in the field statement. INPUTS now can be used to represent the four input bits. The logic equations then can easily be shortened using the equality operation. Whenever INPUTS is equal to the specified constant or range of constants, the resultant expression will be true.

```
Name       LAB-EX1A;
Partno     L105-1;
Date       06/30/93;
Revision   01;
Designer   Greg Moss;
Company    Digi-Lab, Inc.;
Assembly   Example Board;
Location   U101;
Device     G16V8A;
Format     j;

      /*****************************************/
      /* example circuit design using a PLD    */
      /* circuit detects various input values */
      /*    and produces multiple outputs      */
      /*****************************************/

            /**  Input pins  **/
Pin  1  =  D;
Pin  2  =  C;
Pin  3  =  B;
Pin  4  =  A;

            /**  Output pins  **/
Pin 12 =  GT9;   /* GT9 hi output if DCBA > 9    */
Pin 13 = !LT4;   /* LT9 low output if DCBA < 4   */
Pin 14 =  RNG;   /* RNG hi out if 6 < DCBA < 11  */
Pin 15 = !TEN;   /* TEN low output if DCBA = 10  */

      /**    Declarations and Intermediate
               Variable Definitions       **/
field INPUTS  =  [D,C,B,A];  /* assigns the set of
                  bits to the name INPUTS */

            /**  Logic Equations  **/
GT9  =  INPUTS:[A..F];
LT4  =  INPUTS:[0,1,2,3];
RNG  =  INPUTS:[7..A];
TEN  =  INPUTS:'d'10;
```

Fig. 7-6 Alternate CUPL logic description file for example 7-1

Example 7-2

Design a logic circuit that will output a binary value equal to the square of a 4-bit input value.

```
Name        SQUARE;
Partno      L105-2;
Date        02/04/91;
Revision    03;
Designer    Greg Moss;
Company     Digi-Lab, Inc.;
Assembly    Generator board;
Location    U210;
Device      G16V8A;
Format      j;

/************************************************/
/* Generates the square of an input value using */
/* the truth table design entry technique.      */
/************************************************/

/**   Inputs  **/
Pin [2..5] = [I3..0];    /* Data Input Value    */

/**   Outputs  **/
Pin [12..19] = [N0..7];  /* Square Output Value */

/** Declarations and Intermediate
                Variable Definitions **/
field data_in = [I3..0];
field square = [N7..0];

/** Logic Description  --  truth table format **/
table  data_in  =>  square    {
                0   =>    'd'0;
                1   =>    'd'1;
                2   =>    'd'4;
                3   =>    'd'9;
                4   =>    'd'16;
                5   =>    'd'25;
                6   =>    'd'36;
                7   =>    'd'49;
                8   =>    'd'64;
                9   =>    'd'81;
                A   =>    'd'100;
                B   =>    'd'121;
                C   =>    'd'144;
                D   =>    'd'169;
                E   =>    'd'196;
                F   =>    'd'225;
            }
```

Fig. 7-7 CUPL logic description file for example 7-2

A possible CUPL logic description file solution is shown in Fig. 7-7. This solution uses a truth table design entry technique to define the desired function. The 4 input bits have been grouped together and named "data_in," while the 8 output bits are grouped under the name "square." A truth table format is declared using the keyword "table" followed by the name of the input bit field, the table assignment symbol "=>", the name of the output bit field, and then the list of input and output assignments, which is enclosed in braces { }.

Errors are reported on-screen during compilation of the logic description file and will be logged in the ".LST" file if the "Listing file" option is selected. If, for example, the following error was made in the output pin assignment statement of the logic description file:

$$\text{Pin } [12..18] = [N0..7]; \ /* \text{ Square Output Value } */$$

then the resultant SQUARE.LST file would be as shown in Fig. 7-8. The error message is indicating that a total of 7 pins have been assigned to 8 variable names, which is a mismatch in size. The error pointer is pointing to the end of the line where the error occurred.

Example 7-3

Implement a 4-channel multiplexer using a GAL16V8. The logic expression for this circuit is:

$$Y = (D0 \ \overline{SELB} \ \overline{SELA} + D1 \ \overline{SELB} \ SELA$$
$$+ D2 \ SELB \ \overline{SELA} + D3 \ SELB \ SELA) \ \overline{EN}$$

An example CUPL logic description file to implement this combinational circuit is given in Fig. 7-9. The active-low input signal level for EN has been specified in the pin assignment statement, while the logic equation indicates that the EN signal has to be asserted (or true) to produce the desired logic function. List notation has been utilized to assign pins 2 through 5, respectively, to input variables D0 through D3. The "D" variable specifications are accomplished using CUPL's indexed variable notation. The input variables SELA and SELB are also assigned to pins 6 and 7, respectively, using the list notation technique. The list notation provides a very convenient shortcut. This example also illustrates the use of intermediate variable definitions. Each of the four possible combinations of the two select controls has been assigned a variable name to make the writing of the logic equation less complex.

```
LISTING FOR LOGIC DESCRIPTION FILE: C:\CUPL40\DESIGNS\SQUARE.pld

CUPL: Universal Compiler for Programmable Logic
Version 4.0a Serial# XX-XXX-XXXX
Copyright (C)  1983,1990 Logical Devices, Inc.
Created Mon Jul 05 10:42:56 1993

    1:Name        SQUARE;
    2:Partno      L105-2;
    3:Date        02/04/91;
    4:Revision    03;
    5:Designer    Greg Moss;
    6:Company     Digi-Lab, Inc.;
    7:Assembly    Generator board;
    8:Location    U210;
    9:Device      G16V8A;
   10:Format      j;
   11:
   12:/***********************************************/
   13:/* Generates the square of an input value using */
   14:/* the truth table design entry technique.      */
   15:/***********************************************/
   16:
   17:/**   Inputs   **/
   18:Pin [2..5] = [I3..0];    /* Data Input Value     */
   19:
   20:/**   Outputs   **/
   21:Pin [12..18] = [N0..7];  /* Square Output Value */
                        ^
[0012ca] vector size mismatch:  lhs size = 7, rhs size = 8
   22:
   23:/** Declarations and Intermediate
   24:                  Variable Definitions **/
   25:field data_in = [I3..0];
   26:field square = [N7..0];
   27:
   28:/** Logic Description  --  truth table format **/
   29:table   data_in  =>   square   {
   30:             0   =>   'd'0;
   31:             1   =>   'd'1;
   32:             2   =>   'd'4;
   33:             3   =>   'd'9;
   34:             4   =>   'd'16;
   35:             5   =>   'd'25;
   36:             6   =>   'd'36;
   37:             7   =>   'd'49;
   38:             8   =>   'd'64;
   39:             9   =>   'd'81;
   40:             A   =>   'd'100;
   41:             B   =>   'd'121;
   42:             C   =>   'd'144;
   43:             D   =>   'd'169;
   44:             E   =>   'd'196;
   45:             F   =>   'd'225;
   46:         }
```

Fig. 7-8 CUPL Listing file for error in example 7-2

```
         Name         4CH_MUX;
         Partno       L105-3;
         Date         06/29/93;
         Revision     01;
         Designer     Greg Moss;
         Company      Digi-Lab, Inc.;
         Assembly     Multiplexer Board;
         Location     U315;
         Device       G16V8A;
         Format       j;

/******************************************************/
/*    PLD design for a 4-input multiplexer circuit    */
/******************************************************/

/**   Input Pin Assignments  **/
Pin   1     = !EN;           /* Enable control - active low  */
Pin [2..5]  = [D0..3];    /* Input data (list)              */
Pin [6,7]   = [SELA,SELB];     /* Select controls (list) */

/**   Output Pin Assignments  **/
Pin   19    = Y;             /* Multiplexer output           */

/**   Declarations & Intermediate Variable Definitions **/
/* Defining select combinations for:     SELB  SELA  */
SEL0 = !SELB &  !SELA;                 /*   0     0    */
SEL1 = !SELB &   SELA;                 /*   0     1    */
SEL2 =  SELB &  !SELA;                 /*   1     0    */
SEL3 =  SELB &   SELA;                 /*   1     1    */

/**   Logic Equations  **/
Y   =  ( D0   &   SEL0
    #     D1   &   SEL1
    #     D2   &   SEL2
    #     D3   &   SEL3 )   &   EN;
```

Fig. 7-9 CUPL logic description file for example 7-3

Laboratory Projects

Design PLD logic circuits for the following applications. Use a text editor to create (and edit) the design's logic description file. Compile the logic description file to produce a JEDEC output file. Program a GAL16V8 with the JEDEC file and test each of your circuit designs in the lab.

7.1 Pattern generator
Design a logic circuit that will output the pattern illustrated by the following timing diagram. The inputs are DCBA and the outputs are WXYZ.

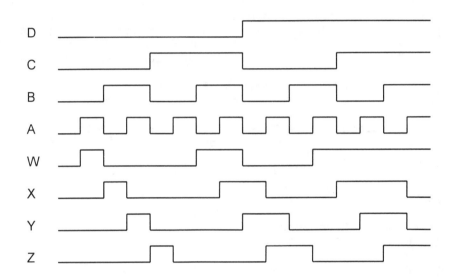

7.2   2421-to-5421-BCD code converter
Design and construct a 2421-BCD-to-5421-BCD code converter. The truth table for
this design is given below. The inputs are labeled DCBA and the outputs are WXYZ.
Note that in this situation, we care about only 10 of the 16 possible input combinations.
The other 6 input combinations are listed at the bottom of the truth table and are
labeled as "invalid inputs." The output for each of these input conditions is given a
default output value of 1111.

		2	4	2	1	5	4	2	1
		D	C	B	A	W	X	Y	Z
		0	0	0	0	0	0	0	0
		0	0	0	1	0	0	0	1
		0	0	1	0	0	0	1	0
		0	0	1	1	0	0	1	1
		0	1	0	0	0	1	0	0
		1	0	1	1	1	0	0	0
		1	1	0	0	1	0	0	1
		1	1	0	1	1	0	1	0
		1	1	1	0	1	0	1	1
		1	1	1	1	1	1	0	0
i	i	0	1	0	1	1	1	1	1
n	n	0	1	1	0	1	1	1	1
v	p	0	1	1	1	1	1	1	1
a	u	1	0	0	0	1	1	1	1
l	t	1	0	0	1	1	1	1	1
i	s	1	0	1	0	1	1	1	1
d									

7.3   Two's complementer
Design a logic circuit that will produce a 5-bit output ($X4$ $X3$ $X2$ $X1$ $X0$) that is equal
to the two's complement of a 5-bit input value ($I4$ $I3$ $I2$ $I1$ $I0$).

7.4   BCD-to-binary converter
Design a logic circuit that will convert a 5-bit BCD input into its equivalent 4-bit
binary value. Since the output is only 4 bits long, the largest number that is to be
converted is the decimal value 15. This converter circuit should also have an output
called ERR that will be high if the BCD input value is not in the range of 0 through 15.
Hints: Use the truth table design entry technique to define valid input conditions and
resultant outputs. Write a logic equation using the equality operator to detect the
ranges of input values that should produce a high output for ERR.

7.5   Programmable logic unit

Design a programmable logic circuit that will perform the logic operations on the two 4-bit inputs. X and Y are controls that determine which of the four functions is to be performed by the logic circuit. A and B represent two different 4-bit inputs and F represents the resultant 4-bit output that will be produced. Each of the output bits will be a function of corresponding A-bit and B-bit and the X and Y controls. For example, F3 is dependent on A3, B3, X, and Y, while F2 is dependent on A2, B2, X, and Y. Hint: The easiest solution is to write a <u>set</u> of four (one for each F output) logic equations in the following form (where n is 0 through 3):

```
Fn   =   (An # Bn)    &   (!X & !Y)
     #   (An & Bn)    &   (!X &  Y)
     #   (An $ Bn)    &   ( X & !Y)
     #    (!An)       &   ( X &  Y);
```

X	Y	Operation
0	0	F = A # B
0	1	F = A & B
1	0	F = A $ B
1	1	F = !A

inputs:

A = (A3 A2 A1 A0)
B = (B3 B2 B1 B0)

output:

F = (F3 F2 F1 F0)

Experiment 14

Name _____

TROUBLESHOOTING EXCLUSIVE-OR AND COMBINATORIAL CIRCUITS

OBJECTIVES

1. Troubleshoot 7486 IC faults.
2. Troubleshoot combinatorial circuits.

TEXT REFERENCES

Read sections 4.6 and 4.9 to 4.13. Also read Appendix A of this manual, and review Experiment 3.

EQUIPMENT NEEDED

Components
7486 IC;
2 toggle (spdt) switches.

Instruments
0–5 volt DC power supply;
logic pulser;
logic probe.

DISCUSSION

In Experiment 3, you learned how to troubleshoot the basic gates. You repeated this exercise in Experiment 6 with NAND and NOR gates. Before proceeding to troubleshoot combinations of these gates, you should spend a few minutes learning to troubleshoot the exclusive-OR, since it is found in many digital applications. Since the IC faults of the 7486 are isolated by using the techniques developed in the earlier troubleshooting exercises, we will concentrate on the faults that produce symptoms peculiar to the exclusive-OR circuit. You will then be asked to troubleshoot a combination circuit using the procedures found in this lab manual and the text.

PROCEDURE

a) Refer to Figure 14-1, and wire a 7486 EX-OR gate as shown. Recall that when the inputs to an EX-OR gate are both the same, the output is LOW. Therefore, if the output of an EX-OR appears to be stuck LOW, one possible trouble might be shorted inputs. Touch the probe tip to one of the inputs and the pulser to the other input. You should observe that the pulsing on one of the inputs is detected by the probe on the other. This indicates a short in the EX-OR's inputs.

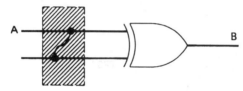

Figure 14-1

b) Refer to Figure 14-2, and wire a 7486 EX-OR gate as shown. Connect point A to a data switch and set the switch HIGH, but leave points B and C disconnected. Place the probe tip on point C, and observe that the output is LOW. Toggle the data switch, and observe that the output is always the inverse of the level at A. If the EX-OR is connected as a controlled inverter, this gate would be behaving properly. Now place the probe tip on point D. You should observe that the level there is floating. This tells you that the input (point D) is open. To verify that the open is external, place the pulser tip on point D and the probe tip on point C. Set the data switch at A to LOW. You should observe that the probe now indicates a pulsing condition. (If the open had been internal, you would still see a LOW at point C. You would also not detect a floating condition at the suspect input's pin.)

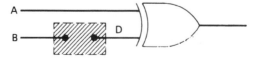

Figure 14-2

c) *Troubleshooting combinatorial circuits:*

1) Tear off the circuit diagram (Figure 14-2) and study it carefully, including the notes in the lower right-hand corner. Note the following:

- D, C, B, and A are inputs to the logic circuit.

- Each IC is identified as Z1, Z2, etc. Logic gates with the same Z number are on the same IC chip. For example, the two NAND gates labeled "Z4" are on the same 7400 NAND gate chip.

- The numbers on each logic gate input and output are pin numbers on the IC chip.

- The "balloons" TP1, TP2, etc., indicate test points that will be checked during testing or troubleshooting.

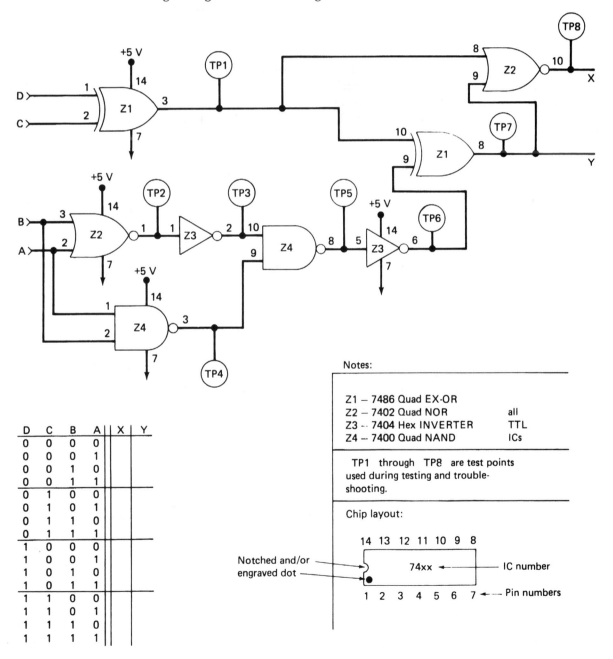

D	C	B	A	X	Y
0	0	0	0		
0	0	0	1		
0	0	1	0		
0	0	1	1		
0	1	0	0		
0	1	0	1		
0	1	1	0		
0	1	1	1		
1	0	0	0		
1	0	0	1		
1	0	1	0		
1	0	1	1		
1	1	0	0		
1	1	0	1		
1	1	1	0		
1	1	1	1		

Notes:

Z1 — 7486 Quad EX-OR
Z2 — 7402 Quad NOR   all
Z3 — 7404 Hex INVERTER   TTL
Z4 — 7400 Quad NAND   ICs

TP1 through TP8 are test points used during testing and trouble-shooting.

Chip layout:

14 13 12 11 10 9 8

Notched and/or engraved dot

74xx   IC number

1 2 3 4 5 6 7   Pin numbers

Figure 14-3

2) The four ICs used in this circuit should be inserted into the circuit board with a left-to-right orientation (i.e., Z1 on the left, then Z2 and Z3, with Z4 on the right). Wire the circuit according to Figure 14-3.

3) Connect inputs A, B, C, and D to toggle switches. Use your logic probe to test the circuit operation by trying each of the 16 input conditions and monitoring the outputs X and Y with the logic probe.

4) If the results do not match your predicted values, you will have to troubleshoot your circuit by following the logic levels through the circuit, starting at the inputs. Use your logic probe and pulser to locate the fault.

5) Once the circuit is operating normally, have your instructor or lab assistant introduce a fault, then use your troubleshooting procedure to locate this fault.

6) Repeat step 5 as frequently as time permits.

FLIP-FLOPS I: SET/CLEAR LATCHES AND CLOCKED FLIP-FLOPS

OBJECTIVES

1. To investigate the operation of the NOR gate SET/CLEAR latch.
2. To investigate the operation of the NAND gate SET/CLEAR latch.
3. To investigate the operation of an edge-triggered J-K flip-flop, the 74LS76 IC.
4. To investigate the operation of an edge-triggered D flip-flop, the 7474 IC.

TEXT REFERENCES

Read sections 5.1, 5.2, 5.4 through 5.7, and 5.9.

EQUIPMENT NEEDED

Components
7400 IC (2);
7402 IC (2);
7474 IC;
74LS76 IC;
normally HIGH pushbutton switch (2) and normally LOW pushbutton switch (2), all debounced;
2 LED monitors.

Instruments
0–5 volt DC power supply;
pulse or square wave generator;
dual trace oscilloscope;
logic probe (optional).

DISCUSSION

All of the previous experiments have been concerned with learning the fundamentals of logic gates and combinatorial circuits. Recall that an output of such a device or circuit responds to changes in its inputs and that when its inputs are removed, the output may not be sustained. In this experiment, you will be introduced to a device that can sustain a given output even when its inputs are removed. Such a device is said to possess memory. Examples of memory devices include flip-flops, which are the topic for this experiment. The following classes of flip-flops are investigated in this experiment:

- SET/CLEAR latches
- Edge-triggered J-K flip-flops
- Edge-triggered D flip-flops

SET/CLEAR Latches

The most fundamental flip-flop is the SET/CLEAR latch. Two types of SET/CLEAR latches are investigated in the current experiment:

- NAND gate SET/CLEAR latch
- NOR gate SET/CLEAR latch

The input levels to these devices determine the outputs. SET/CLEAR latches do not have a clock input, and so they are said to operate *asynchronously*.

Edge-Triggered J-K Flip-Flops

The J-K flip-flop eliminates the ambiguous condition. In place of this invalid condition, the J-K has a "toggle" condition, a characteristic of this flip-flop. Normally, a J-K flip-flop can be operated synchronously, since its J and K inputs need a separate clock to cause the flip-flop to change states. A J-K flip-flop can also be operated asynchronously and have SET and CLEAR inputs to facilitate this.

Edge-Triggered D Flip-Flops

The D flip-flop is a J-K flip-flop with an inverter between the J and the K inputs. This causes the flip-flop to SET or CLEAR with only one synchronous signal input. Like the J-K flip-flop, the D flip-flop also has an asynchronous mode.

PROCEDURE

a) *NOR gate SET/CLEAR latch:* Examine closely and then wire the NOR gate latch shown in Figure 15-1. Connect normally LOW pushbutton switches to the CLEAR and SET inputs to the circuit. You will monitor circuit outputs Q and Q̄ with LED monitors.

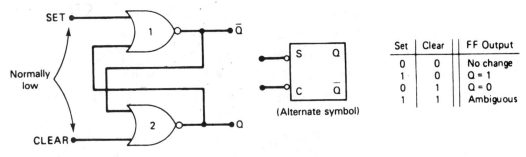

Figure 15-1

Set	Clear	FF Output
0	0	No change
1	0	Q = 1
0	1	Q = 0
1	1	Ambiguous

(Alternate symbol)

b) Turn the power supply on, and note the states of both LEDs: Q = _1_ ; $\overline{Q}$ = _0_ .

Predicting the states of a latch when power is first applied is impossible, so the values just recorded are random.

Clear Q by momentarily pulsing the CLEAR input HIGH. If Q is already HIGH, pulsing the CLEAR input will have no effect on the circuit.

c) Pulse the SET input HIGH, and observe the effects on the circuit outputs: Q = _1_ ; $\overline{Q}$ = _0_ .

Note that releasing the pushbutton does not cause Q to change from its new state. Why? _Because the chip has a memory_

Now pulse the SET input HIGH again. What effect does this have on the circuit outputs? _The output changed from high to low_ X

pulsing SET again
no effect of should
output is
already high

d) Pulse the CLEAR input HIGH, and observe that Q changes back to LOW and stays LOW even after the pushbutton is released.

e) Alternately pulse the SET and CLEAR inputs HIGH several times. Note that the outputs are always at opposite states.

f) Press and hold the SET and CLEAR inputs HIGH at the same time. Note that both outputs are now LOW. Release the pushbuttons, and note the states of the outputs. Are they both still LOW? _NO_ .

Now pulse both SET and CLEAR inputs simultaneously several times, and note the effects on the outputs. If you pulse the circuit in this manner enough times, you will probably get random results. This is because the circuit response to this input condition is unpredictable.

g) *NAND gate SET/CLEAR latch:* Examine closely and then wire the NAND gate SET/CLEAR latch shown in Figure 15-2. Connect normally HIGH pushbutton switches to the SET and CLEAR inputs of the circuit.

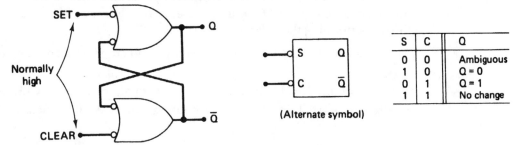

S	C	Q
0	0	Ambiguous
1	0	Q = 0
0	1	Q = 1
1	1	No change

(Alternate symbol)

Figure 15-2

h) Turn the power supply on. Pulse the SET input LOW, and verify that Q is HIGH and $\overline{Q}$ is LOW. Now pulse the CLEAR input LOW, and observe that the latch is cleared (Q = 0) and stays cleared even after the pushbutton is released.

i) Alternately pulse the SET and CLEAR inputs LOW several times. Observe that the outputs are always at opposite states.

j) Pulse both SET and CLEAR inputs LOW simultaneously, and observe the effects on the circuit outputs.

k) *Edge-triggered J-K flip-flop—74LS76 IC:* Refer to the data sheet for a 7476 IC. Note that there are three versions of this flip-flop: the 7476 and the 74H76 dual pulse-triggered master/slave J-K, and the 74LS76 dual edge-triggered J-K. The pin layout diagram given by the data sheet is the same for all three, but the operation of the edge-triggered and pulse-triggered versions are slightly different. You will test a 7476 IC in Experiment 16.

Draw the pin layout diagram for the 74LS76 IC:

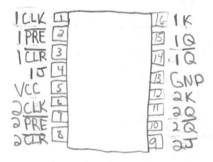

Install a 74LS76 IC on the circuit board, and make the following connections:

1) Connect V_{cc} and DC SET to +5 V, GND to power ground.
2) Connect toggle switches to J and K inputs.
3) Connect a normally LOW pushbutton switch to the clock (CLK) input.
4) Connect a normally HIGH pushbutton switch to DC CLEAR.
5) Connect LED monitors to outputs Q and $\overline{Q}$ (or use a logic probe to monitor the outputs).

Turn the power supply on, and observe the states of Q and $\overline{Q}$. If Q = 1, then pulse DC CLEAR momentarily LOW. Note that this input clears the flip-flop immediately without a clock signal and that the input is active LOW.

l) *74LS76 synchronous operation:* In this step, you will observe that the J and K inputs can be used to change the output state of the flip-flop. You will also observe that in order for these inputs to effect a change, a clock pulse must be applied. For this reason, the J, K, and CLK inputs are referred to as *synchronous* inputs. Verify this by performing the following steps:

1) Change the J and K input switch settings, and observe that nothing happens to Q.
2) Set J = 1 and K = 1, and apply a positive-going transition at CLK. Do this b pressing and holding the CLK pushbutton switch. What happens to Q? _LOW_

3) Repeat step 2 using a negative-going transition at CLK. Do this by releasing the pushbutton switch. What happens to Q? *goes high*. This proves that the flip-flop responds to only negative-going transitions. Apply several more pulses to the CLK input. What happens? *Nothing*.

4) If Q is LOW, pulse the CLK input so that Q is HIGH. Set J = K = 0, and note that nothing happens to Q. Pulse the CLK input momentarily, and observe that nothing happens to Q. Why?
   Because J and K equal 0

5) Set J = 0 and K = 1, and note that nothing happens to Q. Pulse the CLK input momentarily. What happens to Q?
   it switches states, it goes high ~~should have gone low, resets the FF~~ *J = 0*

   Apply several more pulses to the CLK input, and observe that Q remains in the LOW state.

6) Change J to 1 and then back to 0, and note that nothing happens to Q. Pulse the CLK input momentarily. You should observe that Q remains LOW. This proves that the J and K input states present *at the time of the proper clock transition* are the ones transferred to the flip-flop output.

7) Set J = 1, K = 0. Note that nothing happens to Q. Apply a clock pulse, and observe that Q will go HIGH. Apply several more clock pulses. What happens to Q?
   It stays high

   m) Disconnect the pushbutton switch at the CLK input, and replace it with the output of a square wave generator set to 1 MHz (or the highest frequency obtainable). Connect the oscilloscope to observe the clock signal and output Q. Draw the waveforms displayed on the oscilloscope on Timing Diagram 15-1.

   Verify that the flip-flop changes states on the negative-going transitions and does not change states on the positive-going transitions. What is the frequency of the Q waveform compared to the clock waveform? *481 kHz*.

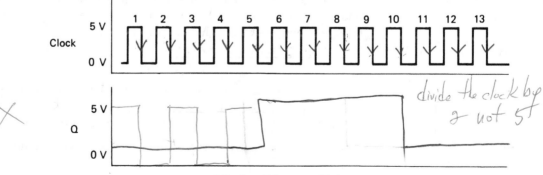

Timing Diagram 15-1

divide the clock by 2 not 5

   n) *74LS76 asynchronous operation:* The DC SET and DC CLEAR inputs are *asynchronous* inputs that operate independently from the synchronous inputs (J, K, CLK). The asynchronous inputs *override* the synchronous inputs when activated. Verify this by holding the DC CLEAR input LOW and observe that the flip-flop output stops toggling even though clock pulses are still being applied. Q will remain LOW, until the first clock pulse after the DC CLEAR pushbutton is released.

o) Disconnect the jumper connection from DC SET to V_{cc} at the V_{cc} end only, and touch this wire to ground. You should now observe that the flip-flop output stops toggling and remains HIGH as long as DC SET is held LOW.

p) *Edge-triggered D flip-flop—7474 IC:* Refer to the data sheet for a 7474 IC and draw its pin layout diagram:

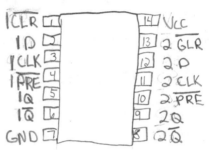

The 7474 IC has two individual positive edge-triggered D flip-flops with separate clock inputs and DC SET and DC CLEAR inputs.

Install a 7474 IC on the circuit board, and make the following connections to one of the D flip-flops:

1) Connect V_{cc} and DC SET to +5 V, GND to power ground.
2) Connect a toggle switch to the D input.
3) Connect a normally HIGH pushbutton switch to the CLK input.
4) Connect a normally HIGH pushbutton switch to DC CLEAR.
5) Connect LED monitors to Q and $\overline{Q}$ (or monitor the outputs with a logic probe)

q) *7474 synchronous operation:* Apply power and monitor the Q output. Observe that nothing happens when you toggle the D input switch back and forth. This is because the D input is a synchronous input that operates with the CLK input.

Clear Q to 0 by momentarily pulsing the DC CLEAR input LOW. Set D to and apply a negative-going transition at CLK. Do this by pressing and holding the CLK pushbutton LOW. What happens to Q?
_____Q stays low_____

Now apply a positive-going pulse at CLK by releasing the pushbutton switch. What happens? __Q tracks with the CLK__. This proves that the flip-flop responds only to positive-going transitions.

Make D = 0, and pulse CLK momentarily. This should clear Q back to 0.

r) *7474 asynchronous operation:* For both DC SET and DC CLEAR, verify the following:

1) The inputs are active LOW and do not require a pulse at CLK to become activated.
2) The inputs override the synchronous input signals.

s) *Review:* This concludes the first set of exercises on flip-flops and latches. In Experiment 16, you will continue your investigation of latches and flip-flops with D latches and master/slave flip-flops. To test your understanding of the principles demonstrated in this experiment, answer the following questions:

1. The Q output of a NAND gate latch can change from 1 to 0 only when S = __1__ and C = __0__, while a NOR gate latch can change from 1 to 0 only when S = __0__ and C = __1__.
2. The CLEAR conditions for a NAND gate latch are S = __1__ and C = __0__, while the CLEAR conditions for a NOR gate latch are S = __0__ and C = __1__.
3. The J and K input levels of a 74LS76 J-K flip-flop are transferred to the Q and $\overline{Q}$ outputs on the ____NGT____ at CLK.
4. The DC SET and DC CLEAR inputs to a 74LS76 J-K flip-flop are active LOW inputs and [operate with, operate independently from] the CLK signal. ✗
5. The D input level of a 7474 D flip-flop is transferred to the Q output of the flip-flop on the ____PGT____ at CLK.

Experiment 16

Name _Aaron Woods_
Marc Melsume
Mike Caboneme

FLIP-FLOPS II: D LATCH; MASTER/SLAVE FLIP-FLOPS

OBJECTIVES

1. To investigate the operation of a D latch, the 7475 IC.
2. To investigate the operation of a master/slave flip-flop, the 7476 IC.
3. To investigate the operation of a master/slave flip-flop with data lock-out, the 74111 IC.

TEXT REFERENCES

Read sections 5.8, 5.9, and 5.13.

EQUIPMENT NEEDED

Components
7475 IC;
7476 IC;
74111 IC;
normally HIGH pushbutton switch and normally LOW pushbutton switch, both debounced;
2 LED monitors.

Instruments
0–5 volt DC power supply;
logic probe (optional).

DISCUSSION

In this experiment, you are to investigate the behavior of the 7475 D-latch and master/slave flip-flops. The D latch is level-triggered and is frequently used to interface one processing unit with another. You will be asked to compare this flip-flop with the 7474 D flip-flop you examined in Experiment 15. Also in Experiment 15, you investigated edge-triggered flip-flops. Recall that these flip-flops have set-up and hold times that must be satisfied if the circuits which employ them are to work properly. In this experiment, you will examine the 7476 and 74111 J-K flip-flops. Both of these flip-flops have a set-up time of zero. But you will also discover that the 7476 is susceptible to input glitches and that the 74111 uses a data lockout feature to reduce its susceptibility to glitches. While master/slave flip-flops are still being used, they are being replaced in newer equipment with improved edge-triggered flip-flops.

PROCEDURE

a) *7475 IC D latch operation*: Refer to the data sheet for a 7475 IC, and draw its pin layout diagram:

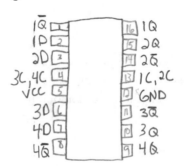

Note that the 7475 has four D latches. The latch CLK inputs are tied together in pairs resulting in dual two-bit D latches. You will use only one of the D latches for this experiment, so examine Figure 16-1 closely for the proper connections to be made.

b) Install a 7475 IC on the circuit board, and make the connections shown in Figure 16-1. Connect a toggle switch to D_1, a normally LOW pushbutton switch to CLK, and LED monitors to Q_1 and $\overline{Q}_1$. When the circuit is completed, perform the following steps:

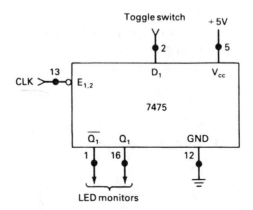

Figure 16-1

1) Turn the power supply on and monitor the outputs of the latch. Change the toggle switch back and forth a few times, and note that there is no effect on Q_1. This is because the latch is in the latch mode, and the data inputs are not enabled. Set $D_1 = 0$.

2) Press and hold the CLK input HIGH. Observe that Q_1 is LOW. Change D_1 back and forth a few times. What happens to Q_1? *Changes state*
Now set $D_1 = 1$, and release the CLK pushbutton. What happens to Q_1?
Q_1 is high

3) Change D_1 back and forth several times. Observe that Q_1 does not change. This proves that the data at D_1 is *latched* on the negative-going transition of the clock signal and that the output at Q_1 *follows* the data at D_1 while the clock signal is HIGH.

c) *7476 master/slave J-K flip-flop operation*: The 7476 IC is identical to the 74LS76 IC that was tested in Experiment 15, except that the flip-flop circuits are pulse-triggered instead of edge-triggered. This will permit you to observe the differences between edge-triggered flip-flops and master/slave flip-flops.

Install a 7476 IC on the circuit board, and make the following connections to one of the J-K flip-flops:

1) Connect V_{cc} and DC SET to +5 V, GND to power ground.
2) Connect toggle switches to the J and K inputs.
3) Connect a normally LOW pushbutton to CLK.
4) Connect a normally HIGH pushbutton switch to DC CLEAR.
5) Connect LED monitors to Q and $\overline{Q}$ (or monitor the outputs with a logic probe).

d) *7476 synchronous operation*: To test the synchronous operation of the 7476, do the following steps:

1) Set J = 1 and K = 0. Turn the power on and note the states of Q and $\overline{Q}$. If the flip-flop is not cleared (Q = 0), then pulse the DC CLEAR input LOW momentarily.

2) Press and hold the CLK input HIGH. You should observe that this has no effect on the outputs. Now release the pushbutton. What happens to Q?
Q = 0, and $\overline{Q}$ = 1

Pulse the CLK input several more times, and note that this has no effect on the outputs.

3) Change J to 0. Note that this has no effect on the outputs. Pulse the CLK input several times. You should observe that this also has no effect on the outputs. Why?
Because the CLK is already set @ high

4) Change K to 1, and note that Q does not change. Press and hold the CLK input HIGH. What happens to Q? *Nothing*. Now release the CLK pushbutton. What happens to Q now?
nothing *goes low* ✗

Pulse the CLK input several more times, and note that Q does not change.

5) Change J to 1. Note that Q remains LOW. Press and hold the CLK
pushbutton HIGH. What happens to Q? __nothing__.
Release the pushbutton. What happens to Q now? __Q goes high__.
Pulse the CLK input several more times. You should observe that Q changes
states on each CLK pulse.

_____ yes Q changes states on each CLK pulse.

e) In step d, you should have observed that the flip-flop loaded the J and K
inputs only when the CLK is HIGH, and they were transferred to Q and $\overline{Q}$ on a
negative-going transition at CLK. Now you will observe the chief disadvantage of
the master/slave: data at the J and K inputs can affect the flip-flop outputs any time
while the CLK input is HIGH.

Set J = 0 and K = 1. Clear the flip-flop by momentarily pulsing DC CLEAR
to LOW. Press and hold the CLK pushbutton HIGH. Change J to 1 and then back
to 0. Now release the pushbutton. You should observe that Q changes to 1 even
though J = 0 and K = 1 at the time of the negative-going transition. This demonstrates
that, should an unwanted glitch or noise spike occur on J or K while the CLK input
is HIGH, it may cause the flip-flop outputs to be invalid when CLK goes LOW.

f) *7476 asynchronous operation:* The DC SET and DC CLEAR inputs to the
7476 operate in the same manner as the asynchronous inputs of the 74LS76. Verify
that this is so.

Skip

g) *74111 master/slave J-K flip-flop operation:* Refer to the data sheet for a 74111
IC, and draw its pin layout diagram:

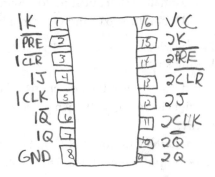

Note that this IC has dual J-K flip-flops similar to the 7476. However, the two
ICs are not pin compatible, and the 74111 has the data lockout feature. It is this
feature that we need to investigate.

Install a 74111 on the circuit board, and make the following connections to
one of the flip-flops:

1) Connect V_{cc} and DC SET to +5 V, GND to power ground.
2) Connect toggle switches to the J and K inputs.
3) Connect a normally LOW pushbutton switch to CLK.
4) Connect a normally HIGH pushbutton switch to DC CLEAR.
5) Connect LED monitors to Q and $\overline{Q}$ (or monitor the outputs with a logic
   probe).

Verify that the flip-flop operates according to its state table by repeating step
d above.

Set J = 0 and K = 1. Clear the flip-flop by momentarily pulsing DC CLEAR to LOW. Press and hold the CLK pushbutton HIGH. Change J to 1 and then back to 0. Now release the CLK pushbutton. You should observe that Q does not change. How does this differ from the 7476? ___*Skip*___.
Does this demonstrate that the 74111 J-K flip-flop is not susceptible to glitches while the clock is HIGH? *Skip*.

(h) *Review:* This concludes the exercises on flip-flops. To test your understanding of the principles covered in this experiment, answer the following questions:

1. The data input of a 7475 D latch is enabled when the CLK input is *high*.
   The data present at the D input is latched to the output when *enabled is low*

2. A 7476 J-K flip-flop transfers the data at the J and K inputs to Q and $\overline{Q}$ when   X
   needs a pulse trigger   *NGT of the clock occurs*

3. Based on your observations, explain how a single 7475 D latch operates differently from a 7474 D flip-flop.
   The 7475 D Latch operates differently from a 7474 D FF because the 7475 D Latch you need it to be enabled in order for the chip to change states.

latch - level triggered
FF - edge triggered

4. Based on your observations, explain how a 7476 J-K flip-flop operates differently from a 74LS76 J-K flip-flop.
   The 7476 J-K FF operates differently from a 74LS76 J-K FF because the 74LS76 J-K FF is faster and uses

5. Discuss how the data lockout feature works. *less power.*
   ← *Skip*

TROUBLESHOOTING FLIP-FLOP CIRCUITS

OBJECTIVES

1. To practice troubleshooting counting circuits containing IC flip-flops.
2. To practice troubleshooting register circuits containing IC flip-flops.
3. To investigate a flip-flop device timing problem, clock skew.

TEXT REFERENCES

Read sections 5.3 and 5.24.

EQUIPMENT NEEDED

Components
7400 IC;
7474 IC (2);
74LS76 IC (2);
normally HIGH pushbutton switch (2) and normally LOW pushbutton switch (2), all debounced;
4 LED monitors.

Instruments
0–5 volt DC power supply;
pulse or square wave generator;
dual trace oscilloscope;
ohmmeter;
logic pulser;
logic probe.

DISCUSSION

Circuits containing flip-flops can develop many of the faults that occur in combinatorial circuits. For example, flip-flops can develop opens and shorts at their inputs and outputs the same as gates do. Unlike gates, however, flip-flops possess memory, and it is this characteristic that can cause flip-flop circuits to behave differently than combinatorial circuits. For example, when trying to determine the cause for a given flip-flop output condition, you must remember that the signals causing the condition may not be present at the inputs to the flip-flop.

In the current experiment, you will first construct a simple asynchronous counting circuit and verify that the counter operates properly. Remember, it is rather difficult to troubleshoot a circuit without knowing how the circuit normally works. You will then have someone put a "bug" (fault) into the circuit for you to find. As always, do not look for the bug, and even if you should suspect what the bug is, use your troubleshooting techniques to isolate the problem. Also, before coming into the lab to perform the experiments, place various bugs into the circuit on paper and try to predict the response of the circuit.

The second exercise is similar to the first. The device used here is a shift register that is synchronous. The last exercise will give you an opportunity to investigate one type of timing problem in flip-flop circuits referred to as clock skew.

PROCEDURE

a) *Troubleshooting flip-flop counters:* Examine the circuit and its timing diagram in Figure 19-1. Since you will be clocking the counter manually at first, use Table 19-1 to make a state table for the counter. Construct the counter. Use a pushbutton switch to clear the counter. Use a logic pulser, if available, to clock the counter and a logic probe to monitor the output of each flip-flop. If a pulser is not available, use a debounced pushbutton switch.

Table 19-1

Clock	Output State		
Pulse	X_2	X_1	X_0
0	0	0	0
1			
2			
3			
4			
5			
6			
7			
8			

b) To begin the exercise, have your instructor or lab assistant place a fault into your counter while your back is turned. Now test the circuit and make a state table using Table 19-2. If the two are different, your circuit is indeed not operating correctly. In the space provided below, list as many possible faults as you can which could cause the circuit to malfunction in this manner.

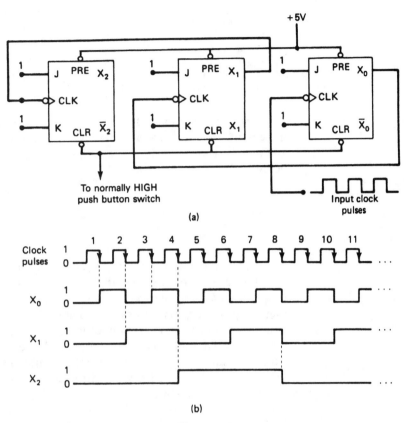

(a)

(b)

Figure 19-1

Table 19-2

Clock	Output State		
Pulse	X_2	X_1	X_0
0	0	0	0
1			
2			
3			
4			
5			
6			
7			
8			

c) Once you have listed as many faults as you can, proceed to troubleshoot the circuit. When you have isolated the bug, remove it and check the circuit once again. When you have done this, write a description of the bug in the space provided below.

d) In the preceding steps, you clocked the counter manually and used a state table to troubleshoot the circuit. In practice, some counters are used to divide the frequency of a signal, and in some counters it is not easy to clock the circuit manually. In fact, in many cases it is desirable to use the clock of the system that is being examined whenever troubleshooting a counter circuit. In these cases, a timing diagram and a dual trace oscilloscope could be used to troubleshoot the counter. Connect a square wave generator to the counter and use the oscilloscope to monitor the outputs. Compare the waveforms on the oscilloscope to those of Figure 19-1. If you removed the bug from steps b and c successfully, they should be the same. If they are not the same, you still have not removed the bug and should do so now. Now have your instructor or laboratory assistant introduce a new bug into your circuit. Draw a timing diagram for the counter in the space provided below and compare these waveforms to those of Figure 19-1 They should differ depending on the bug that was installed. Use the oscilloscope to isolate the circuit fault.

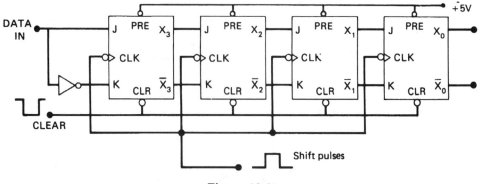

Figure 19-2

Table 19-3

Shift	Output State			
Pulse	X_3	X_2	X_1	X_0
0	0	0	0	0
1	1	0	0	0
2				
3				
4				
5				

e) *Troubleshooting flip-flop shift registers:* Examine the circuit and timing diagram of Figure 19-2. Use Table 19-3 to make a state table for the circuit. Construct the circuit. If a pulser is available, use the pulser for the clock. If a pulser is not available, connect a normally HIGH pushbutton switch (debounced) to the circuit's clock input. Connect the circuit's CLEAR input to a normally HIGH pushbutton switch. Connect a toggle switch to the data input (DATA IN).

f) Pulse the CLEAR input LOW momentarily to clear the register. Set the data input switch to HIGH. Pulse the clock input once and then set the data input switch LOW. Test the register by pulsing the clock enough times to cause the register to go through all of its remaining states, and check the output of each flip-flop after each clock pulse. Compare your observations with Table 19-3. When the register is operating correctly, have your instructor introduce a fault into the register circuit.

g) Test your circuit, and make a state table using Table 19-4. Compare your observations with Table 19-3. If they are not the same, you must troubleshoot. Begin by listing in the space provided below as many possible faults as you can that would cause the circuit to behave the way it currently does.

Table 19-4

Shift	Output State			
Pulse	X_3	X_2	X_1	X_0
0	0	0	0	0
1	1	0	0	0
2				
3				
4				
5				

h) Use the pulser (or debounced switch) and probe to isolate the fault. When you believe you have found the fault, write a brief description of the bug below.

i) *Troubleshooting timing problems—clock skew:* Construct the circuit in Figure 19-3. If a logic pulser is available, use the pulser to clock the circuit. Connect a normally HIGH pushbutton switch to the CLEAR circuit. You will monitor the flip-flop outputs with a logic probe.

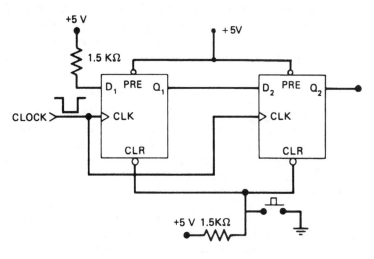

Figure 19-3

j) Test the circuit using the timing diagram provided in Figure 19.4. When the circuit is operating correctly, modify the circuit according to Figure 19.5. Now retest the circuit. You should notice that the circuit may not be functioning correctly, due to the additional propogational delay inserted in this step. If it still works correctly, add two inverters between the NAND gate and the CLK input of FF2, and retest the circuit operation.

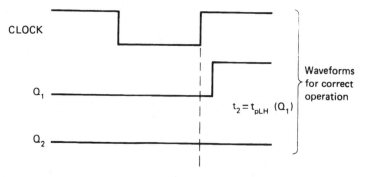

Figure 19-4

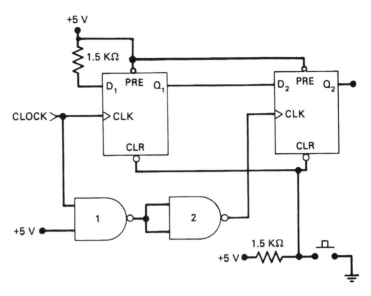

Figure 19-5

k) *Review*: This concludes the exercises on troubleshooting flip-flop devices. To test your understanding of the principles investigated in this experiment, answer the following questions:

1. What would happen to the counter in Figure 19-1 if $\overline{X}_1$ becomes shorted to ground?

2. In Figure 19-3, if FF_1 and FF_2 are both 74LS74 IC D flip-flops, and G_1 and G_2 are 74L00 IC NAND gates, would it seem likely that clock skew could be a problem? _____ .

3. Answer review question 2 if FF_1 and FF_2 are both 74LS74 IC D flip-flops and G_1 and G_2 are 7400 IC NAND gates. _____

BINARY ADDERS AND 2'S COMPLEMENT SYSTEM

OBJECTIVES

1. To investigate the operation of a half adder.
2. To investigate the operation of a full adder.
3. To investigate the operation of a two-bit ripple adder.
4. To investigate the operation of a 7483A IC adder.
5. To investigate the operation of a 2's complement adder/subtractor circuit.

TEXT REFERENCES

Read sections 6.1 through 6.4 and sections 6.9 through 6.15.

EQUIPMENT NEEDED

Components
7400 IC;
7404 IC;
7432 IC;
7474 IC (4);
7483A IC;
7486 IC;
6 toggle switches;
normally HIGH pushbutton switch;
normally LOW pushbutton switch (2);
10 LED monitors.

Instrument

0–5 volt DC power supply.

DISCUSSION

At the heart of digital computers and calculators is the arithmetic unit. Depending on the system, this unit can range in complexity from the very simple, such as an adder, to a unit that possesses the capabilities of computing values for special functions, such as trigonometric and logarithmic functions. No matter how complex the unit is, its most important function is still addition.

At a minimum, arithmetic units usually consist of two flip-flop registers, one of which is called the *accumulator*, and the arithmetic circuits, which are special combinatorial circuits. The arithmetic circuit is fed data (operands) by the two registers and stores its answer into the accumulator.

In the current experiment, you will investigate one type of arithmetic circuit, the parallel binary adder. This circuit adds two binary numbers by operating on pairs of bits (a bit from one operand and the corresponding bit from the other operand) with units called full adders or half adders and generating carry bits that are fed to the next highest significant adder. Full adders have a third input to receive the carry bit output of the previous adder. Half adders do not and are thus used only to add the least significant bits of the two numbers being added. You will then investigate an IC four-bit parallel adder, the 7483A, and use this IC to construct a 2's complement adder/subtractor.

PROCEDURE

a) *Half adder:* In review question 3, Experiment 12, you were asked to design the circuit for a half adder. Redraw your circuit in the space provided below.

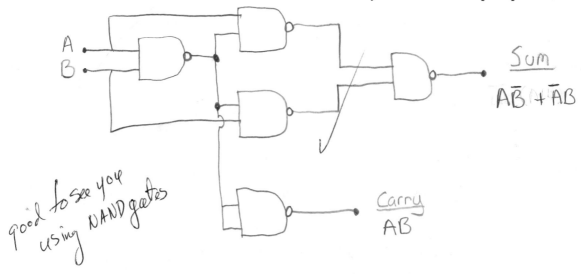

good to see you using NAND gates

b) Construct the half adder. Connect toggle switches to the two inputs and LED monitors to both outputs. When construction is completed, test the half adder, using Table 20-1 to record your observations on the Sum and Carry outputs.

Table 20-1

Inputs		Outputs	
A	B	S	C
0	0	0	0
0	1	1	0
1	0	1	0
1	1	0	1

c) *Full adder:* Draw the circuit for a full adder:

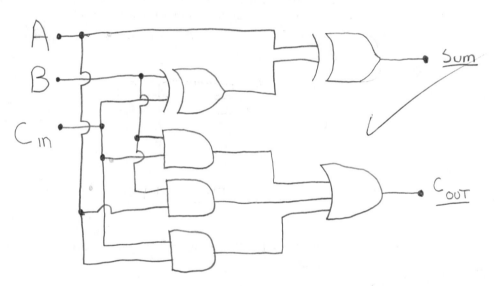

d) Construct the full adder. Connect toggle switches to each input and LED monitors to both outputs. When construction is completed, test the full adder, using Table 20-2 to record your observations on the sum and carry outputs.

Table 20-2

Inputs			Outputs	
A	B	C_i	S	C
0	0	0	0	0
0	0	1	1	0
0	1	0	1	0
0	1	1	0	1
1	0	0	1	0
1	0	1	0	1
1	1	0	0	1
1	1	1	1	1

e) *Two-bit ripple adder:* Connect the half adder and full adder together, according to the diagram shown in Figure 20-1 to form a two-bit ripple adder.

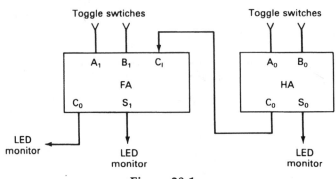

Figure 20-1

Test the operation of the adder by setting the toggle switches to several different values and observing the sum and carry indicated by the LED monitors. Demonstrate the circuit operation for your instructor.

f) *7483A IC adder operation:* Refer to the data sheet for a 7483A IC, and draw its pin layout diagram:

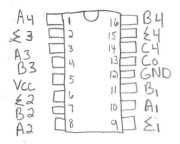

g) Install a 7483A IC on the circuit board, and make the following connections:

1) Connect V_{cc} to +5 V and GND to power ground.
2) Connect C_0 to power ground.
3) Connect toggle switches to inputs A_0 through A_3 and B_0 through B_3.
4) Connect LED monitors to sum outputs S_0 through S_3 and also to C_4.

Table 20-3

Inputs								Outputs				
A_3	A_2	A_1	A_0	B_3	B_2	B_1	B_0	C_4	S_3	S_2	S_1	S_0
0	0	1	1	0	0	0	1	0	0	0	1	1
0	1	1	1	1	0	0	1	1	0	0	0	0
1	0	1	1	0	1	0	1	0	1	1	0	1
1	1	1	1	1	1	1	1	1	1	1	1	0

h) Verify that the adder is operating correctly by entering the input values listed in Table 20-3 and recording your observations on the outputs in the table.

i) *Adder/Subtractor:* Examine the circuit of Figure 20-2. The circuit is for a parallel adder/subtractor using the 2's complement number system. Investigate the possibility of simplifying the circuit somewhat by examining the AND-OR circuits. The right simplification will permit you to replace the ADD and SUB control lines with a single control line, X. When X = 0, the circuit will function as an adder; when X = 1, it will function as a subtractor. When you believe that you have found a way to simplify the circuit, draw the simplified diagram below, and show it to your instructor or laboratory assistant. HINT: consider using exclusive-OR circuits as controlled inverters.

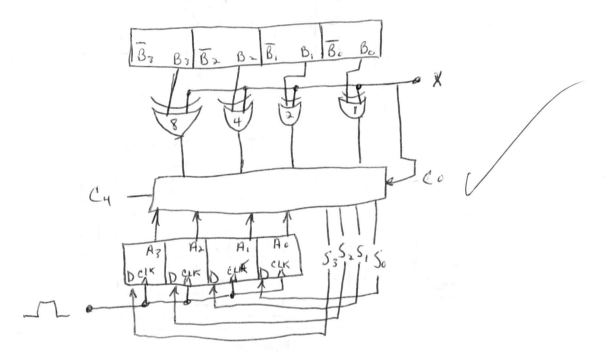

j) Construct the circuit you drew in step i. Connect toggle switches to each D input of register B. Also, connect a toggle switch to control line X. Connect LED monitors to the 7483A sum outputs (S_3 through S_0) and carry output C_4, switch X, and register A outputs (A_3 through A_0).

The clock inputs of register A flip-flops should be connected to a single normally LOW pushbutton switch (ADD/SUB pulse input). The clock inputs of register B should all be tied to a single normally LOW pushbutton switch (TRANSFER line, not shown). Tie the DC SET inputs for both registers A and B HIGH. Finally, tie the DC CLEAR inputs for register A to a normally HIGH pushbutton switch, so that the register may be cleared to begin a new sequence of operations.

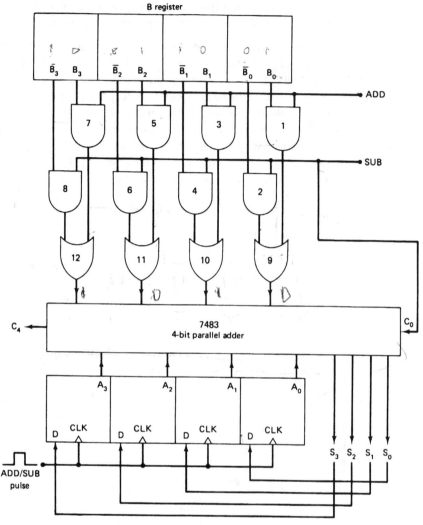

Figure 20-2

k) The circuit operates in the following manner:

1) To clear the unit, pulse the DC CLEAR pushbutton switch momentarily LOW.
2) To ADD a number to register A, set X to 0. To SUBTRACT a number from register A, set X to 1.
3) To enter a number to be added or subtracted, set toggle switches B_3 through B_0 to the value of the number, then pulse the TRANSFER line momentarily HIGH to clock the data into register B. The LED monitors at the 7483A sum and carry outputs should now indicate the new sum (or difference) of [A] and [B].
4) Pulse the ADD/SUB line momentarily HIGH to clock the sum outputs from the 7483A into register A. The LEDs at the outputs of register A should now indicate the new accumulated sum (or difference).
5) Repeat steps 2–4 until all numbers have been added (or subtracted). The final result will be indicated by the register A output monitors.

l) Perform the following operations with the adder/subtractor unit:

1) 1 + 2 + 3 + 4 = __10__.
2) +7 + (-1) + (-2) + (-3) = __1__.
3) +1 - (-3) - (-2) = __0__. -12
4) -3 + (-2) + (-3) - (+4) = __-12__.
5) 9 - 1 - 3 - 2 = __3__. 8
6) +1 - (+5) - (+4) = __-8__.
7) 5 - 4 - 6 - 7 = __-12__.

m) *Review:* This concludes the exercises on binary adders. To test your understanding of the principles investigated in this experiment, answer the following questions:

1. A half adder may be made from a full adder by _taken Cout_.
2. How many outputs must an adder have if it is to add two 8-bit numbers?
   __8__. 9 X

3. What is the range of SIGNED numbers that a 7483A adder can operate on?
   __8 Bit__.   X   sign 1   XXX   3 Maquitude bits -2^U to 2N-1
                                                    = -8 to +7
4. Explain how register A, in the 2's complement adder/subtractor, acts like an accumulator in a digital arithmetic unit.

X

11.3　Recycling asynchronous counter 3

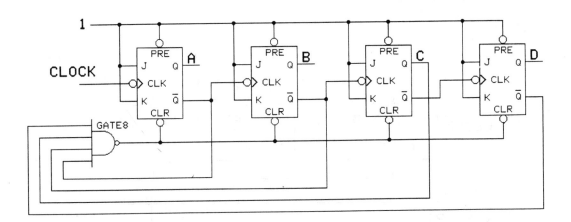

11.4　Recycling asynchronous counter 4

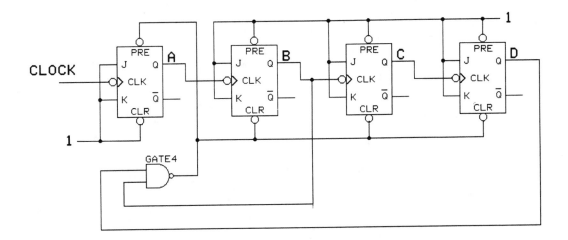

11.5   Self-stopping asynchronous counter
Determine the count sequence produced after an active-low RESTART pulse has been
applied to the counter.

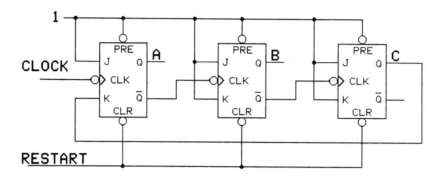

SYNCHRONOUS COUNTERS

Objectives

- To analyze synchronous counter circuits to predict their theoretical operation.
- To construct and test synchronous counter circuit designs.

Suggested Parts				
74LS00	74LS08	74LS32	74LS20	74LS112A

<u>Synchronous Counters</u>

Synchronous or parallel counters are triggered by a common clocking signal applied to each flip-flop. Because of this clocking arrangement, all flip-flops react to their individual synchronous control inputs at the same time. The count sequence depends on the control signals input to each flip-flop. Additionally, the flip-flop asynchronous control inputs, preset and clear, may be used to modify the count sequence.

Example 12-1

Analyze the synchronous counter circuit given in Fig. 12-1. Draw the state transition diagram (include all 8 possible states) for the counter. Also draw the counter's timing diagram. Determine the modulus for the counter.

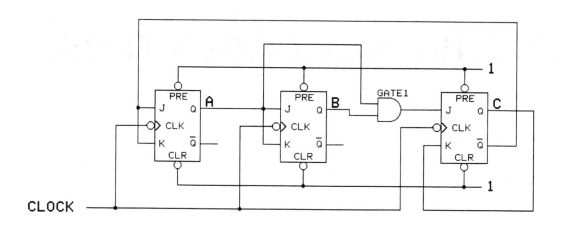

Fig. 12-1 Synchronous counter schematic for example 12-1

To analyze the counter, the circuit excitation (or present state - next state) table given in Table 12-1 is produced. The counter is assumed to start at state 000. The analysis indicates that the counter is a mod-5 counter.

CLOCK	Present State C B A			J_C	K_C	J_B	K_B	J_A	K_A	Next State C B A		
0	0	0	0	0	0	0	0	1	1	0	0	1
1	0	0	1	0	0	1	1	1	1	0	1	0
2	0	1	0	0	0	0	0	1	1	0	1	1
3	0	1	1	1	0	1	1	1	1	1	0	0
4	1	0	0	0	1	0	0	0	0	0	0	0
	1	0	1	0	1	1	1	0	0	0	1	1
	1	1	0	0	1	0	0	0	0	0	1	0
	1	1	1	1	1	1	1	0	0	0	0	1

Table 12-1 Complete present state - next state table for example 12-1

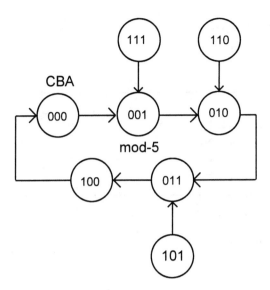

Fig. 12-2 State transition diagram for synchronous counter in example 12-1

Laboratory Projects

Analyze the following synchronous counters. For each counter, determine the counter's modulus and sketch its timing diagram (show the clock input and the flip-flops' Q outputs). Construct and test the operation of the counter circuits. Use an oscilloscope to compare the output waveforms for each of the counters with your theoretical prediction.

12.1   Synchronous counter 1

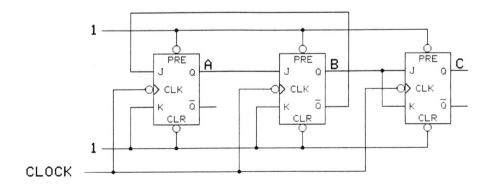

12.2 Synchronous counter 2

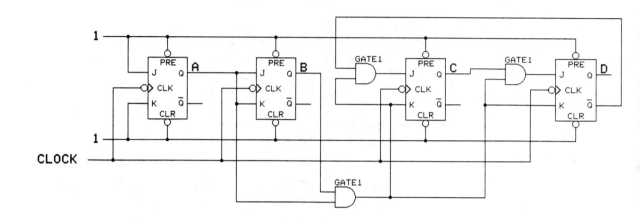

12.3 Synchronous counter 3

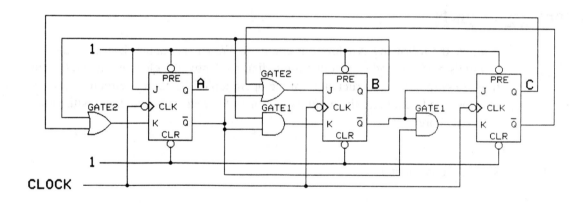

12.4 Synchronous counter 4

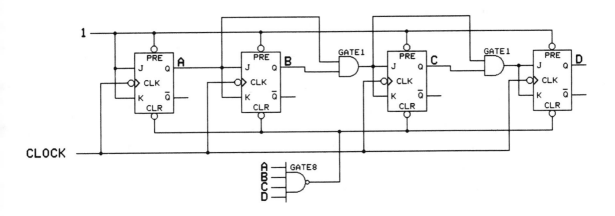

12.5 Synchronous counter 5

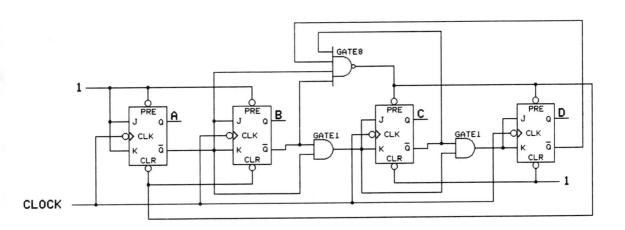

BCD IC COUNTERS

OBJECTIVES

1. To investigate the operation of the 7490 IC counter.
2. To demonstrate that BCD counters may be displayed directly with seven-segment display units.
3. To investigate the cascading of 7490 IC counters.

TEXT REFERENCES

Read sections 7.1 through 7.3 and sections 7.11, 7.13, and section 9.3.

EQUIPMENT NEEDED

Components

7446 IC (2);
7490 IC (2);
FND507 seven-segment display units (2);
130 ohm resistors (14);
normally HIGH pushbutton switch (debounced).

Instruments

0–5 volt DC power supply;
pulse or square wave generator;
dual trace oscilloscope.

DISCUSSION

A special IC asynchronous counter is the 7490 BCD counter. There are many applications in digital systems for MOD-10 counters, and since many of these systems use BCD interfaces, counters like the 7490 are often included in the design. An example where BCD is employed is the output indicator of a frequency counter (see Experiment 24).

7490 IC Counter

The 7490 is similar to the 7493. It contains a single toggle flip-flop, a MOD-5 counter, and a gated reset circuit, which can be wired together externally to configure the counter as a BCD counter, which counts from 0 to 9. It may also be configured as a divide-by-10 counter, which does not count sequentially, and therefore is not a BCD counter.

Also, like the 7493, the counter can be wired to produce a counter that has a MOD-number less than 10, although this is not done often in practice. You should be aware that the MOD-5 counter internal to the 7490 is a three-bit counter with a MOD-number that has been reduced from 8 to 5 by internal wiring. The 7490 is often cascaded with other counters whenever the desired MOD-number has the numbers ten and/or five as factors. For example, cascading a 7493 wired as a four-bit counter with a 7490 wired as a BCD counter will result in a counter with a MOD-number of 16 x 10 = 160.

In the current experiment, you will investigate the 7490 operating in both of its primary modes, the symmetrical MOD-10 and BCD MOD-10 modes. You will also investigate cascading two BCD counters to form a MOD-100 counter.

BCD Displays

It is often desirable to display the count of a BCD counter. In many applications, a seven-segment LED display is used. The outputs of BCD counters must be converted from BCD into seven-segment codes and then applied to the seven-segment devices through current booster circuits called *drivers*. Both of these functions are found in the 7446 IC BCD-to-seven-segment decoder/driver. In this experiment, you will learn how to connect a 7446 and a seven-segment LED device to function as a BCD display unit.

PROCEDURE

a) Refer to the data sheet for the 7490 IC. This IC contains four flip-flops, which may be arranged as a BCD counter. To do this, the output of flip-flop A must be tied externally to the input of flip-flop B. The MSB of this counter is Q_3, and the LSB is Q_0. The counter's MOD-number may be changed by making the appropriate external connections. The operation of this counter is similar to that of the 7493, which was investigated in Experiment 21.

Draw the pin layout diagram for this IC:

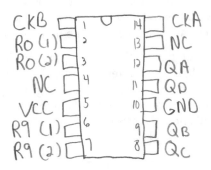

b) *7490 IC operation—symmetrical MOD-10 configuration:* There are two ways to configure the 7490 as a MOD-10 counter. In this step you will investigate the symmetrical MOD-10 configuration. Install a 7490 IC on the circuit board, and wire the counter so that it is like that of Figure 22-1. Connect a normally HIGH pushbutton switch to $\overline{CP}_1$. Connect LED monitors to Q_0, Q_1, Q_2, and Q_3 (Q_0 = MSB; Q_1 = LSB).

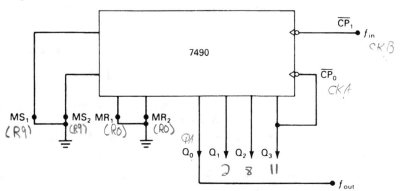

Figure 22-1

c) Pulse $\overline{CP}_1$ repeatedly, and observe the count sequence displayed on the LEDs. Record your observations in Table 22-1. Note that the counter does have ten different states, but the order in which they occur is not the normal binary sequence.

Table 22-1

Input Pulse Applied	Q3	Q2	Q1	Q0	Decimal Number
None	0	0	0	0	0
1	0	0	0	1	2
2	0	0	1	0	4
3	0	0	1	1	6
4	0	1	0	0	8
5	0	1	0	1	2
6	0	1	1	0	3
7	0	1	1	1	5
8	0	1	1	1	7
9	1	0	0	0	9
10	1	0	0	1	0
	0	0	0	0	

d) Disconnect the pushbutton switch, and apply a 10 kHz square wave to $\overline{CP}_1$. Observe the output at Q_0 on the oscilloscope. You should observe that the waveform is a 1 kHz square wave. The square wave signal was obtained by altering the counting sequence while maintaining 10 states.

e) *BCD MOD-10 configuration:* The second way the 7490 can be configured as a MOD-10 counter is the BCD configuration. Rearrange the wiring of the 7490 so that the circuit is like that of Figure 22-2. Connect a normally HIGH pushbutton switch to $\overline{CP}_0$. Connect LED monitors to outputs Q_0, Q_1, Q_2, and Q_3. This time Q_0 = LSB and Q_3 = MSB.

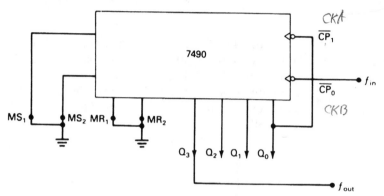

Figure 22-2

f) Pulse $\overline{CP}_0$ repeatedly and observe the count sequence displayed on the LEDs. Record your observations in Table 22-2. You should observe that the sequence is now normal binary and that there are still 10 different states.

Table 22-2

Input Pulse Applied	Output States Q_3 Q_2 Q_1 Q_0				Decimal Number
None	0	0	0	0	0
1	0	0	0	1	1
2	0	0	1	0	2
3	0	0	1	1	3
4	0	1	0	0	4
5	0	1	0	1	5
6	0	1	1	0	6
7	0	1	1	1	7
8	1	0	0	0	8
9	1	0	0	1	9
10	0	0	0	0	10

g) Now disconnect the pushbutton switch from the counter input, and apply a 10 kHz square wave in its place. Observe the signal at Q_3, and draw it in Timing Diagram 22-1. Note that the signal is 1 kHz but not a square wave.

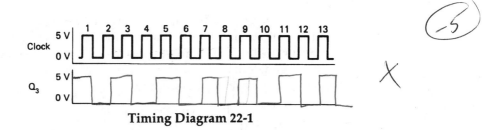

Timing Diagram 22-1

h) *Displaying BCD counters:* The count of the BCD counter can be more conveniently displayed in decimal. One of the most common devices used to display BCD counters is the seven-segment LED driven by a BCD-to-seven-segment decoder/driver, such as a 7446 IC. The seven segments that make up the display device each consist of one or two LEDs, and all are connected in a common cathode or common anode arrangement. The decimal digits are formed by turning on the appropriate segments (see Figure 22-3). The decoder/driver unit decodes a BCD number and supplies the correct levels at its outputs that will cause a seven-segment display unit to display the correct decimal digit.

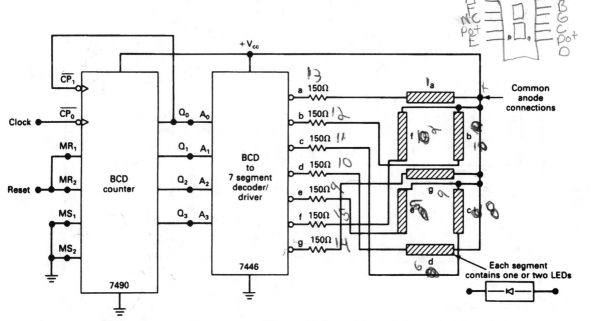

Figure 22-3

Refer to the data sheet for a 7446 IC, and draw its pin layout diagram:

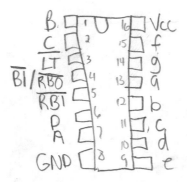

Now examine the circuit of Figure 22-3, and then construct it. Connect a normally LOW pushbutton switch to the reset-to-zero pins. Connect a square wave generator set to a low frequency, and observe that the seven-segment unit is counting in decimal. Pulse the reset pushbutton switch, and note that the counter resets to 0, then continues counting.

Demonstrate the counter for your instructor.

i) *Cascading BCD counters:* BCD counters may be cascaded to count in decimal fashion. For example, two BCD counters may be cascaded to count from 00 to 99. The input counter of such an arrangement will count units, while the output counter will count tens. Refer to Figure 22-4, and cascade two 7490 ICs together to perform this function. Use seven-segment display units to display the counters' outputs. Demonstrate the counter to your instructor when it is operating correctly.

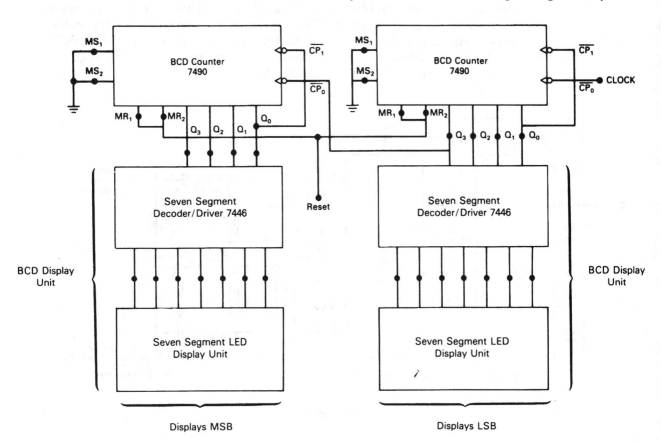

Figure 22-4

j) *Review:* This completes the exercises on BCD counters. To test your
understanding of the principles covered in this experiment, answer the following
questions:

1. Based on your observations, does the count sequence of a counter determine
   the MOD-number of a counter? __Yes__ ✗. NO

2. Four 7490 IC counters are all configured to count BCD and are cascaded
   together. What is the MOD-number of the resulting counter? __15__. What is
   the highest decimal number that can be displayed by the counter? __9999__. ✓

$16 \times 16 \times 10 \times 10 = 10,000$

✗

3. Draw a diagram showing how you would convert a 7490 BCD counter into a
   MOD-6 counter. HINT: use the reset-to-zero inputs.

−25

SEQUENTIAL CIRCUIT DESIGN USING PROGRAMMABLE LOGIC DEVICES

Objective

- To design and implement sequential logic circuits using programmable logic devices (PLDs).

Suggested Part
GAL16V8

Sequential Circuits Using PLDs

Many programmable logic devices contain flip-flops and, therefore, can also be used to implement sequential circuits. The design and implementation of sequential circuits using CUPL is carried out in much the same fashion as for combinatorial circuits. The flip-flops contained in most PLDs are D type flip-flops in which the D inputs are produced by the programmable AND/OR gate structure in the PLD. A registered output pin is defined in the logic equations by using the pin modifier ".D" attached to the output pin name. CUPL also provides a convenient means to define many types of sequential circuits called state machine entry. State machine entry uses a "present-state, next-state" format to define the desired sequence of states. The operation of a sequential circuit can also be easily controlled by external signals in the state machine definition. While very flexible and easy to implement for relatively low modulus counters, the state machine entry is somewhat cumbersome for higher mods. The high level language framework of CUPL provides many other options for defining sequential circuits.

The GAL16V8 can be programmed to provide registered outputs on any of its eight output pins. Whenever at least one of the outputs from the GAL16V8 uses a D flip-flop to produce the output, the chip is said to be programmed in the registered mode. In the registered mode of operation, pin 1 is automatically configured to be the clock pin for all flip-flops used (synchronous clocking) and pin 11 is the common tristate output enable pin (active-low) for all registered outputs (but not combinational outputs). Neither of these two pins can be defined to be any other type of input to the PLD when it is configured for a registered output.

Example 14-1

Design a counter using a GAL16V8 that produces the 4-bit, irregular, recycling sequence given in the timing diagram of Fig. 14-1.

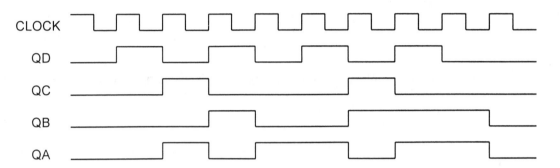

Fig. 14-1 Timing diagram for sequential design example 14-1

A CUPL logic description file solution is shown in Fig. 14-2. Pin 1 is the clock input and pin 11 is the tristate output enable control for the flip-flops. The tristate control was not specified for this application and, therefore, pin 11 should be grounded to permanently enable the flip-flop outputs for this counter. The "$define" command is a CUPL preprocessor command. The "$define" command is used to replace a given character string by another specified operator, number, or variable name. In this example file, each of the 16 binary combinations that is possible with 4-bits is given the variable names of S0 through S15. The names are arbitrary and this application will use only nine of the states, but all of the possible 4-bit counter states have been defined for our convenience so that any 4-bit counter sequence can be easily defined by minor changes in this file. The "$" symbol is the first character for all preprocessor commands and it must be placed in column 1 of the line. Preprocessor command lines do not end with a semicolon. The logic definition (equations) section uses the state machine entry format (indicated by the keyword "sequence") to describe the sequence for this counter. The output bits of the counter are listed after "sequence."

```
Name       IRREGSEQ;              Partno     L155-17A;
Date       07/17/93;              Revision   01;
Designer   Greg Moss;             Company    Digi-Lab;
Assembly   Example board;         Location   U121;
Device     G16V8A;                Format     j;

/****************************************************/
/*  Synchronous counter with irregular sequence     */
/*   0 -> 8 -> 5 -> A -> 1 -> 9 -> 6 -> B -> 3 -> 0  */
/****************************************************/

/**  Inputs  **/
Pin  1  =  CLK;                    /* CLOCK INPUT    */
Pin 11  =  !OE;                    /* OUTPUT ENABLE  */

/**  Outputs  **/
Pin [14..17]  =  [QA,QB,QC,QD];    /* COUNTER OUTPUTS */

/** Declarations and Intermediate Variable Definitions **/
field irregcnt = [QD,QC,QB,QA];         /* counter bits */

$define S0  'b'0000              /* define counter states */
$define S1  'b'0001
$define S2  'b'0010
$define S3  'b'0011
$define S4  'b'0100
$define S5  'b'0101
$define S6  'b'0110
$define S7  'b'0111
$define S8  'b'1000
$define S9  'b'1001
$define S10 'b'1010
$define S11 'b'1011
$define S12 'b'1100
$define S13 'b'1101
$define S14 'b'1110
$define S15 'b'1111

/** Logic Definition **/
sequence    irregcnt    {   present S0      next S8;
                            present S8      next S5;
                            present S5      next S10;
                            present S10     next S1;
                            present S1      next S9;
                            present S9      next S6;
                            present S6      next S11;
                            present S11     next S3;
                            present S3      next S0;
                        }
```

Fig. 14-2 CUPL design logic description file for example 14-1

In this example, the output bits have been assigned a field name. The braces {} mark the beginning and end of the state machine description. The sequence desired is represented in a series of present state and next state combinations. The desired sequence can be easily changed by simply changing the order of the states. Each present state must be unique in the sequence description.

Example 14-2

Design an up/down, recycling decade counter using a GAL16V8. The mod-10 counter also has count enable, count direction, and counter reset controls. The counter should also produce a ripple carry output signal that goes low for the last state in the up count or down count sequence.

CLR	ENABLE	DIR	function
0	0	X	HOLD
0	1	0	COUNT UP
0	1	1	COUNT DOWN
1	X	X	CLEAR

A CUPL design solution is shown in Fig. 14-3. In this logic description file, the count enable and direction control bits are grouped together as a field and intermediate variables are defined for the count up and count down modes of operation. The ten counter states are given labels with the "$define" command and the count sequence is described in the state machine format. In this case, the next state that will be produced by the counter is dependent on the three external control inputs (CLR, ENABLE, and DIR). For each present state, if the counter is not being cleared and the "up" bit combination is asserted, then the next state will be the resulting up count state. If, on the other hand, the counter is not being cleared and the "down" bit combination is asserted, then the resulting next state would be the previous value in a down count sequence. If CLR is active, then the next state will always be 0000. The default condition would exist if the counter is not enabled and the count should remain in the same state. The ripple carry output signal should be asserted under two different circumstances. It should be active during the state "S0" if the counter is counting down or during state "S9" if the counter is counting up. The keyword "OUT" is used to assert the combinational output signal "ripple" (which is active-low) during the proper state.

```
Name      MOD10;                    Partno    L155-17A;
Date      07/17/93;                 Revision  01;
Designer  Greg Moss;                Company   Digi-Lab;
Assembly  Example board;            Location  U129;
Device    G16V8A;                   Format    j;

/*********************************************************/
/* up/down decade counter with synchronous clear        */
/* counter also has an asynchronous ripple carry output */
/*********************************************************/

/**   Inputs   **/
pin 1 = CLK;              /* Counter clock            */
pin 2 = CLR;              /* Counter clear input      */
pin 3 = DIR;             /* Counter direction input   */
pin 4 = ENABLE;          /* Counter enable           */
pin 11 = !OE;            /* Register output enable    */

/**   Outputs   **/
pin [19..16] = [Q3..0];      /* Counter outputs      */
pin 15 = !ripple;            /* Ripple carry out      */


/** Declarations and Intermediate Variable Definitions **/
field counter = [Q3..0];         /* counter bit field  */
field mode = [ENABLE,DIR];       /* mode control field */

up = mode:2;                     /* define count up mode    */
down = mode:3;                   /* define count down mode  */

$define S0 'b'0000           /* define counter states   */
$define S1 'b'0001
$define S2 'b'0010
$define S3 'b'0011
$define S4 'b'0100
$define S5 'b'0101
$define S6 'b'0110
$define S7 'b'0111
$define S8 'b'1000
$define S9 'b'1001


/** Logic Equations **/

sequence counter    {
    present S0    if  !CLR  &  up        next S1;
                 if  !CLR  &  down      next S9;
                 if   CLR               next S0;
                 default                next S0;
                     if down     OUT  ripple;
    present S1    if  !CLR  &  up        next S2;
                 if  !CLR  &  down      next S0;
                 if   CLR               next S0;
                 default                next S1;
    present S2    if  !CLR  &  up        next S3;
                 if  !CLR  &  down      next S1;
                 if   CLR               next S0;
                 default                next S2;
```

151

```
present S3     if   !CLR   &   up        next S4;
               if   !CLR   &   down      next S2;
               if    CLR             next S0;
               default               next S3;
present S4     if   !CLR   &   up        next S5;
               if   !CLR   &   down      next S3;
               if    CLR             next S0;
               default               next S4;
present S5     if   !CLR   &   up        next S6;
               if   !CLR   &   down      next S4;
               if    CLR             next S0;
               default               next S5;
present S6     if   !CLR   &   up        next S7;
               if   !CLR   &   down      next S5;
               if    CLR             next S0;
               default               next S6;
present S7     if   !CLR   &   up        next S8;
               if   !CLR   &   down      next S6;
               if    CLR             next S0;
               default               next S7;
present S8     if   !CLR   &   up        next S9;
               if   !CLR   &   down      next S7;
               if    CLR             next S0;
               default               next S8;
present S9     if   !CLR   &   up        next S0;
               if   !CLR   &   down      next S8;
               if    CLR             next S0;
               default               next S9;
                    if up        OUT  ripple;
               }
```

Fig. 14-3 CUPL design logic description file for example 14-2

Example 14-3

Design a mod-100, recycling, BCD counter using a GAL16V8. The two-digit decade counter also needs to have an active-low count enable control EN.

A CUPL design solution is shown in Fig. 14-4. Since describing the count sequence for a mod-100 counter in state machine format would be rather long and tedious, logic equations have been written for the two decade counters. The 4-bits for each of the two decade counters have been grouped together as a field. In writing each of the two decade counter equations, the extension ".D" is used to indicate that the outputs are to be registered outputs. The GAL16V8 will be in registered mode and the equations represent the inputs to each of the D flip-flops. The logic equation for the LSD counter can be interpreted as: If the counter is enabled, after being clocked the LSD will be equal to the decimal value 1 if the LSD currently is equal to 0, or it will be equal to a decimal 2 if it is currently equal to 1, or to 3 if it is currently 2, etc. If the counter is not enabled, then the LSD counter should remain in the same state after it is clocked. The MSD equation is similar, but it must also take into account the state of the LSD counter to determine its count action. The least significant digit must control

```
Name        MOD-100;              Partno    L155-17C;
Date        07/17/93;             Revision  01;
Designer    Greg Moss;            Company   Digi-Lab;
Assembly    Example board;        Location  U126;
Device      G16V8A;               Format    j;

/***********************************************************/
/* Synchronous MOD-100 BCD up counter with enable     */
/***********************************************************/

/**   Inputs   **/
Pin  1  =  CLK;                           /* Clock input    */
Pin  2  =  !EN;                           /* Count enable   */
Pin 11  =  !OE;            /* Register output enable  */

/**   Outputs   **/
Pin [12..15] = [L0..3];        /* Counter LSD output  */
Pin [16..19] = [M0..3];        /* Counter MSD output  */


/**   Declarations and Intermediate Variable Definitions
**/

field LSD = [L3..0];
field MSD = [M3..0];


/**   Logic Equations   **/

LSD.D  =  (   ['d'1]   &   LSD:0
          #   ['d'2]   &   LSD:1
          #   ['d'3]   &   LSD:2
          #   ['d'4]   &   LSD:3
          #   ['d'5]   &   LSD:4
          #   ['d'6]   &   LSD:5
          #   ['d'7]   &   LSD:6
          #   ['d'8]   &   LSD:7
          #   ['d'9]   &   LSD:8
          #   ['d'0]   &   LSD:9  )   &   EN
          #   LSD                      &   !EN;

MSD.D  =  ((  ['d'1]   &   MSD:0
          #   ['d'2]   &   MSD:1
          #   ['d'3]   &   MSD:2
          #   ['d'4]   &   MSD:3
          #   ['d'5]   &   MSD:4
          #   ['d'6]   &   MSD:5
          #   ['d'7]   &   MSD:6
          #   ['d'8]   &   MSD:7
          #   ['d'9]   &   MSD:8
          #   ['d'0]   &   MSD:9  )   &   LSD:9
          #   MSD  &   LSD:[0..8]  )   &   EN
          #   MSD                      &   !EN;
```

Fig. 14-4 CUPL design logic description file for example 14-3

the most significant digit to count 0 through 9, and then 10 through 19, and 20 through 29, etc. The MSD will increment on the next clock only when the LSD is equal to 9. The MSD should remain in the same state while LSD is in the states of 0 through 8.

Example 14-4

Design a mod-64, recycling, up counter using a GAL16V8. The counter will also be used to generate two active-high timing signals (TIME1 and TIME2). TIME1 should be asserted when the 6-bit counter is in the hexadecimal states 16 through 20 (inclusive). TIME2 should be asserted when the counter is in the hexadecimal states 2A through 3C.

A CUPL design solution is shown in Fig. 14-5. The logic equations have the ".d" extension to produce registered outputs in the GAL16V8. The least significant bit must change states with each clock cycle. Therefore, the inverse of the current output is fed into the D input of flip-flop Q0. The XOR function can be used to determine the input for each of the other D-type flip-flops. In the logic equations for Q2 through Q5, the D input for each flip-flop will be the current output bit exclusive ORed with the ANDing of the set of bits that are lower in significance than this output bit.

A convenient shortcut notation is utilized in this solution where a set of variables given in the brackets are to be operated on with the function specified after the equality operator. For example:

[Q1..0]:& is equivalent to (Q1 & Q0)
[Q2..0]:& is equivalent to (Q2 & Q1 & Q0)

```
Name        MOD-64;              Partno    L155-17D;
Date        07/17/93;            Revision  01;
Designer    Greg Moss;           Company   Digi-Lab;
Assembly    Example board;       Location  U142;
Device      G16V8A;              Format    j;
/**********************************************************/
/* mod-64 counter defined using the XOR function and the  */
/* ANDing of a set of variables with the equality operator */
/**********************************************************/

/** Inputs **/

pin 1 = CLK;                     /* Counter clock input    */
pin 11 = !OE;                    /* Register output enable  */

/** Outputs **/

pin [19..14] = [Q5..0];          /* Counter outputs        */
pin 13 = TIME1;                  /* Output waveform #1      */
pin 12 = TIME2;                  /* Output waveform #2      */


/** Declarations and Intermediate Variable Definitions  **/

field  counter = [Q5..0];


/** Logic Equations **/

Q0.d    =    !Q0;
Q1.d    =    (Q1  $  Q0);
Q2.d    =    (Q2  $  [Q1..0]:&);
Q3.d    =    (Q3  $  [Q2..0]:&);
Q4.d    =    (Q4  $  [Q3..0]:&);
Q5.d    =    (Q5  $  [Q4..0]:&);

TIME1   =    counter:[16..20];
TIME2   =    counter:[2A..3C];
```

Fig. 14-5 CUPL design logic description file for example 14-4

Example 14-5

Design a mod-16, recycling, up/down, binary counter using a GAL16V8. The counter can also be parallel loaded with a 4-bit number (D3 D2 D1 D0) or reset to 0. The 3-bit function control (M2 M1 M0) for the counter is described in the following table.

M2	M1	M0	Function
0	0	X	HOLD
0	1	X	LOAD
1	0	0	COUNT UP
1	0	1	COUNT DOWN
1	1	X	RESET

A CUPL solution file is shown in Fig. 14-6. In this design, bit fields are declared and all 4-bit combinations are assigned names to use. The various functional modes are also given convenient variable names. The complex equation describes the logic for each of the five different functional modes of operation for the counter.

```
Name       LOADCNTR;              Partno     L155-17E;
Date       07/20/93;              Revision   01;
Designer   G. Moss;               Company    Digi-Lab;
Assembly   Controller;            Location   U922;
Device     G16V8A;                Format     j;

/********************************************************/
/*  Mod-16 binary up/down counter with parallel load   */
/********************************************************/

                /****   Inputs   ****/

pin 1 = clk;                /* Counter clock              */
pin [2..4] = [M2..0];       /* Counter function controls  */
pin [5..8] = [D3..0];       /* Parallel data inputs       */
pin 11 = !oe;               /* Register output enable     */


                /****   Outputs   ****/

pin [12..15] = [Q0..3];     /* Counter outputs            */


                /**** Definitions ****/

field counter = [Q3..0];    /* counter bit field          */
field data    = [D3..0];    /* data input field           */
field mode    = [M2..0];    /* function control field     */

hold       =   mode:[0..1];  /* define functions          */
load       =   mode:[2..3];
count_up   =   mode:4;
count_dn   =   mode:5;
reset      =   mode:[6..7];

$define S0   'b'0000         /* define counter states     */
$define S1   'b'0001
$define S2   'b'0010
$define S3   'b'0011
$define S4   'b'0100
$define S5   'b'0101
$define S6   'b'0110
$define S7   'b'0111
$define S8   'b'1000
$define S9   'b'1001
$define SA   'b'1010
$define SB   'b'1011
$define SC   'b'1100
$define SD   'b'1101
$define SE   'b'1110
$define SF   'b'1111
```

157

```
                 /**** Logic Equations ****/

counter.d   =
                                    /* hold data mode     */
        counter  &  hold

                                    /* parallel load mode */
     #   data     &  load

                                    /* count up mode       */
     #   (   S1  &  counter:S0
            # S2  &  counter:S1
            # S3  &  counter:S2
            # S4  &  counter:S3
            # S5  &  counter:S4
            # S6  &  counter:S5
            # S7  &  counter:S6
            # S8  &  counter:S7
            # S9  &  counter:S8
            # SA  &  counter:S9
            # SB  &  counter:SA
            # SC  &  counter:SB
            # SD  &  counter:SC
            # SE  &  counter:SD
            # SF  &  counter:SE
            # S0  &  counter:SF )  &  count_up

                                    /* count down mode      */
     #   (   SF  &  counter:S0
            # S0  &  counter:S1
            # S1  &  counter:S2
            # S2  &  counter:S3
            # S3  &  counter:S4
            # S4  &  counter:S5
            # S5  &  counter:S6
            # S6  &  counter:S7
            # S7  &  counter:S8
            # S8  &  counter:S9
            # S9  &  counter:SA
            # SA  &  counter:SB
            # SB  &  counter:SC
            # SC  &  counter:SD
            # SD  &  counter:SE
            # SE  &  counter:SF )  &  count_dn

                                    /* reset mode          */
     #   S0  &  reset;
```

Fig. 14-6 CUPL design logic description file for example 14-5

Laboratory Projects

14.1   Custom sequential circuit
Design a custom sequential circuit using a GAL16V8 that will produce the sequence
given in the following state diagram.

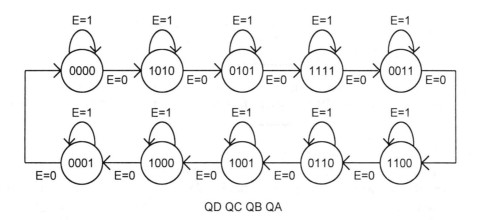

QD QC QB QA

14.2   Gray code counter
Design a 4-bit, up/down, recycling Gray code counter using a GAL16V8. The count
direction is controlled by a signal called F, as indicated in the following function table.
Label counter outputs Q_3, Q_2, Q_1, and Q_0. The circuit also should produce an output
signal called INDEX, which goes low whenever the counter state is 0000.

F	operation
0	Count Up
1	Count Down

	Gray code sequence				
	Q_3	Q_2	Q_1	Q_0	
	0	0	0	0	
c	0	0	0	1	⇑
o	0	0	1	1	
u	0	0	1	0	⇑
n	0	1	1	0	
t	0	1	1	1	c
	0	1	0	1	o
u	0	1	0	0	u
p	1	1	0	0	n
	1	1	0	1	t
	1	1	1	1	
⇓	1	1	1	0	d
	1	0	1	0	o
⇓	1	0	1	1	w
	1	0	0	1	n
	1	0	0	0	

14.3   Mod-16 binary counter

Design a mod-16, recycling, binary counter using a GAL16V8. The counter's function table is given below. The counter should also produce an active-low ripple carry output signal called CARRY.

C1	C0	operation
0	0	Reset
0	1	Count Down
1	0	Count Up
1	1	Hold Count

14.4   Mod-60 BCD counter

Design a mod-60, recycling, BCD counter using a GAL16V8. The counter should have an active-low reset (RES) signal. The count sequence will be 0 through 59_{10} in BCD.

14.5   Mod-128 binary counter

Design a mod-128, recycling, binary up-counter using a GAL16V8. The counter should have an active-high count enable called EN. Also produce an active-high pulse output signal called PULSE. The pulse will end when the counter recycles. The pulse width will be controlled by an input signal called W as shown in the table below.

W	PULSE width
0	4 clock periods
1	8 clock periods

14.6   Mod-200 binary counter

Design a mod-200, recycling, binary up-counter using a GAL16V8. Hint: Define an intermediate variable that decodes the desired final counter state and then include this variable in the logic equations for an 8-bit binary counter.

14.7   Stepper motor sequence controller

Design a half-step sequencer to control a stepper motor using a GAL16V8. The sequencer should produce the appropriate sequence of states to drive the motor either clockwise (CW) or counterclockwise (CCW). The stepper direction is controlled by the signal CW. The stepper enable is called STEP. The function table is given below. Make sure the sequencer is self-starting.

STEP	CW	function
0	X	HALT
1	0	CCW
1	1	CW

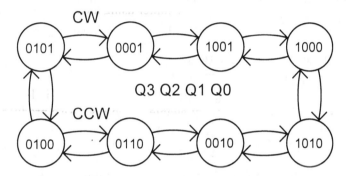

Half-step sequence for stepper motor control

14.8   Variable frequency divider

Design a variable frequency divider using a GAL16V8. The frequency divider should divide the input frequency by one of four different factors. The divide-by factor is controlled by two mode controls as described by the following function table. The mode controls are used to change the modulus of the counter used for the frequency division. The output waveform will be high for two clock cycles starting at state zero.

M1	M0	divide by:
0	0	5
0	1	10
1	0	12
1	1	15

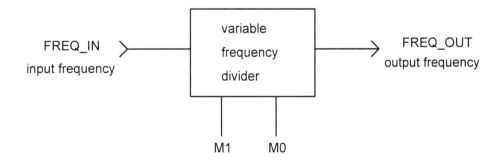

14.9   Digital lock
Design a digital lock circuit using a GAL16V8. The lock will have a 4-bit data input and an ENTER signal. Use a mod-5 binary counter to keep track of the sequencing through the combination. The ENTER signal is the clock signal for the counter. A 4-number lock combination sequence (established in the design) will be required to unlock the combination lock. Each input number (4-bit value) will be applied and then the ENTER signal will be asserted (active-high). The machine states must be sequenced in the proper order to unlock the lock. The "START" state, or STATE0, is followed by the intermediate states STATE1, then STATE2, then STATE3, and then finally STATE4, which "UNLOCKs" the lock. If an incorrect input combination is "ENTERed" during any counter state, the counter will return to STATE0. The state transition diagram for the digital lock is shown below.

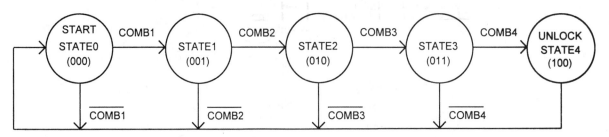

Returns to STATE0 if any incorrect combination is applied

DESIGNING WITH COUNTERS AND REGISTERS

OBJECTIVES

1. To practice designing systems using IC counters.
2. To practice designing systems using IC registers.

TEXT REFERENCE

Read Chapter 7.

EQUIPMENT NEEDED

Components and instruments are selected by the student according to her or his design needs.

DISCUSSION

The exercises below will give you an opportunity to practice designing devices using flip-flops, counters, and registers. Before constructing any of these projects, you should check with your instructor as to which exercises are to be completed from design through construction and testing. You should also be sure you know what documentation is required to be turned in.

For your own personal records, you should keep a notebook containing all draft schematics and text from each project as well as a copy of the final schematic and text. When a proposed solution does not work, make a notation on the back of its schematic about what is wrong and why. If you practice this technique, you will seldom repeat the same mistakes on other design projects. You will appreciate your efforts when you are assigned large projects.

PROCEDURE

a) *System clock :* Design a clock with a 100 kHz master oscillator and a 6.667 kHz symmetrical TTL compatible clock signal as its output.

b) *Variable timer:* Design a circuit that, when started, will produce a HIGH output for N milliseconds and then a LOW output for 1 second, where N is a number that can vary from 0 to 65,535 and that can be loaded into the circuit using toggle switches. Include in the design a clock oscillator to drive the circuit.

c) *Serial input with handshake:* An interface is a circuit that connects a computer to an external device. An input interface is usually capable of receiving a data word from the device—even if the computer is tied up doing something else—and store it until the computer takes it. Computers are not always ready to receive data from an interface. Similarly, interface circuits are not always ready to send data to the computer, interface units are not always ready to receive data from input devices, and finally, input devices do not always have data to send when the interface circuit is ready to receive. In order that all three units can communicate with each other, a single data line and several control lines, called *handshaking lines*, are used to interconnect them. These control lines help to minimize data loss.

A computer has a serial interface circuit that receives 10 bits of information from an input device and a (HIGH) INPUT DEVICE READY signal, and passes all bits, except the first and last bit, on to the computer in parallel when the computer is ready for it. Figure 28-1 shows the relationship among input device, interface, and computer and the format that the input device uses to send data to the interface. The following is a description of these lines:

• The input data line from the device to the interface is normally HIGH. When data is to be transmitted from the device, the device causes the input line to go LOW for one *bit time* (called the START bit), signalling that the next 10 bits are 8 bits of data followed by 2 (HIGH) STOP bits. Bit time is 100 microseconds in duration. See Figure 28-1.

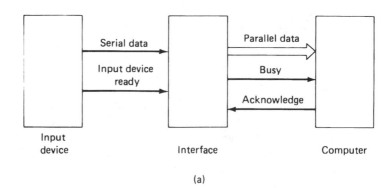

(a)

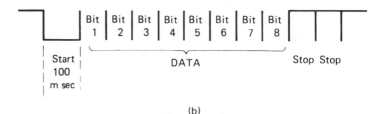

(b)

Figure 28-1

- The BUSY line is a control line from the interface to the computer. When this line is HIGH, the interface is not ready for the computer to take the data. When the line is LOW, the interface is ready.
- The ACKNOWLEDGE line is a control line from the computer to the interface. Whenever the computer has transferred the data from the interface, it drives this line LOW momentarily. The interface responds by forcing the BUSY line HIGH.
- The INPUT DEVICE READY line is a control line from the input device to the interface. As long as this line is LOW, the interface will not shift data serially. On the leading (NGT) edge of the START bit, the device drives this line HIGH, causing the interface to shift data from the input data line. At the end of the STOP bit, the input device forces the INPUT DEVICE READY line LOW, causing the interface to quit shifting data from the input data line. (You can assume that the device will not send data as long as the BUSY line is LOW.)

Design the interface unit.

Experiment 31

USING A LOGIC ANALYZER

OBJECTIVES

1. To learn how to display and interpret digital waveforms using a 7D01 logic analyzer.
2. To practice using the various trigger modes and sources available on the 7D01.

TEXT REFERENCE

Read Appendix B in the back of this manual.

EQUIPMENT NEEDED

Components
7493 IC (2)

Instruments
7D01 logic analyzer;
0–5 volt DC power supply;
pulse or square wave generator;
logic probe.

DISCUSSION

Before attempting this experiment, read and be sure you understand Appendix B in the back of this manual. If your lab uses a logic analyzer other than the one this experiment features, your instructor will explain the differences and/or modify the experiment to fit the lab model.

PROCEDURE

PART 1—INITIAL CHECKOUT

a) 1. Do not connect the data probes to any signals.

2. Set the 7D01 panel controls as follows:

Vertical

POS. (position).. MIDRANGE
MAG. (magnifier) X1
RECORD DISPLAY TIME............................ ∞ (fully clockwise detent)
CLOCK QUALIFIER .... OFF

Horizontal

POS. .... MIDRANGE
MAG. X1
THRESHOLD VOLTAGE .... TTL (+1.4 V)
EXT CLOCK POLARITY .... ↑
SAMPLE INTERVAL .... 1 ms
DATA CHANNELS 0–3
DATA POSITION .... POST-TRIGGER
TRIG SOURCE .... CH. 0 (channel 0)
EXT TRIGGER POLARITY........................... ↑

Word Recognizer (W.R.)

W.R. MODE .... ASYNCH
FILTER.. MIN
CH. 0 through 15.. X (center)
EXTERNAL QUALIFIER.............................. X (center)
PROBE QUALIFIER .... X (center)

b) Turn on the power to the 7D01.

c) Press the MANUAL RESET button (right above the SAMPLE INTERVAL selector). This initiates a new STORE mode. The analyzer is now sampling the various channel inputs every 1 µs.

d) To terminate the STORE mode and begin the DISPLAY mode, a TRIGGER EVENT must occur. With the TRIGGER SOURCE set to CH. 0, the logic analyzer is waiting for a positive transition on the channel 0 probe. Since this will not occur (with the probes not connected) we can use the MANUAL TRIGGER to generate a TRIGGER EVENT. Depress the MANUAL TRIGGER pushbutton.

e) Four waveform traces should appear on the CRT. They will have random logic levels, because the probes are not connected.

f) Verify that the VERT POS and VERT MAG controls can be used to vary the vertical position and spacing of the four traces. The HORIZ POS control should vary the horizontal position of the traces.

g) Change the DATA CHANNELS switch to 0–7. Eight traces should now appear. You may have to vary the VERT POS and MAG controls to get a reasonable display of the eight traces.

h) Change the DATA CHANNELS switch to 0–15 and repeat step g for 16 traces.

i) Set the DATA CHANNELS switch back to 0–3.

j) The four traces should have an intensified zone on the left end, which indicates the TRIGGER EVENT point. If you can't see this, gradually reduce the CRT intensity.

k) You should also see another intensified zone, which indicates the CURSOR point. It will be at some random point on the screen. Verify that it can be horizontally positioned on the screen using the CURSOR COARSE and FINE controls. The readout at the top of the screen will continually indicate the CURSOR position relative to the TRIGGER points in the units of one SAMPLE INTERVAL.

l) Set the CURSOR position to TRIG +45, and answer the following.

1. What is the time duration between the CURSOR and the TRIGGER point?

   _____.

2. What are the logic levels on the four channels at the CURSOR point?

   _____.

3. What is the total time duration from the beginning to the end of the trace?

   _____.

m) Change the DATA POSITION switch to CENTER, and note that the intensified trigger point has moved to the approximate center of the display. Verify that the CURSOR can be positioned before or after the TRIGGER point.

n) Change to PRE-TRIGGER and verify that the trigger point is moved to the right end of the screen.

o) Set the DATA POSITION switch back to POST-TRIGGER.

p) The current display will stay on the screen indefinitely because the DISPLAY TIME has been set to ∞. A new STORE mode can be initiated by depressing the MANUAL RESET pushbutton. Then, a new DISPLAY mode can be initiated by pressing MANUAL TRIGGER. Do this several times.

q) Repeat step q for a shorter display time.

r) Set the DISPLAY TIME back to ∞. Hit MANUAL TRIGGER to obtain the four channel traces.

s) The SAMPLE INTERVAL that is used during the STORE mode can be varied between 10 n sec and 5 m sec. However, there are certain limitations when 8 or 16 channels are being used. When 8 channels are being used, the selected SAMPLE INTERVAL must be 20 ns or greater. For 16-channel operation, the

SAMPLE INTERVAL must be 50 ns or greater. If you try to use a smaller SAMPLE INTERVAL than allowed, a light will blink on the SAMPLE INTERVAL dial. Verify this by changing the DATA CHANNELS switch and the SAMPLE INTERVAL selector switch.

t) If the SAMPLE INTERVAL is set to EXT, the SAMPLE INTERVAL is determined by an external clock signal connected to the appropriate probe.

> NOTE: In this experiment, we will not be using the external SAMPLE CLOCK. Instead, we will use the 7D01's internally-generated, switch-selected SAMPLE INTERVAL.

u) Set the SAMPLE INTERVAL back to 1.0 ms.

PART 2—DISPLAYING COUNTER WAVEFORMS

a) We will now use the logic analyzer to display the waveforms from a 7493 IC counter. Connect a 7493 IC as a MOD-16 counter. Be sure that the master reset inputs are grounded. Connect the power supply to the 7493 IC. Now connect the clock A input of the counter to a pulse generator that is set to 10 kHz. Turn on the pulse generator, and use your logic probe to verify that all of the counter outputs are pulsing.

b) Connect the 7D01's upper data probes to the counter outputs as follows:

Ch. 0 (black wire) .... Output Q_A
Ch. 1 (brown wire) .... Output Q_B
Ch. 2 (red wire) .... Output Q_C
Ch. 3 (orange wire) .... Output Q_D

Also, connect the ground probe (white wire) to the ground of your circuit.

c) The logic analyzer can now be commanded to sample and store these waveforms by pressing the MANUAL RESET button. Do this, and note that a display of the counter waveforms appears almost immediately. This is because the signal connected to channel 0 has produced a positive transition for the TRIGGER EVENT (remember, our TRIG SOURCE is selected as Ch. 0).

> NOTE: If the counter waveforms do not appear, notify your instructor immediately.

d) Check to see that the intensified TRIGGER point occurs when the channel 0 waveform has gone from LOW to HIGH. Also, note the logic levels on the other waveforms at the TRIGGER point. Record them as a four-bit number in the following order:

Ch. 3 _____, Ch. 2 _____, Ch. 1 _____, Ch. 0 _____.

e) Now position the CURSOR so that it coincides with the TRIGGER point. The 4-bit number on the bottom of the display will now indicate the waveform levels at the TRIGGER point. The results should be the same as you recorded in step d.

f) As you move the CURSOR to various other points on the waveforms, the 4-bit number should change to reflect the waveform levels at the CURSOR point. Verify this.

g) The CURSOR can be used to measure approximate time intervals between two points on a waveform. To demonstrate this, position the CURSOR just before one of the positive transitions of the Ch. 0 waveform. Note the CURSOR position relative to the TRIGGER point. Then move the CURSOR to the next Ch. 0's positive transition and note how many SAMPLE INTERVALS the CURSOR has moved. Record this number:

Number of SAMPLE INTERVALS = _____.

Record the measured value of one period of the Ch. 0 waveform. _____.

Compare this to the expected value (remember that the counter is being driven by a 10 kHz clock signal).

h) Use the same method to measure the pulse duration of the waveform on Ch. 2.

Pulse duration of Ch. 2 = _____.

i) The HORIZ MAG control can be used to horizontally magnify the waveforms by a factor of up to 10. Verify its operation.

j) When the waveforms are magnified horizontally, the HORIZ POS control can be used to find any part of the original unmagnified waveforms. Verify this.

k) Return the HORIZ MAG to ×1, and position the CURSOR at the TRIGGER point (TRIG + 0).

l) Press the MANUAL RESET button to initiate a new STORE mode and DISPLAY mode. Find the TRIGGER point on the waveforms; the CURSOR should still be at the TRIGGER point.

m) What are the waveform levels at the TRIGGER point this time? Are they the same as in steps d and e? If they are, then repeat step l until they change.

n) Why has the TRIGGER point changed? (Hint: what is our TRIGGER source?) _____.

o) With four channels, the duration of the waveform display is 1016 SAMPLE INTERVALS, or 1016 μs, since our SAMPLE INTERVAL is 1 μs. If we chose to use eight channels, the duration would be 508 SAMPLE INTERVALS, and the display would not show as many cycles of the counter waveforms. Check this out by switching the DATA CHANNELS to 0–7. Then press MANUAL RESET. You may have to use the VERT POS and VERT MAG controls to get all eight traces on the screen at the same time.

Note that the Ch. 0–Ch. 3 waveform displays are now spread out by a factor of 2 from what they were before, since the total time duration is 508 ms. This is similar to changing the time scale on a conventional scope.

p) Repeat step o for 16 channels, and observe what happens. What is the total time duration of the waveform now? _____.

q) Return to the 4-channel display mode.

r) We can also change the total time duration of the display by changing the SAMPLE INTERVAL. Change it to 2 μs and press MANUAL RESET. The resultant display now represents 1016×2.0 μs = 2032 μs time duration. Thus, there should be twice as many cycles of the various counter waveforms.

s) Change the SAMPLE INTERVAL to 0.5 μs and press MANUAL RESET. The display now represents 1016×0.5 μs = 508 μs. Thus, there are fewer cycles of the waveform being displayed.

t) The SAMPLE INTERVAL is usually made very small whenever we want to take a close look at a specific portion of the waveforms. For example, suppose we want to take a close look at the positive transition of the Ch. 0 waveform. The TRIG SOURCE is already set to Ch. 0, and we are using POST-TRIGGER so that the start of the display will show the positive-going edge of Ch. 0. Set SAMPLE INTERVAL to 10 n sec, and press MANUAL RESET. The display should now show the waveforms spread way out. The rising edge of Ch. 0 can now be examined with a resolution of 10 n sec. The total time duration of the display is only 1016×10 n sec = 10.16 μs. The other channel waveforms are not changing during this time.

u) A large SAMPLE INTERVAL is usually used when we want to see a larger portion of the waveforms. Set SAMPLE INTERVAL to 20 μs, and press MANUAL RESET. The display now represents 1016×20 μs = 20.32 m sec. Thus, there are many cycles of the waveforms crowded into the display. The HORIZ MAG can be used to spread out the display to make it easier to examine the various waveforms.

v) There are two important considerations that limit the maximum size of the SAMPLE INTERVAL:

1. If the interval chosen is too large, glitches or narrow pulses on the waveforms may be missed by the logic analyzer if they happen to occur in the interval between edges of the SAMPLE CLOCK. See Figure 31-1.

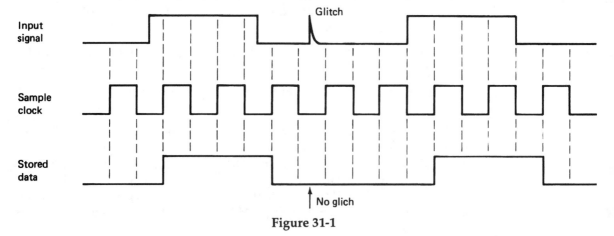

Figure 31-1

2. If the chosen SAMPLE INTERVAL is greater than the narrowest pulse width on the data waveform, the logic analyzer will not produce an accurate display of the waveform. For our waveforms, the narrowest pulse is about 100 μs on Ch. 0, 200 μs on Ch. 1, 400 μs on Ch. 2, and 800 μs on Ch. 3. Try various

SAMPLE INTERVALs greater than 100 µs and observe what happens to the displayed waveforms. Use the HORIZ MAG to spread the waveforms out. *In general, you should never use a SAMPLE INTERVAL greater than 1/2 the width of the narrowest data pulse.*

w) Set SAMPLE INTERVAL back to 1 µs and get a new display.

PART 3—USING AN EXTERNAL TRIGGER SOURCE

a) We have used MANUAL TRIGGER and Ch. 0 as the source for the TRIGGER EVENT. Another possible trigger source is EXT (external). Switch the TRIGGER SOURCE selector to EXT.

b) Press MANUAL RESET to initiate a new STORE mode. Note that the display does not appear. This is because no TRIGGER EVENT has occurred, since there is no signal connected to the EXT TRIG input jack.

c) Connect a 1× or BNC-to-alligator probe (*do NOT use a 10×probe*) from the EXT TRIG jack to a normally LOW pushbutton.

d) Press the pushbutton switch. The logic analyzer should now display the various waveforms, because the positive transition from the pushbutton output has produced the TRIGGER EVENT.

e) Change the EXT TRIG POLARITY switch to negative-going transition, and then press MANUAL RESET. Again, there is no display, because a TRIGGER EVENT hasn't occurred yet.

f) Press the pushbutton and hold it down. Why doesn't the display appear? Release the pushbutton. The display should now appear.

PART 4—USING THE WORD RECOGNIZER AS THE TRIGGER SOURCE

a) The WORD RECOGNIZER is used to generate a TRIGGER EVENT when a specific word (pattern of 0s and 1s) is present on the input data channels. For example, you might want to generate a TRIGGER when the 16 data inputs are at 1001101100101111. This binary pattern is called the TRIGGER WORD.

There are 16 three-position switches (one for each channel) that select the state of each data channel for the desired TRIGGER WORD. For example, if the desired TRIGGER WORD is 1010111000010110, the switches for channels 15, 13, 11, 10, 9, 4, 2, and 1 should be set HIGH, and the switches for the other channels should be set LOW.

Whenever a data channel is not being used, the WORD RECOGNIZER switch should be set to the middle position (X) so that it is not part of the TRIGGER WORD. Even when a data channel is being used, you can set its WR switch to X if you don't want that particular data channel to be part of the TRIGGER WORD.

b) Set the 16 WR channel switches to XXXXXXXXXXXX0101. The TRIGGER WORD is thus 0101 for the four channels we are using.

c) Set the TRIG SOURCE to WR. Then press the MANUAL RESET button.

d) Position the CURSOR at the TRIGGER point (TRIG + 0). The TRIGGER should occur when the waveform levels are 0101.

e) Display the four waveforms with a TRIGGER point at 1011. Demonstrate this to your instructor or lab assistant.

f) The WR MODE switch is currently in the ASYNC position. In this position, the WR generates a TRIGGER EVENT as soon as the conditions on the WR channel switches are met. *It does not wait for a clock signal.*

If this switch is placed in the SYNC position, the WR will generate a TRIGGER EVENT when the WR conditions are met *and* the active edge of the EXTERNAL SAMPLE CLOCK occurs. This position is used *only* when the SAMPLE INTERVAL switch is set to EXT and the external system clock is connected to the "C" probe on the Ch. 0–7 connector.

Since we are using the logic analyzer's internal SAMPLE CLOCK, the WR MODE has to be set to ASYNC or the WR will not produce a trigger. Verify this by switching to SYNC and hitting MANUAL RESET. Note that there is no display.

Return to the ASYNC mode. The display should appear.

g) There are two other switches that are part of the WR operation. One is the EXTERNAL QUALIFIER switch. It can be used to add one more condition to those needed to produce a WR TRIGGER. The other switch is the PROBE QUALIFIER. Let's examine the EXT QUALIFIER switch first.

1) Set the EXT QUALIFIER switch to HIGH.
2) Connect a toggle switch to the EXT TRIG/QUALIFIER INPUT jack (this is a dual purpose jack). Set the toggle switch to LOW.
3) Press MANUAL RESET. Note that there is no display, even though the data inputs satisfy the WR channel switch settings, because the level at the QUALIFIER INPUT does not match the EXTERNAL QUALIFIER switch setting.
4) Set the toggle switch HIGH, and note that the display appears, since the EXTERNAL QUALIFIER condition is now satisfied. The TRIGGER point on the waveform should still be 1011 (the settings on the WR channel switches).
5) Set EXT QUALIFIER back to X, and disconnect the QUALIFIER INPUT.

h) The PROBE QUALIFIER switch operates the same as the EXT QUALIFIER switch, except that it specifies the logic level required at the PROBE QUALIFIER input that is connected to the "Q" probe on the Ch. 8–15 connector.

1) Set the PROBE QUALIFIER switch to HIGH, and connect the Q probe to a toggle switch that is in the LOW state.
2) Press MANUAL RESET, and note that no display appears because the Q input is not HIGH.
3) Set the toggle switch connected to the Q probe to HIGH, and the display should appear. The TRIGGER point should still be at 1011.
4) Set the PROBE QUALIFIER switch back to X, and disconnect the Q probe.

i) The WR FILTER control (lower right-hand corner) is used to control the amount of time that the WR conditions have to be satisfied for the WR to generate a TRIGGER. This time requirement can be varied from 10 n sec to around 300 n sec. For example, if the WR FILTER setting is 100 n sec, then the WR will not generate a TRIGGER EVENT unless the WR conditions (WR channel switches and qualifiers) are met for 100 n sec or longer.

The WR FILTER can be used to prevent erratic triggering of the WR in situations where glitches or "race" conditions cause the WR conditions to be satisfied. This is demonstrated in the next step.

j) Make sure that the CURSOR is still positioned at the TRIGGER point.

k) Set the WR for a TRIGGER WORD of 0000.

l) 1) Set the DISPLAY TIME for a few seconds. The logic analyzer will now automatically perform a new STORE and DISPLAY mode every few seconds.

2) Examine each new display, and note the readout of the waveform levels at the TRIGGER point. Since the WR is set for a TRIGGER WORD of 0000, you expect the levels at the TRIGGER point to be 0000. However, you will see the levels at the TRIGGER point varying randomly (e.g., 0000, 1000, 0100, 0010). How can this happen if we selected 0000 for the WR TRIGGER WORD?

The answer is that the 0000 condition can occur momentarily at various points on the counter waveforms as the flip-flops are in transition from one state to another. An example is shown in Figure 31-2. Examine the waveforms where the transition is being made from 0111 to 1000. Because of its propagation delay, flip-flop D doesn't go HIGH until after C has gone LOW. Thus, for a few nanoseconds, the 0000 condition is present. This can be recognized by the WR, which will then generate a TRIGGER.

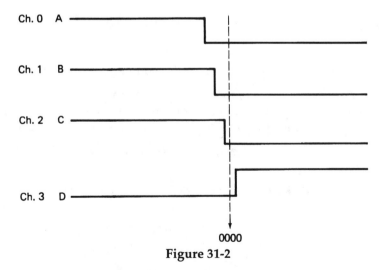

Figure 31-2

m) We can prevent this erratic operation by setting the WR FILTER high enough so that the momentary occurrences of the 0000 TRIGGER WORD will be ignored by the WR, and it will respond only to the stable 0000 condition that occurs on the waveform.

Gradually increase the WR FILTER setting until the display always shows 0000 at the TRIGGER point.

Demonstrate this to the instructor or lab assistant.

n) We can use the logic analyzer to display the race condition depicted in Figure 31-2. To do so, however, we will have to use a much smaller SAMPLE INTERVAL, since the propagation delays between flip-flops is very small.

1) Set the WR for a TRIGGER WORD of 1000.
2) Change SAMPLE INTERVAL to 10 n sec.
3) Set DISPLAY TIME to ∞ and examine the waveforms. They should appear as in Figure 31-2. You can spread them out with the HORIZ MAG control.
4) Move the CURSOR to the point on the waveforms where the temporary 0000 condition occurs. Measure and record the duration of this 0000 condition.

PART 5—DETECTING GLITCHES WITH THE
LOGIC ANALYZER

a) Very narrow glitches can be detected and displayed by using a very small SAMPLE INTERVAL. To demonstrate this, we have to somehow generate a glitch. One way to do this is to change our MOD-16 counter to a MOD-10 counter by connecting the outputs of flip-flops D and B back to the counter RESET inputs. This will produce a glitch at the B output as the counter reaches 1010 and immediately gets cleared back to 0000. See the waveform in Figure 31-3.

Ch. 1   B

Figure 31-3

b) Wire the 7493 IC counter as a MOD-10 counter.

c) Try to figure out a way to display the glitch. If you want to use the WR to trigger on the glitch, remember to reduce the WR FILTER to minimum because the glitch is very narrow. Demonstrate this to your instructor or lab assistant.

d) Measure and record the duration of the glitch: _____.

PART 6—EIGHT-CHANNEL OPERATION

a) Set SAMPLE INTERVAL to 1 ms.

b) Connect the channel 4–7 probes to the same counter waveforms as channels 0–3, in the same order.

c) Set the DATA CHANNELS switch for eight-channel operation.

d) Set WR for a TRIGGER WORD of 00010001.

e) Press MANUAL RESET.

f) Find the TRIGGER point on the waveforms. It should occur at 00010001.

g) Repeat for a TRIGGER WORD of 01010101.

h) Repeat for a TRIGGER WORD of 01010001. Why is there no display?

IC DECODERS

OBJECTIVES

1. To investigate the operation of a 1-of-8 decoder IC, the 74LS138.
2. To investigate the operation of a BCD-to-decimal decoder IC, the 7442.
3. To examine the outputs of a decoder with a logic analyzer.
4. To investigate a method of eliminating glitches from decoder outputs.

TEXT REFERENCES

Read sections 9.1 and 9.2.

EQUIPMENT NEEDED

Components
7402 IC;
7408 IC;
7442 IC;
7493 IC;
74121 IC;
74LS138 IC;
4 toggle switches;
normally HIGH pushbutton switch, debounced;
4 LED monitors;
1 k-ohm potentiometer;
270 and 330 pF capacitors.

Instruments
0–5 volt DC power supply;
pulse or square wave generator;
dual trace oscilloscope;
logic probe;
logic analyzer (optional).

DISCUSSION

You are already familiar with decoders, having investigated counter decoding in previous experiments. You are now ready to investigate representative examples of IC decoders. In this experiment you will study the behavior of two popular IC decoders, the 74LS138 and 7442.

74LS138 Decoder

The 74LS138 is an octal (1-of-8) decoder. It is frequently used to decode special binary codes called addresses in small computer systems. Its eight outputs are active LOW and it has three enable inputs and three data inputs. For a given octal code, one—and only one—of the eight outputs will go LOW if the chip is enabled. If the chip is not enabled, all of the outputs will remain HIGH no matter what data is present at the inputs.

7442 BCD-to-Decimal Decoder

In an earlier experiment, you investigated a special IC called a BCD-to-seven-segment decoder/driver. You found that it decoded a BCD counter and provided the necessary translation and power to drive a seven-segment LED display unit. The 7442 is a BCD-to-decimal (1-of-10) decoder, but, like the 74LS138, only one of its outputs will go LOW when a *valid* BCD code is at the data inputs. Unlike the 74LS138, the 7442 has no enables.

PROCEDURE

a) Refer to the data sheet for a 74LS138 IC and draw its pin layout diagram:

The 74LS138 can operate as a 1-of-8 decoder or a 3-line-to-8-line demultiplexer. In this experiment you will investigate the decoder function. The demultiplexer function will be covered in Experiment 34. Study the data sheet and familiarize yourself with the IC's functions.

b) *74LS138 decoder operation:* Install a 74LS138 on the circuit board. Connect the IC as follows:

1) Connect V_{CC} to +5 V, GND to power ground.
2) Connect toggle switches to select inputs A_2, A_1, and A0, and enable inputs $\overline{E}_1$, $\overline{E}_2$, and E_3. The select inputs will be used to input data.

You will use a logic probe to monitor the ouputs, $\overline{O}_7$ through $\overline{O}_0$.

c) Set E_3 to 1 and $\overline{E}_1 = \overline{E}_2 = 0$. Verify the decoder operating mode by setting inputs A_2, A_1, and A0 to each input combination listed in Table 32-1 and checking the decoder outputs with the logic probe.

d) Now set $\overline{E}_1$ to 1. You should observe that the decoder is now disabled (all outputs are HIGH) and that the select inputs have no effect. Repeat this for $\overline{E}_2$ = 1 and then $E_3 = 0$.

Table 32-1

Select Inputs			Outputs							
A_2	A_1	A_0	$\overline{O}_0$	$\overline{O}_1$	$\overline{O}_2$	$\overline{O}_3$	$\overline{O}_4$	$\overline{O}_5$	$\overline{O}_6$	$\overline{O}_7$
0	0	0								
0	0	1								
0	1	0								
0	1	1								
1	0	0								
1	0	1								
1	1	0								
1	1	1								

e) *Decoder used as a device enabler:* Decoders are often used to select or enable other devices such as memory ICs and peripheral interface adapters. Each device is assigned a device number such as 0, 1, or 2. The device enable input is connected to the corresponding output of a decoder, and whenever the decoder receives the binary code for the device at its inputs, the decoder will activate the device. Let the four NOR gates of a 7402 IC simulate four devices numbered 0, 1, 2, and 3. One input of each NOR gate is connected to a toggle switch to represent data. Draw a diagram showing how a 74LS138 can be used to selectively enable the four gates.

Show your diagram to your instructor for approval. Then construct the circuit and test it, using a logic probe to monitor the outputs of the NOR gates.

f) *BCD decoder operation—7442 IC:* Refer to the data sheet for a 7442 IC and draw its pin layout diagram:

You should note that the 7442 has four inputs, A_3 through A_0, and ten outputs, $\overline{O}_9$ through $\overline{O}_0$. You should also note that this decoder has no enable inputs.

g) Install a 7442 IC on the circuit board and also a 7493 IC counter. You will use the counter to supply the binary data to the 7442. Connect V_{cc} to +5 V and GND to power ground on each IC. Wire the 7493 as a MOD-16 counter and connect its outputs to the corresponding inputs of the 7442 (A_0 to Q_0, A_1 to Q_1, A_2 to Q_2, and A_3 to Q_3). Use a pushbutton switch to clock the counter. You will monitor the output of the decoder with a logic probe.

Clear the counter outputs. Verify that $\overline{O}_0$ is now LOW and the rest of the outputs are HIGH. Single-step the counter through its count sequence, and verify that the appropriate decoder output is LOW for each count, and that the rest of the outputs are HIGH. You should observe that any count greater than 1001 is not decoded. In other words, all outputs should be HIGH for any invalid BCD code.

h) *Observing decoder outputs with a logic analyzer:* If a logic analyzer is not available, go on to step i. Otherwise, connect the decoder outputs $\overline{O}_7$ through $\overline{O}_0$ to logic analyzer channels 0–7, respectively. Set the analyzer controls as follows (consult with your instructor to learn the exact settings for your particular model):

MODE	Timing Diagram
CLOCK QUALIFIER	Off
THRESHOLD	TTL
EXTERNAL CLOCK POLARITY	Positive Edge
SAMPLE INTERVAL	20 n sec
DATA POSITION	Post-Trigger
TRIGGER SOURCE	Word Recognizer (WR)
WR FILTER	MAX
WR DATA	11111110

Apply a 1 MHz square wave to the counter. Start the logic analyzer so that it begins a new store mode. You should observe that the analyzer displays the decoder output waveforms almost immediately. If the screen remains blank, check the WR data switch setting (on some models this is displayed at the top of the screen).

to make sure you set it correctly. If you persist in having difficulty getting a display, consult with your instructor.

Observe the waveforms, and note that they go LOW one at a time as the counter goes through its count sequence. You may see glitches on some of the waveforms.

Repeat this procedure several times. You may note that any glitches that appear may vary as to position on the screen. This is because they are very narrow, and even with a 20 n sec sample interval, the logic analyzer does not always pick them up.

Use the cursor to measure the approximate duration of one of the decoder output pulses. Record your value: _____.

The WR FILTER was set to MAX so that the WR would not be triggered by a glitch on the $\overline{O}_0$ waveform. If possible, set the WR FILTER to MIN, and repeat the measurement several times. You should see that the logic analyzer occasionally triggers on one of these glitches.

i) *Eliminating decoder glitches:* If you did not have access to a logic analyzer to do the last step, you should first apply a 1 MHz square wave to the counter input (or highest frequency obtainable) and observe decoder output $\overline{O}_0$ for glitches. Depending on the quality of your oscilloscope, you should be able to spot a few that occur randomly.

Glitches can cause serious problems, as you are already aware. You have seen one way to possibly eliminate glitches by using synchronous counters instead of asynchronous. Since that method is not always satisfactory, you will now employ another method, strobing the decoder. Strobing requires the decoder to have an enable input, like the 74LS138. The 7442 does not have an enable input. However, you can convert the 7442 into a 1-of-8 decoder WITH an enable. To do this, you simply use data inputs A_0, A_1, and A_2 as usual, and use the A_3 input as an enable. Since outputs $\overline{O}_8$ and $\overline{O}_9$ will not be needed, they will not be connected. When A_3 is set LOW, the 7442 outputs $\overline{O}_0$–$\overline{O}_7$ will respond to the correct data input. With A_3 HIGH, they cannot respond.

Disconnect input A_3 from the counter, and connect it to a toggle switch. Set the toggle switch HIGH. Set the square wave generator to a low frequency and verify with the logic probe that none of the decoder outputs $\overline{O}_0$–$\overline{O}_7$ are activated at any time. Set the toggle switch LOW, and verify that the decoder now acts like a 1-of-8 decoder.

j) Set up the circuitry shown in Figure 32-1. Note that the enable input (A_3) of the 7442 is to be driven by a pulse delay circuit consisting of a 74121 IC one shot. Note also the values of R_t and C_t. R_t is selected to be variable, since you will have to adjust t_p slightly in order to achieve a delay of slightly more than 0.5 microseconds.

Assuming that the count is 111 prior to the first clock pulse, draw the predicted signals at the enable input and decoder output $\overline{O}_0$.

k) With the dual trace oscilloscope, display the OS output and the output of the square wave generator. Adjust R_t so that t_p is slightly more than 0.5 microsecond. If this is not possible, change the value of C_t to 330 pF.

l) If a logic analyzer is available, get a display of the decoder waveforms $\overline{O}_7$ through $\overline{O}_0$ on the analyzer. You should observe no more glitches. If there are still some, try increasing t_p slightly. If this doesn't work, check your OS connections.

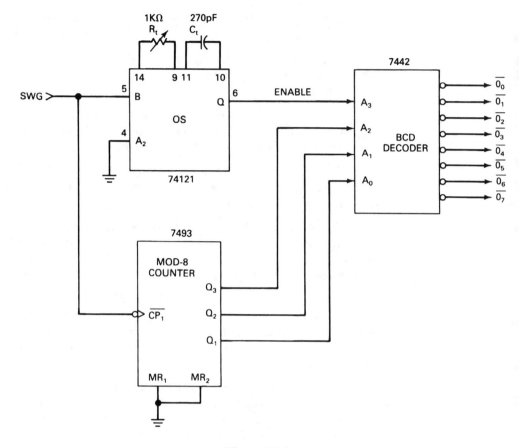

Figure 32-1

m) Once you have no glitches, reduce t_p gradually while observing the outputs of the decoder. You should, at some point, see the glitches return. This is because t_p is too narrow and the decoder is enabled during counter flip-flop transitions.

Demonstrate your circuit to your instructor.

n) *Review:* This concludes the exercises on decoders. To test your understanding of the principles covered in this experiment, answer the following questions:

1. Give a few examples of decoder applications.

2. Give the conditions necessary for the 74LS138 to decode input data.

3. In using the logic analyzer, if the WR data word is set to 11101111 when observing the 7442 outputs $\overline{O_7}$–$\overline{O_0}$, on what output will the logic analyzer be triggered?
_____.

4. Can you think of other devices you have tested where the logic analyzer might have been useful?

5. If the clock signal used in steps j–m had been 2 MHz, what value of OS t_p would have been necessary? _____.

Experiment 33

Name

IC ENCODERS

OBJECTIVES

1. To investigate the operation of a decimal-to-BCD encoder, the 74147 IC.
2. To investigate the application of the 74147 IC in key encoding.

TEXT REFERENCE

Read section 9.4.

EQUIPMENT NEEDED

Components
7404 IC;
7408 IC;
7476 IC;
74121 IC;
74147 IC;
74192 IC;
4 toggle switches;
normally HIGH pushbutton switch, debounced;
4 LED monitors;
33 k-ohm resistor;
1 μF capacitor;
decimal or hex keyboard with normally open contacts (recommended).

197

Instruments

0–5 volt DC power supply;

accurate 1 Hz square wave source;

storage oscilloscope (recommended), time interval counter, or nonstorage oscilloscope set at very low sweep speed.

DISCUSSION

In Experiment 32, you investigated IC decoders. Recall that for a given N-bit code received by the decoder, one and only one output became active. In this experiment, you will investigate the opposite of decoding: encoding. An encoder takes a single input and produces an N-bit code. For example, an octal encoder gives a three-bit code for a given octal input (digits 0–7) and a BCD encoder gives a four-bit code for a given decimal input (digits 0–9).

In the current experiment, you will investigate a 74147 IC decimal-to-BCD encoder. You were introduced to this IC in Experiment 1. You will use this encoder to interface a keypad with a programmable timer circuit, so that you can input (preset) the amount of time desired by pushing a single key.

PROCEDURE

a) Refer to the data sheet for the 74147. Note that the inputs are active LOW. Grounding one (and only one) input will result in a binary code being produced at

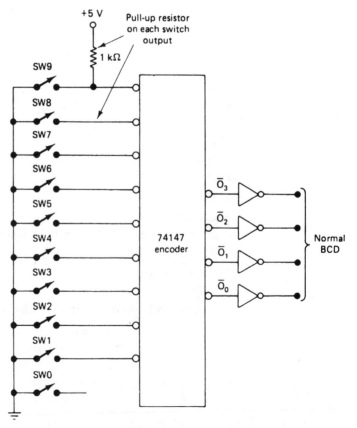

Figure 33-1

the encoder outputs, which represent the number of the input activated. Note also that the outputs are active LOW. Therefore the output code will be *inverted* BCD.

b) Install 74147 and 7404 ICs on the circuit board. Connect them as shown in Figure 33-1. Connect V_{CC} to +5 V and GND to power ground for both ICs. Connect LED monitors to the output of the inverters. If a keyboard is available, connect it to the inputs of the 74147. If not, simply touch a small length of wire to ground, and use this wire to activate the inputs. Verify that the 74147 operates as a decimal-to-BCD encoder.

c) Study the programmable timer circuit in Figure 33-2. You will construct and test this circuit using toggle switches to provide the binary inputs to the counter. Once the circuit operates satisfactorily, you will then replace the toggle switches with the encoder unit you currently have on the board.

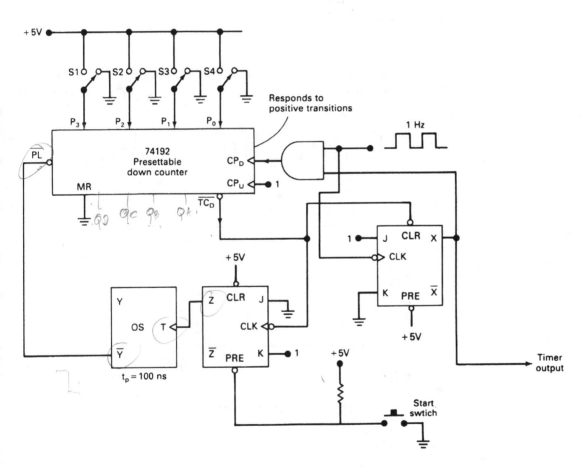

Figure 33-2

The timer output is normally LOW, and then it goes HIGH for 1–9 seconds, depending on the counter's preset conditions. The counter will be a 74192 BCD presettable UP/DOWN counter operated in the DOWN mode. The accuracy of the circuit depends on the accuracy of the 1 Hz square wave.

Refer to the data sheet for the 74192 IC counter. Note that its pin layout is the same as the 74193 and that it is functionally equivalent to a 74193 that is wired to operate as a MOD-10 counter.

Now complete the following circuit description:

1) Assume $S_1 = S_2 = 0$ and $S_3 = S_4 = 1$. Initially the counter is at 000 and $\overline{TC_D} = 0$.
2) Pressing the START switch produces a [positive-, negative-] going transition at Z.
3) This causes the OS, whose $\overline{Y}$ output goes _____, to activate the 74192 $\overline{PL}$ input. This loads the counter with _____, and as a result, $\overline{TC_D}$ goes _____.
4) Flip-flop X now goes to ____ on the next [positive-, negative-] going transition of the 1 Hz timing signal, causing the AND gate to allow the _____ to pass through into the counter.
5) The counter begins counting at _____. When the count reaches zero and CP_D is LOW, $\overline{TC_D}$ goes ____ and clears _____ to 0. This disables (inhibits) the _____ from getting through the AND gate to the counter.
6) The counter stays at 0000 until _____.

___d) Draw the expected waveforms for the 1 Hz clock, START, Z, Y, X, CP_D, and $\overline{TC_D}$. Assume that switches S1–S4 are set as above. Use Timing Diagram 33-1.

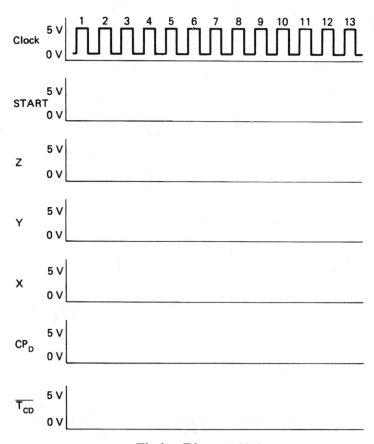

Timing Diagram 33-1

e) Show the results of steps c and d to the instructor before continuing.

f) Construct the programmable timer. Check its operation for several settings of switches S_1–S_4. Use either the storage oscilloscope or the time interval counter to measure the timer output. A nonstorage oscilloscope set at a very slow sweep can be used if necessary.

g) When the circuit is working as expected, press the START switch, and keep it depressed until after the output returns LOW. What happens when the START switch is pressed again? _____.

Draw a circuit that, when added to the programmable timer, will prevent this from happening. Obtain approval from your instructor or laboratory assistant and then install the modification before continuing.

h) Now remove switches S_1–S_4 and replace them with the outputs of the encoder circuit. Test the operation of the circuit by pressing and holding a key (or activating a 74147 input) and pressing the START switch. The timer output should be a pulse whose duration, in seconds, corresponds to the key pressed (or input of the 74147 activated).

i) Demonstrate the programmable timer for your instructor.

j) *Review:* This concludes the exercises on encoders. To test your understanding of the principles covered in this experiment, answer the following questions:

1. Why can't the START switch be connected directly to the OS?

2. Why can't the output of the timer be taken directly from $\overline{TC_D}$?

3. Explain the results you obtained in step g.

Experiment 34

Name_____

IC MULTIPLEXERS AND DEMULTIPLEXERS

OBJECTIVES

1. To investigate the operation of a 1-of-8 multiplexer, the 74151 IC.
2. To investigate the operation of a frequency selector.
3. To investigate the operation of a 3-line-to-8-line demultiplexer, the 74LS138 IC.
4. To investigate the application of multiplexers and demultiplexers in a synchronous data transmission system.

TEXT REFERENCES

Read sections 9.7 through 9.9.

EQUIPMENT NEEDED

Components
7404 IC;
7408 IC;
7474 IC (2);
74LS76 IC (4);
74121 IC (2);
74LS138 IC;
74151 IC;
74194A IC (4);
8 toggle switches;
normally HIGH pushbutton switch, debounced;
student selected capacitors and resistors.

Instruments
0–5 volt DC power supply;
pulse or square wave generator;
dual trace oscilloscope;
logic analyzer (optional).

DISCUSSION

Switches used to select data from several input sources are common in electronic systems. Digital systems use electronic circuits to simulate data selector switches called multiplexers. The multiplexer consists of several inputs, one output, and a number of SELECT inputs. When a binary code is applied to the SELECT inputs, the data with the input number represented by the code will be routed to the output. In the current experiment, you will investigate the operation of a 74151 IC, an 8-line-to-1-line multiplexer with a complementary output, and an enable. You will then use the multiplexer in a frequency selector.

The opposite of multiplexing is demultiplexing. A demultiplexer receives a single data line and distributes it over several outputs. Each output is selected by SELECT inputs, and each gets a "slice" of the data present on the input line. In this experiment, you will discover that the 74LS138 IC, whose decoder function was investigated in Experiment 32, can also be used as 1-line-to-8-line demultiplexer.

Finally, an elaborate, but not too complex, synchronous data transmission system is investigated. This system makes use of both the multiplexer and demultiplexer and is representative of serial communication on a small scale. You will use this system in Experiment 35, which is a troubleshooting exercise.

> Note: The completed transmission system may be used in Experiment 35. Verify this with your instructor before disassembling the circuit.

PROCEDURE

a) Refer to the data sheet for a 74151 IC and draw its pin layout diagram:

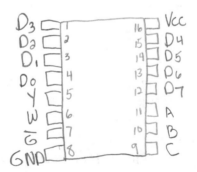

Note that the 74151 has two complementary outputs and an enable input.

b) *74151 IC operation*: Install a 74151 IC and a 7493 IC. Connect V_{CC} to +5 V and GND to ground for each IC. Wire the 7493 as a MOD-8 counter. Wire the remaining pins on the 74151 as follows:

1) Connect toggle switches to each of its eight inputs.
2) Connect select inputs S_2 through S_0 to outputs Q_2 through Q_0, respectively, of the counter.
3) Connect the enable input, $\overline{E}$, to ground.

Set the toggle switches so that $I_0 = I_2 = I_4 = I_6 = I_7 = 0$ and $I_1 = I_3 = I_5 = 1$. Set the clock counter to 1 kHz, and observe the output at Z and the counter clock with the dual trace oscilloscope. Trigger the oscilloscope sweep on Q_2 to get a stable display of the Z waveform. Draw the waveforms displayed on the oscilloscope. Use Timing Diagram 34-1.

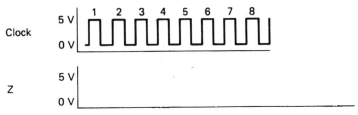

Timing Diagram 34-1

You should observe that the output at Z is the serial representation of the data at the multiplexer input. Toggle the I_2 data switch and observe the effect on the output. You should be able to locate the position of the input channel's data by observing the change in the output.

c) Lift the enable input momentarily. What happens?

nothing happens

d) *Frequency selector*: Figure 34-1 shows a circuit for a frequency selector. The 74151 IC multiplexer is fed various square wave frequencies with I_3 the highest and I_0 the lowest. Inputs I_4–I_7 are kept LOW. The data select inputs of the 74151, S_1–S_0, are used to select any of the square waves to be output at Z.

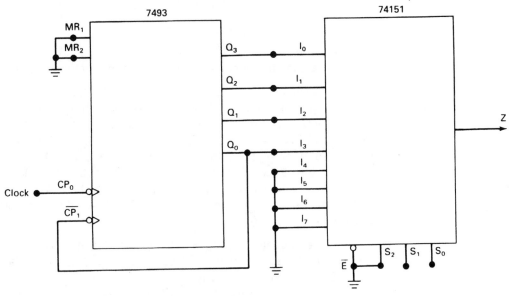

Figure 34-1

e) Wire the circuit of Figure 34-1. Use the SWG set at 5 kHz for the counter clock. Connect toggle switches to select inputs S_1 and S_0, and set them both to HIGH. If you are using an oscilloscope to monitor the circuit waveforms, use one vertical input to monitor Z and the other input to monitor the 74151 data inputs I_0–I_3. If you are using a logic analyzer, connect the logic analyzer to display I_1 through I_4 on channels 0–3 and the multiplexer output, Z, on channel 4. Use a sample interval that allows you to observe several cycles of the lowest frequency waveform to be displayed. Draw the waveforms that you observe on the logic analyzer, using Timing Diagram 34-2.

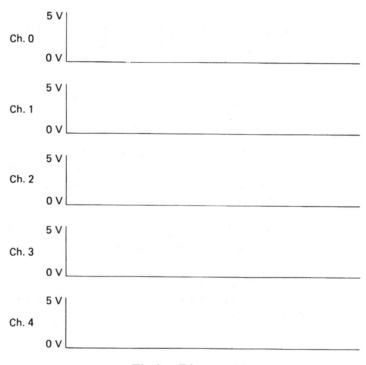

Timing Diagram 34-2

f) Vary the select inputs to produce other frequencies at output Z. Demonstrate the frequency selector for your instructor or laboratory assistant.

g) *Demultiplexer operation of the 74LS138 IC:* You are already familiar with the decoder operation of the 74LS138 (Experiment 32). You will now investigate its demultiplexer operation. Install the 74LS138 IC on the circuit board. Connect V_{cc} to +5 V and GND to power ground. Then wire the circuit of Figure 34-2. Connect the output of the 74151 multiplexer, Z, to the E_1 input of the 74LS138. Connect the other two enable inputs as shown in Figure 34-2. Connect the select inputs of the 74LS138 to the corresponding select inputs of the 74151. You will monitor outputs O_0–O_3 of the 74LS138 and inputs I_0–I_3 of the 74151 with the logic analyzer, if available, or oscilloscope.

h) Set the select inputs to 011, and monitor input I_3 of the 74151 and output $\overline{O}_3$ of the 74LS138. Are the waveforms the same? _____. Verify that all other outputs of the demultiplexer are inactive.

Set the select switches to several other values and verify that the signal at the selected demultiplexer output is the same as the selected multiplexer input.

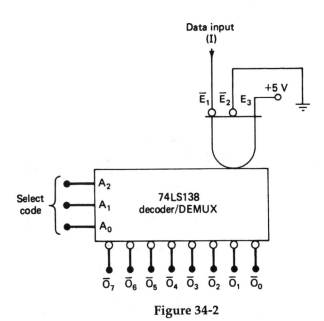

Figure 34-2

i) *Application of multiplexers and demultiplexers—synchronous data transmission system:* Now that you have verified the demultiplexer operation of the 74LS138 and have observed multiplexers and demultiplexers in the same circuit, you will build a synchronous data transmission system that makes use of these two operations. The operation of the data transmission system is described in the text, section 9.9. Review the operation of the system carefully, and then fill in the following statements:

Transmitter section operation:

Each register A, B, C, and D is configured as a _____ shift register. Each register will shift on the [PGT, NGT] of the shift pulse from AND gate 2. The *word counter* _____ the register data that will appear at Z. This counter counts from _____ to _____. The *bit counter* makes sure that _____ data bits from each register are transmitted through the _____ before advancing to the next register. This counter advances one count per _____ so that after _____ pulses, it recycles to 0. The word counter is incremented by _____. The Z signal contains _____ bits from each register for a total of _____ bits. The transmission system is controlled by

_____.

Receiver section operation:

The receiver _____ the Z signal into _____ sets of data and _____ them to their respective outputs.

j) Construct the circuit of Figure 34-3. Use the following ICs (or their equivalent):

1) Registers A, B, C, and D - 74194 (4)
2) Multiplexer - 74151.
3) Demultiplexer - 74LS138.
4) Flip-flops W, X, and Y - 7474 (2)
5) MOD-4 counters - 74LS76 (4).
6) One-shots ($t_p = 1\ \mu S$) - 74121 (2).

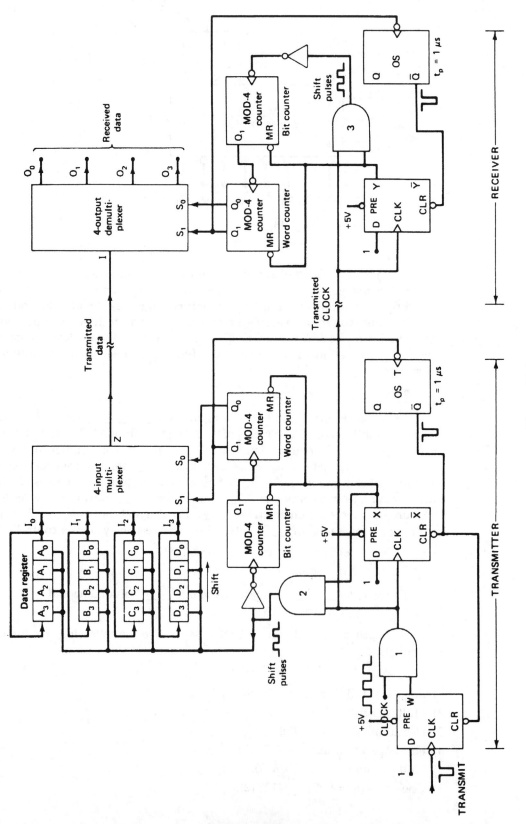

Figure 34-3

k) The 74194 ICs are to be wired as ring counters with parallel load capability. Connect a single toggle switch to all the register S_1 inputs. Connect all S_0 inputs to V_{cc}. The parallel data inputs will be permanently wired as follows:

Register A - [0110]
Register B - [1001]
Register C - [1011]
Register D - [0100]

The registers must be loaded manually before applying a TRANSMIT pulse. To accomplish this, set S_1 HIGH, and pulse the clock inputs LOW using a normally HIGH pushbutton switch. Then set S_1 LOW, and remove the pushbutton switch from the clock inputs.

Connect the output of AND gate 2 to the clock inputs of the registers. Output Q_D of each register should be connected to the appropriate multiplexer input and also to the right serial input SR SER. Connect the $\overline{Q}$ output of the flip-flop W to S_1 of each register.

Review Experiment 27 if necessary for the correct wiring of the 74194A as a ring counter.

l) Wire a normally HIGH pushbutton to the clock input of flip-flop W to provide the TRANSMIT pulse, and complete the rest of the circuit wiring according to the figure. Monitor the demultiplexer outputs with an oscilloscope or logic analyzer if one is available.

m) Test the circuit, and verify that the outputs of the demultiplexer are serial representations of the data stored in the corresponding register. Refer to Timing Diagram 34-3 for the waveforms that you should obtain.

If the system does not work properly, use a pushbutton switch for the clock input, and check out the operation of the circuit step-by-step.

n) Once the circuit is operating successfully, temporarily lift the connection at $\overline{MR}$ of the receiver word counter. What happens?

Reconnect the wire you just lifted. Now temporarily lift the connections at S_0 and S_1 of the 74151 IC. What happens?

Reconnect the select inputs, and demonstrate the circuit for your instructor.

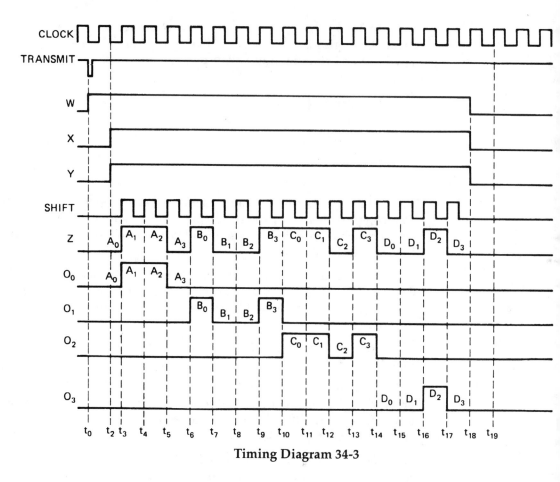

Timing Diagram 34-3

o) *Review*: This concludes the exercises on multiplexers and demultiplexers. To test your understanding of the principles covered in this experiment, answer the following questions:

1. In the data transmission system, what circuit modifications would be necessary to increase the number of channels to eight?

2. What would happen if register A's SR SER input became shorted to V_{cc}?

3. Draw a circuit diagram showing how three 74151 multiplexers can be arranged to form a 1-of-24 multiplexer.

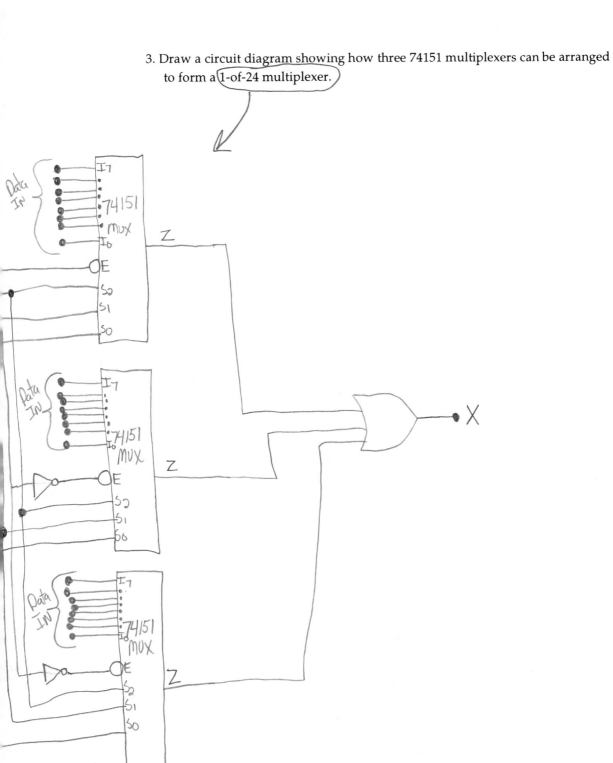

TROUBLESHOOTING SYSTEMS CONTAINING MSI LOGIC CIRCUITS

OBJECTIVE

To practice troubleshooting systems containing MSI logic circuits.

TEXT REFERENCES

Read sections 9.6 and 9.11.

EQUIPMENT NEEDED

Components
74151 IC;
74LS76 IC (2);
74LS138 IC;
7493 IC;
toggle switches (8);
LED monitors (11);
OR
functioning circuit from Experiment 34.

Instruments
0–5 volt DC power supply;
logic probe;
logic analyzer (optional);
oscilloscope;
pulse generator or SWG.

DISCUSSION

Before beginning this exercise, check with your instructor to determine which exercise you are to do. Also, reread the text assignment, and work through the examples in each section. This experiment will help you to gain confidence in your ability to reason out a troubleshooting problem using what the author of the text refers to as observation/analysis.

PROCEDURE

a) *Troubleshooting a parallel-to-serial converter*: Examine Figure 35-1 closely. It is the circuit for a parallel-to-serial converter using a multiplexer and a counter. Construct the circuit, and test it until you have it operational.

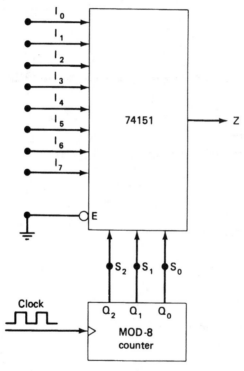

Figure 35-1

b) Have your lab partner or another student insert a fault into the circuit while you are not looking. Do not look for the bug yet. Now examine the circuit with a scope. Connect one vertical input to the clock and the other to the output of the converter. On a separate sheet of paper, draw the waveforms that you observe. Using your observations, narrow the location of the bug to a few possible faults. Then use this list and your test equipment to find the fault. Repeat this step as many times as possible.

c) Have your instructor place a bug in your circuit, and then repeat step b. Place your observations, list of possible faults, and your final solution on a separate sheet of paper.

d) *Troubleshooting a security monitoring system*: Examine Figure 35-2 closely. It is the circuit for a security monitoring system. Construct the circuit, using toggle switches for the door switches. Use a pulse generator set to a frequency sufficiently low (so that the LEDs can be monitored) to clock the counter. Test the system until you have it operational. Now review Example 9.6 in the text.

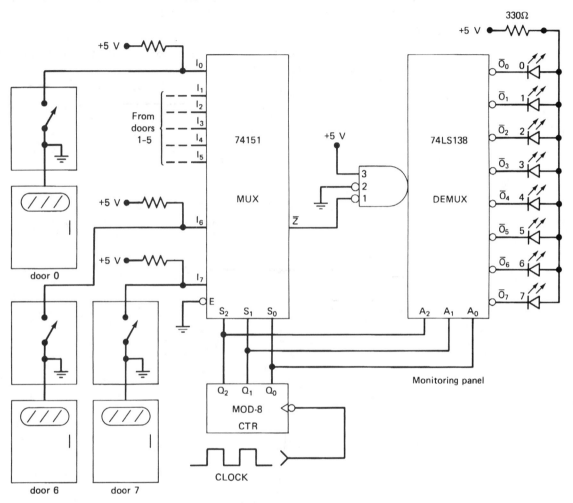

Figure 35-2

e) Have your lab partner or another student insert a fault into the circuit while you are not looking. Do not look for the bug yet. On a separate sheet of paper, draw a table that shows which LEDs are flashing (if any) for any door that opens. Also note the state of the LEDs when all doors are closed. Using your observations, narrow the location of the bug to a few possible faults. Use this list and your test equipment to find the fault. Repeat this step as many times as possible.

f) Have your instructor or laboratory assistant place a bug in your circuit, and then repeat step e. Place your observations, list of possible faults, and your final solution on a separate sheet of paper.

g) If you are to troubleshoot the synchronous data transmission system, make sure that it is functional before beginning the exercise; otherwise, you may be chasing down several bugs instead of just one. Also review Example 9.14 in the text. When you are ready, have your lab partner insert a bug into the circuit while you are not looking. Monitor the MUX and DEMUX outputs with the oscilloscope (or logic analyzer, if available) during one transmission cycle, and draw the waveforms on a separate sheet of paper. Now study the observations, and try to narrow the location of the fault to a small area in the system. List what you think are the possible faults on the same sheet of paper as your observations, then proceed to look for the fault with your troubleshooting tools. Write a description of the fault on the sheet of paper containing your other data. Repeat this step as often as time permits.

h) When you are ready, ask your instructor or laboratory assistant to place a bug in your system. Repeat step g.

Experiment 38

Name _____

DIGITAL-TO-ANALOG CONVERTERS

OBJECTIVE

To investigate the operation of a two-digit BCD-to-Analog-Converter.

TEXT REFERENCES

Read sections 10.1 through 10.5.

EQUIPMENT NEEDED

Components

MC1408 (or DAC0808) (2); √
LM324 op-amp; √
7446 IC (2); √
7490 IC(2); √
seven-segment display unit (2); √
1 k-ohm resistor (2); √
1 k-ohm potentiometer (two 10-turn potentiometers are recommended); √
5 k-ohm potentiometers (two 10-turn potentiometers are recommended); √
18 k-ohm resistor; √
180 k-ohm resistor (2); √
0.1 mF ceramic disc capacitor (2);
normally HIGH pushbutton switch, debounced. √

Instruments

0–5 volt DC power supply; √
+12 volt DC power supply; √
- 12 volt DC power supply; √
DVM;√
pulse or square wave generator. √

DISCUSSION

In today's modern processing systems, one will rarely find a completely analog or completely digital system. Hybrid systems, which combine digital with analog, are predominant. We have already discovered the basic difference between analog and digital signals, and we know that they are incompatible, as are the devices that produce them. However, we also know that there are more analog than digital variables in the real world. If a digital system requires an input from an analog variable, we must find a way to convert the variable from analog to digital. Of course, the reverse is also true. In the current experiment and the next, you will investigate devices which perform these conversions.

Digital-to-Analog Conversion

A very simple digital-to-analog converter (DAC) is the summing amplifier circuit you most likely encountered in an electronic devices course (see Figure 38-1). The inputs of the summing amplifier are applied to an op-amp through the resistor network, and the output of the op-amp will be proportional to the sum of the weighted input currents. In practice, such a circuit is used only when accuracy is not important. IC digital-to-analog converters provide very good accuracy and are found in many applications. In this experiment, you will investigate an IC digital-to-analog convertor, the MC1408. The MC1408 is an 8-bit DAC with current output. You will also contruct a two digit BCD-to-analog converters, which will be used in Experiment 39 to complete a simple digital voltmeter (DVM).

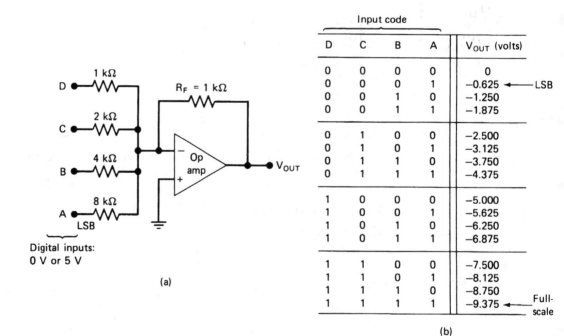

| Input code | | | | |
D	C	B	A	V_{OUT} (volts)
0	0	0	0	0
0	0	0	1	−0.625 ←——LSB
0	0	1	0	−1.250
0	0	1	1	−1.875
0	1	0	0	−2.500
0	1	0	1	−3.125
0	1	1	0	−3.750
0	1	1	1	−4.375
1	0	0	0	−5.000
1	0	0	1	−5.625
1	0	1	0	−6.250
1	0	1	1	−6.875
1	1	0	0	−7.500
1	1	0	1	−8.125
1	1	1	0	−8.750
1	1	1	1	−9.375 ←——Full-scale

(a)

(b)

Figure 38-1

PROCEDURE

a) Refer to the data sheet for an MC1408 IC, and draw its pin layout diagram:

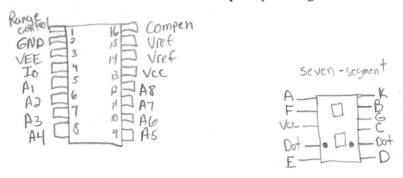

The MC1408 accepts an 8 bit input (at D_7 through D_0) and produces an output *current* that is proportional to the binary input value. Its full-scale (F.S.) rating is 2 mA.

b) Examine and then construct the circuit in Figure 38-2. You will use this circuit later in this experiment and Experiment 39, so do not disconnect the circuit until Experiment 39 has been completed.

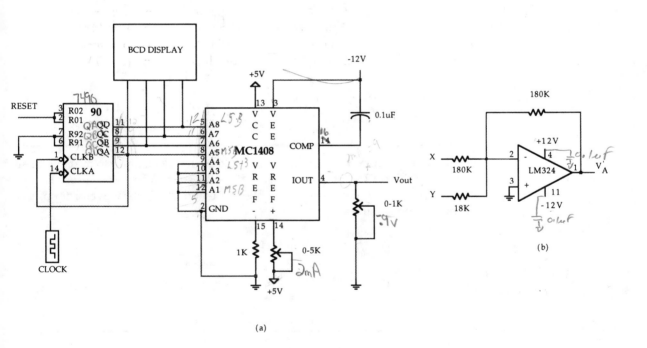

Figure 38-2

c) For each BCD value in Table 38-1, compute the corresponding value at point V_{out} and place the values in the table under V_{out} (expected).

d) Calibrate the unit by using the following procedure:

    1. Insert a milliameter between the 0-5K potentiometer and VREF + of the DAC.

2. Apply power to the circuit and adjust the 0-5K potentiometer until the milliameter reads 2 mA.

3. Remove the power and disconnect the milliameter. Reconnect the potentiometer to the DAC and connect the DVM to point V_{out}. Connect a normally-LOW pushbutton switch to the clock input of the 7490 counter.

4. Set the counter to 9 and adjust the 0-1K potentiometer until the voltage at point V_{out} is -0.9V $\pm$ 0.001V, as measured with the DVM.

5. Pulse the counter through its counting range (0-9) and record the output at point V_{out} in Table 38-1 under First Unit V_{out} (observed).

6. Compare the results in steps c and 5 above. How close in agreement are they? *very close in agreement.*

Table 38-1

BCD Input	V_{out} Expected	First Unit V_{out} Observed	Second Unit V_{out} Observed
0	-0.0V ✓	-0.01 ✓	-0.00 ✓
1	-0.1 ✓	-0.09 ✓	-0.10 ✓
2	-0.2 ✓	-0.19 ✓	-0.20 ✓
3	0.3 ✓	-0.29 ✓	0.30 ✓
4	-0.4 ✓	-0.39 ✓	0.41 ✓
5	0.5 ✓	-0.49 ✓	0.51 ✓
6	-0.6 ✓	-0.59 ✓	0.61 ✓
7	-0.7 ✓	-0.69 ✓	0.71 ✓
8	0.8 ✓	-0.79 ✓	0.80 ✓
9	0.9 ✓	-0.89 ✓	0.90 ✓

e) Disconnect the pushbutton switch from the clock input to the counter and replace it with a TTL-compatible signal from the squarewave generator. Examine the signal at point Vout with an oscilloscope and draw the waveform observed using Timing Diagram 38-1.

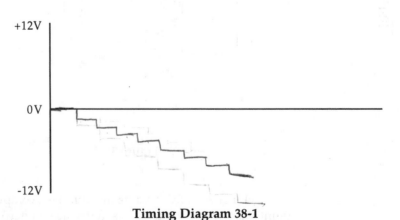

Timing Diagram 38-1

f) Construct and calibrate a second unit as in steps b-e. Use Second Unit V_{out} of Table 38-1 to record your calibration results. This unit will also be used later in this experiment and in Experiment 39, so do not disconnect it until then.

g) Construct the summing amplifier of Figure 38-2(b) and connect each of the DAC units to one of its inputs.

h) Pulse the counter so that the BCD input is 09. Measure V_A' with the DVM. It should indicate a value close to +0.9 V. Adjust the 0-1 k-ohm potentiometer at the LSD output, if necessary, until V_A' is as close to +0.9V as possible.

i) Now set the BCD count to 90. The voltage at V_A' should now be close to +9.0 V. If necessary, adjust the 1 k-ohm potentiometer at the MSD output to bring this value as close as possible to +9.0 V. The BCD-to-analog converter is now calibrated.

j) Remove the toggle switches and install a MOD-100 BCD counter in their place as shown in Figure 38-2. Also connect BCD display units to display the counter. Clock the MOD-100 counter with a pushbutton.

k) Fill in the expected values of V_A' for each BCD number listed in Table 38-2.

Table 38-2

BCD Input	V_A' expected	V_A' observed
00		
05		
10		
15		
20		
25		
30		
35		
40		
45		
50		
55		
60		
65		
70		
75		
80		
85		
90		
95		
99		

l) Step the counter through its count sequence, stopping every five counts and reading V_A'. Record these values in the table. If any reading is off by more than 0.05 V from the expected value, notify your instructor or laboratory assistant.

m) Remove the pushbutton switch connected to the counter clock input, and replace it with the output of the square wave generator. Set the square wave generator to 1 kHz. Connect the oscilloscope to V_A', and draw the waveform displayed using Timing Diagram 38-2.

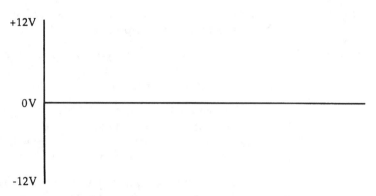

Timing Diagram 38-2

n) *Review*: This concludes the exercises on digital-to-analog converters. Do not disassemble the converter you have on the circuit board at this time. It will be used in Experiment 39.

To test your understanding of the principles covered in this experiment, answer the following questions:

1. What is the percent resolution of the BCD-to-analog converter you constructed? _____ %.

2. What problems would you have encountered had you not calibrated the DAC outputs before using them in the two-digit converter?

Experiment 39

Name _Daniel Woods_

Marc Melcusone

Mike Glomm

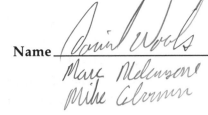

ANALOG-TO-DIGITAL CONVERTERS

OBJECTIVES

1. To investigate the operation of a TTL compatible comparator circuit.
2. To investigate the operation of a digital-ramp analog-to-digital converter in a 2-digit DVM circuit.

TEXT REFERENCES

Read sections 10.6 and 10.7.

EQUIPMENT NEEDED

Components
MC1408 (or DAC0808) (2); ✓
LM324 op-amp; ✓
7446 IC (2); ✓
7490 IC (2); ✓
seven-segment display unit (2); ✓
4.7 V zener diode;
1.5 k-ohm potentiometer (two 10-turn potentiometers recommended);
5 k-ohm potentiometer; ✓
18 k-ohm resistor; ✓
180 k-ohm resistor (2); ✓
student-selected resistors and capacitors;
8 toggle switches;
normally HIGH pushbutton switch, debounced.

Instruments

0–5 volt DC power supply;

+15 volt DC power supply;

-15 volt DC power supply;

DVM;

pulse or square wave generator.

DISCUSSION

In Experiment 38, you investigated the DAC. You used DACs to construct a two-digit BCD-to-analog converter. Analog-to-digital converters (ADCs) and digital computers work together to measure real world variables. Thus the ADCs extend a digital computer by acting as an interface to sensors that convert analog quantities into voltages or current. In this way, whenever the computer needs information on a variable, it acts like a digital voltmeter, measures the quantity, and then stores the measurement in memory for future use.

In the current experiment, you will first investigate a comparator circuit that is TTL compatible. This type of circuit is used quite frequently in hybrid systems. It is also a component in an analog-to-digital converter. You will then complete your two-digit DVM circuit by constructing a digital-ramp ADC.

PROCEDURE

a) *TTL compatible comparator*: To construct a counter-ramp ADC, you need to add only a comparator circuit to the output of a counter-driven DAC, like the one you constructed in Experiment 38. Since the comparator output will be used to control a TTL gate, it is desirable to have the output of this comparator TTL compatible.

Examine the circuit of Figure 39-1. The circuit has two inputs. One is V_A', the input from the DAC output, and the other is V_A, the analog input. Note the zener diode at the comparator output. Since the digital output is negative or 0, the analog input must also be negative. The purpose of this diode is to limit the output excursions to a range of about -0.7 V to 4.7 V, making the output of the comparator TTL compatible.

Suppose the analog input is -2 V. If $V_A' = -1.5$ V, then the op-amp input difference will be positive, causing the output to swing positive toward +15 V. The zener diode limits this swing to +4.7 V. On the other hand, if $V_A' = -2.5$ V, the input difference will be negative, causing the output to swing negative toward -15 V. The zener diode this time will be forward-biased, so the voltage at the output will be -0.7 V, the voltage drop across the zener.

Construct the comparator. Connect one end of the 5 k-ohm potentiometer to -15 volts and the other to ground. Connect a wire to the wiper of the potentiometer. This wire will be the analog source, V_A.

Connect V_A' from the DAC to the + input of the comparator and the analog source to the - input. Adjust V_A for approximately -5 V. Pulse the MOD-100 counter until a count of around 55 is reached. Measure V_A' and the comparator output voltage, and record the measurement in Table 39-1.

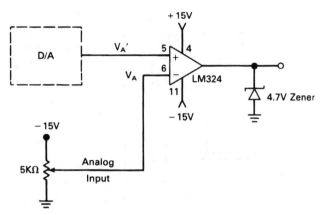

Figure 39-1

Table 39-1

V_A	Count	V_A'	Output
-5 V	55		
-5 V	45		

Now reset the counter, and pulse it until a count of around 45 is reached. Measure V_A' and the comparator output voltage, and record them in Table 39-1.

If the voltages measured above are correct, proceed to the next step. If not, check the calibration of the DACs and the connections between V_A' and the comparator.

b) *Analog-to-digital converter application—Digital voltmeter*: Now that the comparator is operating satisfactorily, you are ready to finish the DVM circuit. Figure 39-2 shows the complete wiring of the DVM. Make the necessary additions to the BCD-to-analog converter and the comparator, which are already on the board. One-shot OS1 controls the display time of the DVM. Its t_p should be made adjustable from about 1 second to 5 seconds or greater. One-shot OS2 provides a clear pulse for the BCD counters, and its t_p should be 10 microseconds. The AND gate is a transmission gate for the counter clock. As long as $V_A < V_A'$, the comparator output is HIGH and the AND gate is enabled, allowing the clock through to the counter. Whenever $V_A > V_A'$, the comparator switches to LOW, inhibiting the AND gate and freezing the counter at its current count.

When you have completed the circuit, disconnect the pushbutton switch from the BCD MOD-100 counter, and apply a 1 kHz square wave as clock input. Set the analog source to -5 V or slightly over. The DVM display should display 51, which represents -5.1 V. It could, however, be 50 or 52, depending on the accuracy of the calibration of the BCD-to-analog converters. Try several values of V_A between 0 and -10 V and record the results in the space provided below.

c) *Resolution of analog-to-digital converter*: With the lab DVM monitoring V_A, determine what change in V_A is needed to cause the counter display to change by one step. What is the resolution of the ADC? _____.

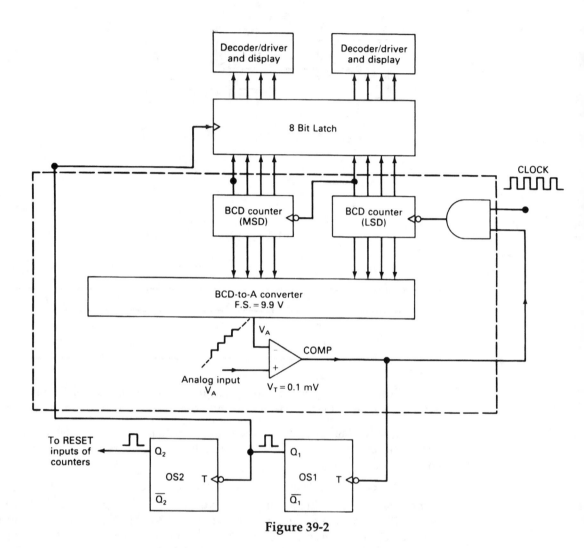

Figure 39-2

d) *Conversion time:* Change the display OS1 circuit so that t_p is 1 millisecond. Connect the dual trace oscilloscope to V_A' and the output of the comparator. Set V_A to -5 V. Observe the waveforms, and draw them, using Timing Diagram 39-1. Be sure to show proper levels. Label the conversion time and display time on the waveforms. Measure and record the conversion times for V_A = -1 V, -5 V, -9 V, and -11 V in Table 39-2.

Table 39-2

V_A	t_C
-1 V	
-5 V	
-9 V	
-11 V	

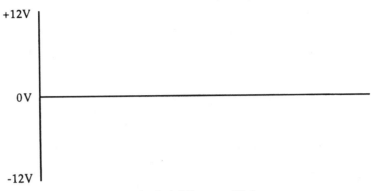

Timing Diagram 39-1

e) In step d, you observed the effect of applying an analog input that is overrange (-11 V). How would you modify the DVM circuit to indicate that V_A is overrange? Draw a circuit showing the modification:

Show the circuit to your instructor for approval, and then add the modification to the DVM. Test the modified DVM. When the DVM is working properly, demonstrate the DVM to your instructor.

f) *Review*: This concludes the exercises on analog-to-digital converters. To test your understanding of the principles covered in this experiment, answer the following questions:

1. Why were the (constructed) DVM readings always higher than the actual value of V_A?

2. Explain why V_A has to be a negative value.

Experiment 40

Name _Marc McLansme_
Mike Glomeme

SEMICONDUCTOR RANDOM ACCESS MEMORY (RAM)

OBJECTIVES

1. To investigate the operation of an N-MOS static RAM memory IC.
2. To demonstrate the use of a logic analyzer in examining memory.
3. To demonstrate memory-to-register data transfer.
4. To demonstrate register-to-memory data transfer.

TEXT REFERENCES

Read sections 11.1, 11.2, 11.4, 11.12, 11.13, and 11.14.

EQUIPMENT NEEDED

Components
2114A IC;
7486 IC;
7493 IC;
74125 IC;
74LS139 IC;
74174 IC;
SK-10 circuit board;
10 toggle switches;
normally HIGH pushbutton switch (2), normally LOW pushbutton switch, debounced;
4 LED monitors.

Instruments
0–5 volt DC power supply;

logic probe;

logic analyzer (optional).

DISCUSSION

We know that memory is a characteristic of all useful digital systems. Up to now, we have been using flip-flops and registers for storing data. In Experiment 37, you investigated the tristate register and connected three of them to a data bus system. You discovered that in order to use (access) a particular register, the register has to be enabled. If data is to be stored in (written to) a register, its input must be enabled. If data is to be transferred from (read from) it, its output must be enabled. Recall that a decoder was used to do the enabling (or controlling).

Digital systems normally need hundreds of registers, and the word size needed is usually more than four bits. Memory ICs are available in various sizes, ranging from a few registers to several thousand. Large decoders are needed to access any particular register. For example, selecting one register from a 1024-word (1K) memory requires a 1-of-1024 decoder. How would you like to wire one of those? Rest at ease, for these large devices are included on the memory chip. For the same 1024-word memory, there are 10 special enable lines called address lines, which are used to externally select any register inside the chip.

A memory system that can be written to and read from is generally called read/write memory. However, semiconductor read/write memories are usually referred to as random access memory (RAM). In the current experiment, you will investigate a popular 1K RAM chip, the 2114. The word size of the 2114 is four bits. The number of data lines is four, and the chip is classified as common I/O. The chip must be enabled at the $\overline{CS}$ (chip select) input for the memory system to function. A normally HIGH $\overline{WE}$ (write enable) input keeps the chip in the read mode most of the time. Reading does not destroy the data in the memory. Whenever a WRITE operation is necessary, the $\overline{WE}$ input is pulsed LOW long enough for storage to take place.

PROCEDURE

a) In this experiment, you are to connect a 2114A memory chip to a data bus. Refer to the data sheet for a 2114A IC, and draw its pin layout diagram:

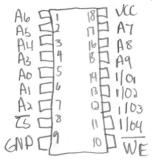

The 2114A is an N-MOS static RAM chip organized as 1024 four-bit words (1024 × 4). Its ten address inputs permit access to any of the 1024 words by applying the correct binary number representing the address to these pins. The addresses range from 0000000000 to 1111111111. Since it is more efficient to express such large binary numbers in *hexadecimal*, we will do so from now on. The range of addresses in hexadecimal is 000_{16} to $3FF_{16}$.

The $\overline{WE}$ input is used to select the READ or WRITE operation. When the input is HIGH, the READ operation is selected; when it is LOW, the WRITE operation is selected.

The $\overline{CS}$ (chip select) input enables the chip, when LOW, so that either the READ or the WRITE can take place. When HIGH, $\overline{CS}$ disables the chip so that neither operation can take place.

The 2114A has four tristate I/O lines, I/O_3 through I/O_0. During a READ operation, the memory word selected by an address will be made available at these pins. During a WRITE operation, the word to be written must be on the lines connected to these pins.

Summarize the memory chip's operations using Table 40-1.

Table 40-1

WE	$\overline{CS}$	Operation
0	1	
1	1	
0	0	
1	0	

b) Examine the circuit of Figure 40-1. The circuit shows how the memory chip will be wired for initial testing. Later you will add other components to the bus. Read through the following steps, and make each connection as directed.

1) Mount a 2114A IC, a 7493 IC, and a 74125 IC on a circuit board. This board will be separate from the board to be used for the data bus. Connect V_{cc} to +5 V and GND to power ground for the three ICs.

2) Wire the 7493 as a MOD-16 counter. Connect the 7493 outputs, Q_3–Q_0 to address inputs A_3–A_0, respectively, of the 2114A memory chip. Make sure address inputs A_4–A_9 are grounded.

3) Connect a toggle switch to the write enable toggle input.

4) Connect a normally HIGH pushbutton switch to the device select clock input ($\overline{CS}$).

5) Connect a normally HIGH pushbutton switch to the address select clock input ($\overline{CP_0}$ input of the 7493).

6) Connect I/O outputs I/O_3–I/O_0 to data bus lines DB_3–DB_0, respectively.

7) Connect the outputs of the 74125 buffers to the data bus.

8) Connect a normally LOW pushbutton switch to the reset input (MR of the 7493). You will use this switch to reset the counter.

You are now ready to test the 2114A. Using the logic probe to monitor the counter outputs, clear the counter by pulsing it until its output is 0000. Set $\overline{WE}$ to HIGH and the data switches to 1001. Use the logic probe to check the data bus levels. The probe should indicate an indeterminate level. Why?

c) *2114 READ operation*: To read data from memory, $\overline{CS}$ must be made LOW while $\overline{WE}$ is HIGH. Press and hold the pushbutton connected to $\overline{CS}$, and check the data bus levels. Since the counter is at 00_{16}, the data stored at that address should

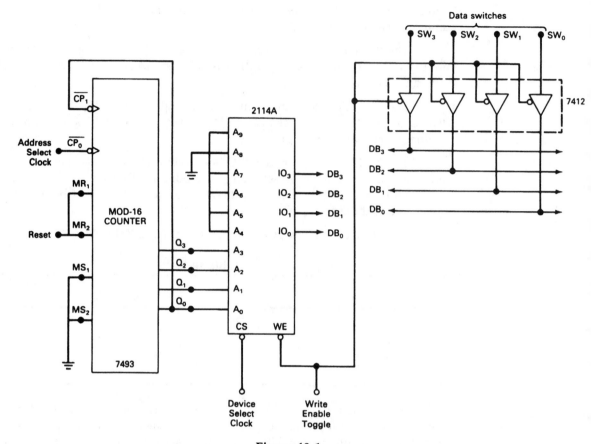

Figure 40-1

be on the data bus. Since nothing has been written into memory, whatever is on the data bus is random. Release the $\overline{CS}$ switch, and pulse the counter to 0001 (01_{16}). Press and hold the $\overline{CS}$ pushbutton switch, and check the bus levels. Again, the levels on the data bus are random. Read the data words in other memory locations in the same manner, and verify that the levels on the data bus are random.

d) *2114A WRITE operation*: To write data to memory, $\overline{CS}$ must be made LOW while $\overline{WE}$ is LOW. Set the address counter to 00_{16}. Set $\overline{WE}$ to LOW. Check the levels on the data bus now. Since the data switch buffers are enabled, the data word on the bus should be 1001. However, the data has not been written yet, since $\overline{CS}$ = 1. Momentarily pulse $\overline{CS}$ LOW. Verify that 1001 has been written to memory location 00_{16} by performing a READ as done in step c.

e) Momentarily disconnect V_{cc} from the 2114A. Then reconnect it, and READ the data word at memory location 00_{16}. It should be lost, since RAM memory is volatile.

f) Store all of the words at the memory locations shown in Table 40-2. Have your instructor check the data.

g) *Using a logic analyzer to examine memory*: If a logic analyzer is not available, go on to step h.

The contents of your memory chip can be displayed in "state table format." In order to sample and display the data, the memory must be cycled continuously

Table 40-2

Address	Data	
	Binary	Hex
00	1111	F
01	1110	E
02	1101	D
03	1100	C
04	1011	B
05	1010	A
06	1001	9
07	1000	8
08	0111	7
09	0110	6
0A	0101	5
0B	0100	4
0C	0011	3
0D	0010	2
0E	0001	1
0F	0000	0

through each of the 16 addresses so that the contents of each memory location are placed on the data bus. Use the following procedure to set up and display memory on the logic analyzer. The instructions are very general, so you may have to consult your instructor for specific details on how to set up your particular logic analyzer.

1) Connect a 10 kHz square wave to the counter clock input.
2) Connect the logic analyzer probes as follows:

    Channels 0–3 to DB$_0$–DB$_3$
    Channels 4–7 to address lines A$_0$–A$_3$
    "C" probe to the 10 kHz clock

3) Set $\overline{WE}$ to 1 (READ mode).
4) Set the logic analyzer sample interval to EXT (positive edge).
5) Set the logic analyzer to trigger on address 0000.
6) Set the logic analyzer to state table mode. Display should be binary.
7) Have the logic analyzer start a sample cycle. Observe the tabular data displayed. Then position the cursor so that the trigger word is at the top of the table. This line should be either highlighted, blinking, or both. The table should show addresses 0000–1111 and their respective data contents. Since $\overline{CS}$ was HIGH, the data will not be correct.
8) Now hold $\overline{CS}$ LOW, and repeat step 7. The table should now display the correct memory data. This time store the sample.
9) Disconnect one of the memory's I/O lines from the data bus. Have the logic analyzer take another sample. Next, use the COMPARE mode to compare the new sample with the sample that you stored. You should observe that the missing I/O line's data position in the display is highlighted in some manner to indicate differences between old and new data.
10) Reconnect the I/O line you disconnected in step 9.

11) Disconnect the square wave generator from the counter, and replace the pushbutton switch there.

h) *Memory-to-register data transfer*: This type of transfer requires close attention to timing. During a READ operation, $\overline{WE}$ is HIGH and the $\overline{CS}$ line is pulsed LOW. After internal delays, the memory produces the data word at the I/O pins. This data can be clocked into the register at this time. For proper operation, the $\overline{CS}$ pulse has to stay LOW long enough to give the data a chance to stabilize on the data bus. If not, the register will latch erroneous data.

Refer to the data sheet for the 2114A, and determine how much time should be allowed for the memory outputs to stabilize before latching them into a register. Record this value: _____.

i) Examine the circuit in Figure 40-2. You are to add a 74LS139 IC and a 74174 IC to the data bus system. Install the 74174 IC onto the component board, and make the connections shown in Figure 40-2. Keep the 74174 $\overline{MR}$ input unconnected; it can be momentarily grounded to clear the register. Also make all other connections not shown that are required for the proper operation of the IC.

j) Make a table of transfer operations like you did in Experiment 37, this time for the new data bus system. Show the table to your instructor or laboratory assistant for approval.

k) Test the operation of the completed data bus system by setting the decoder select inputs to all possible combinations and verifying that the correct input and output devices are selected. What happens when the decoder select inputs are all

Table 40-3

Selects				Data Transfer	
IS_1	IS_0	OS_1	OS_0	To Register	From Register
0	0	0	0		
0	0	0	1	memory	data switches
0	1	0	0		
0	1	0	1		

LOW? _____. Check the memory READ/WRITE operations. Enter the data in Table 40-3 and then verify that the data was written.

l) *Register-to-memory data transfer*: The way the data bus is currently configured, you cannot transfer data from the 74174 to memory. Come up with a circuit modification that will permit this type of data transfer. Keep in mind the following considerations:

1) You cannot tie the register outputs directly to the data bus. Why?

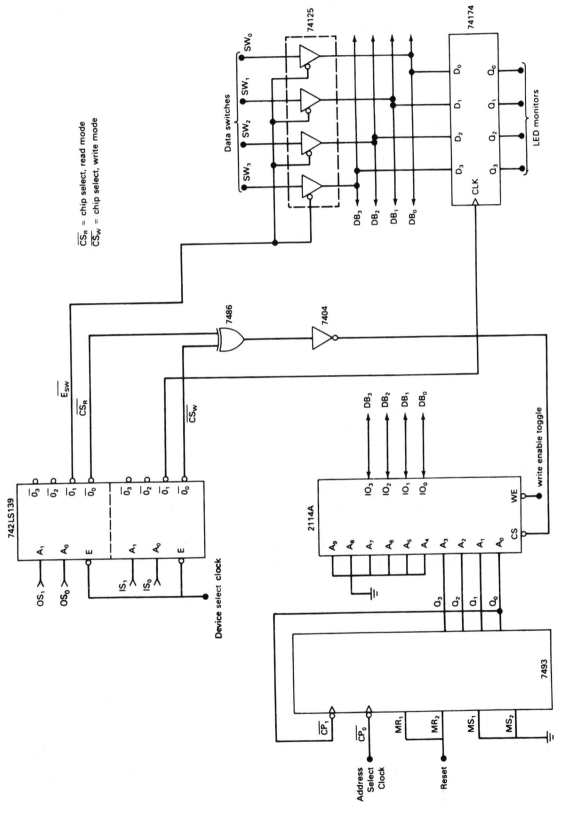

FIGURE 40-2

2) You still want to be able to write a word into memory from the switch inputs.
Thus, you must have some way of selecting either the register or the switches
as the source of data to be placed onto the data bus to be written into memory.
Draw the circuit modification:

Show the circuit to your instructor for approval.

m) Construct your modification, and check it out using the following
sequence of operations:

1) WRITE 1011 from the data switches to memory address 05.
2) READ the contents of address 05, and transfer it to the 74174 register.
3) Clear the register.
4) WRITE 0000 from the register into address 05.
5) READ address 05 to see if it is storing 0000.

Demonstrate this sequence to your instructor.

n) *Review*: This concludes the exercises on RAM memory. To test your understanding of the principles covered in this experiment, answer the following questions.

1. Explain the sequence of events illustrating how data is transferred from memory to the 74174 register.

2. Explain what might happen to memory if the enables to the 74LS139 were NOT pulsed LOW to enable the decoder operation, but rather tied permanently LOW.

3. Explain why timing during memory-to-register data transfer was not a critical factor in performing this experiment.

Appendix A

WIRING AND TROUBLESHOOTING DIGITAL CIRCUITS

OBJECTIVES

1. To discuss general wiring procedures for digital circuits.
2. To introduce the student to formalized troubleshooting procedures.
3. To list some of the common faults found in digital systems.

DISCUSSION

The experiments in this manual are designed to give you hands-on experience with digital circuits. More than that, they provide you with an opportunity to develop sound breadboarding and troubleshooting skills that will be invaluable to you whether you eventually become an engineer or a technician. This appendix will present some very basic information and suggestions concerning each area. It is not meant to replace any laboratory standards. However, much of the information given here can be used as reference material that can be, and should be, reviewed from time to time.

Most of the experiments contain operational testing of various ICs. At times, this may appear to be a tedious undertaking on your part. Don't fall into the trap of treating this sort of experimentation mechanically, taking for granted that an IC will operate just as it did in the classroom lecture. In the classroom, you are working with the ideal. In the lab, you will occasionally work with ICs that are less than ideal. In fact, they may not work at all, or at least not in the manner they were designed to work. If you keep in mind that lab experimentation is not only to verify principles but also to learn to recognize common problems associated with the circuits, you will get more out of the experiments. As you will learn, verification of a circuit's operation is one of the first steps taken in troubleshooting.

A.1 Prototype Circuit Wiring

It is assumed that you will be wiring circuits using a prototype circuit board. Such boards come in different sizes, but most have the following features:

a) Two horizontal rows of holes, one at the top and one at the bottom. The contacts underneath the holes on each of these rows are connected together to form a bus. They are not directly connected to the other holes on the board.

b) At least two sections of holes, with each section arranged so that the holes are in vertical groups called circuit blocks. Each circuit block is isolated from all others. This permits several wires to be joined at common junctions. The two sections are separated by a horizontal gap. This gap separates the sections electrically as well as physically. Thus, a vertical circuit block in the top section of the board is not connected to the block directly below it in the bottom section. ICs will straddle this gap so that each IC pin will be inserted into its own block. Connections to each pin will be brought to its block.

Installing ICs: ICs should be installed or mounted on the board to permit wires going from the top section of the board to the bottom to go between the ICs. It is not advisable to pass wires over ICs, although sometimes it is hard to avoid. Strapping ICs to the board in this manner will present problems if the IC has to be removed. The consequences of this are obvious.

As you mount an IC, check to make sure that none of its pins are being tucked beneath it. If it is necessary to remove an IC, always use an IC puller. *Never* remove an IC with your fingers or with a pair of pliers. The first causes a definite safety hazard, while the second will often result in eventual damage to the IC.

Wiring the circuit: Wires should be dressed so that 3/8" insulation is stripped from each end and the length of wire is no more than needed to make a neat connection between circuit blocks. If the wires are too long, some circuits will malfunction, especially flip-flops and flip-flop devices such as counters. You may have to rearrange the ICs on the board to solve this problem, if it occurs. Another way to solve the problem is by inserting a 2 k-ohm resistor in series with the wire at the input end of the wire.

Have a lab partner call out each connection to be made. Route the wires along the circuit board neatly, bending them smoothly wherever necessary. Avoid bending the wire sharply, since this will increase the likelihood of fracture beneath the insulation, resulting in an open circuit or an intermittent open. Minimize the number of crossovers, that is, wires routed over other wires.

The overall appearance should be neat, not like a bowl of spaghetti. If you have made all of your connections as outlined above, it may not be picture perfect, but the neatness will pay off in reduced troubleshooting time and easier IC replacement.

A.2 Testing the Circuit

Circuit testing is also known as troubleshooting. You are probably accustomed to discrete circuit (e.g., a transistor amplifier) troubleshooting methods. Since each circuit element of a discrete circuit is accessible to the troubleshooter, faulty circuit elements can be isolated by making basic measurements such as voltage, resistance, capacitance, and inductance, using conventional test equipment. Modern digital circuits and systems, on the other hand, consist mainly of digital ICs. The IC's components are not accessible to the troubleshooter, so the troubleshooter must rely on knowledge of the IC's operation(s) in order to isolate the IC as being faulty. The experiments in this manual are designed to give you the necessary experience to test for and recognize proper operation of ICs.

A digital IC is considered defective or faulty if its outputs do not respond correctly, according to its truth table, for each set of input conditions and for each of its various operating modes. A similar statement can be made for digital circuits and systems. Once it has been verified that a circuit or system is not responding correctly, a *fault is said to exist*, and further troubleshooting is indicated. The next troubleshooting step is to *isolate the cause of the fault*, which may be in one or more smaller circuits or subsystems. By progressively isolating smaller circuits, and perhaps smaller subsystems, the troubleshooter will eventually isolate the defective components, which may be one or more ICs and/or discrete components. After *replacing the defective components*, the circuit or system is tested for proper operation once more. Once proper operation is established for all operating modes, the troubleshooter's task is completed.

Now that the student is acquainted with the nature of digital troubleshooting, a procedure for fault isolation is presented. The student should, when applying the procedure in the lab, perform each step in the order given. After sufficient experience with digital circuits is attained, common sense and intuition may lead the student directly to the faulty device and thereby reduce the amount of troubleshooting time.

Step 1: Perform a visual inspection of the system or circuit. Look for loose or damaged connecting wires, cables, and printed circuit (PC) boards, evidence of burning or extreme overheating, missing components, and blown fuses. If the circuit or system is mounted on prototype boards, look for wiring errors, damaged boards, and digital ICs improperly inserted. Also check for incorrect circuit design.

Step 2: Check all power source levels, and confirm that power is actually being applied to the circuit or system.

Step 3: Study all relevant documentation on the circuit or system, such as block diagrams, schematics, and operating instructions. Learn how the circuit or system operates normally.

Step 4: Verify all operating modes of the circuit by running tests.

Step 5: Record results of the tests run in step 4. Test results often show patterns that may lead to the faulty device. Repeat steps 4 and 5 at least once before proceeding to step 6.

Step 6: If the circuit passes all tests, end the procedure. If the circuit fails at least one test, continue to the next step.

Step 7: Analyze the test results recorded above and select a possible location for the fault.

Step 8: Check all signals and static logic levels at this location, and record them. If nothing appears abnormal, return to step 7.

Step 9: Analyze the test results recorded above, and select a possible faulty device.

Step 10: Check the device for proper functioning. If it is a discrete component, take basic Ohm's Law measurements and/or use a device tester to determine if the device is faulty. If the device is an IC, check the IC for proper functioning. This includes checking inputs and outputs for stuck-HIGH and stuck-LOW conditions and other types of digital IC faults (see below, *Common Digital IC Faults*). If the device passes all tests, then return to step 9.

Step 11: Repair or replace the faulty device and return to step 4.

A.3 Common Causes of Faults
in Digital Systems

In this section, several common causes of faults in digital systems are listed along with symptoms given for each cause and steps that may be taken to correct or minimize its effects on the system.

Defective components: Components normally fail because of age, because the maximum voltage or current rating of the device was exceeded due to improper design or because of the breakdown of another component, improper connections, or excessive ambient temperature. In the case of digital ICs, overheating caused by improper connections (especially prototype circuits), overvoltage, or ambient temperature may result in the IC operating only sporadically. After cooling down, the IC will usually operate normally.

IC loading problems: Exceeding the fan-out of a TTL logic output may result in the output voltage dropping below V_{OH}(min) or rising above V_{OL}(max). To verify this condition, the output voltage should be checked for a level of 0 V–0.8 V for a LOW and 2 V–5 V for a HIGH. If not, the excessive fan-out is causing a problem.

CMOS and MOS logic outputs will not be affected significantly by exceeding the fan-out limits. However, any transitions at the output will show an increase in risetime and falltime. This is because each CMOS or MOS input loads the output capacitively (5 pf each input).

Some common symptoms to look for are flip-flops, counters, and flip-flop registers that do not respond to the signal at the clock input. Measure t_R and t_F of the clock signal, and compare the measurements to the minimum required by the flip-flop, counter, or register for proper triggering.

To correct the problem caused by excessive fan-out, a buffer should be used or the fan-out reduced by load splitting. Another solution is to insert a pulse-shaping circuit such as a Schmitt trigger between the overloaded output and the clock input.

Improper signal characteristics: A digital IC may function improperly if logic signals not meeting its requirements are applied to its inputs. Minimum requirements are given for amplitude, pulse duration, and transition times. A signal that fails to meet any one of these requirements can cause the IC to function incorrectly.

Common symptoms brought on by improper signal characteristics include flip-flops, counters, and flip-flop registers that respond incorrectly to signals at clock, clear, and preset inputs.

The characteristic(s) causing the problem must be determined and brought back into specification.

Power supply—Improper levels: Since all IC logic devices use voltage to represent logic levels, trouble with the output level of the supply can cause ICs to function improperly. A common cause of improper power supply levels is overload. This can be particularly true in prototype systems and circuits.

Symptoms of this type of trouble include the condition where logic HIGH at circuit outputs is less than V_{OH}. Disconnecting a few ICs from the power supply will usually cause the level of V_{CC} to rise if this is the case.

Using a larger power supply or redesigning the existing one for higher current output will solve the problem.

Power supply—Poor regulation.   Poor regulation in a power supply will cause V_{CC} to fluctuate when large numbers of logic circuits are switching states. These fluctuations act like noise pulses and can cause false triggering of logic devices. This problem is especially significant in TTL circuits.

A symptom caused by this problem is flip-flops, counters, and registers triggering when they are not supposed to, and triggering instead at the time other devices in the system are changing states. To verify that poor regulation is the problem, V_{CC} should be examined with an oscilloscope. If spikes or pulses are riding on the V_{CC} level causing V_{CC} to drop by more than 0.2 V, then the power supply has poor regulation.

There are two ways to correct this problem: (1) improve the power supply regulation by either replacing or redesigning the current one, or (2) use RF decoupling capacitors (refer to text, Chapter 8).

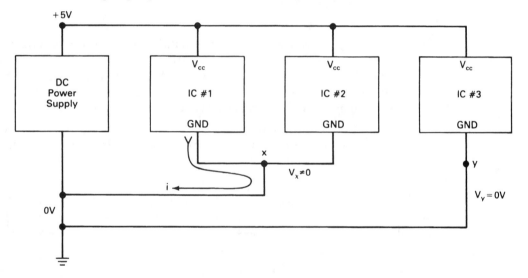

Figure A-1

Grounding problems: Poorly designed ground return circuits can cause the voltage at IC ground pins to be nonzero. This is because currents flowing through the ground system can cause resistive and inductive voltage drops (see Figure A-1). To avoid this problem, all ground wires should have low resistance and inductance, and each IC ground pin should be connected to the power supply separately. PC board ground returns should be large conductive traces.

Noise problems: Circuit noise can be externally or internally generated. Internally generated noise was discussed earlier. Externally generated noise can cause sporadic triggering of logic circuits. Common sources are electromechanical devices (e.g., motors and relays that produce electromagnetic radiation) and electronic power control circuitry using SCRs and TRIACs. This type of problem can be minimized by using special AC power line filtering devices to prevent noise from entering through the AC lines and grounded shields or conducting planes to short radiated noise signals to ground.

A.4 Common Digital IC Faults

Digital IC faults are classified as either internal or external faults. We begin our discussion with internal faults.

Internal digital IC faults: There are four types of internal failures:

1) inputs or outputs shorted to ground or V_{CC}
2) inputs or outputs open
3) shorts between pins (not to ground or V_{CC})
4) internal circuitry failure

These failures are corrected by replacing the faulty IC. A discussion on each type of failure follows.

Short to ground or V_{CC}: This failure causes the inputs or outputs to be either permanently HIGH or permanently LOW (referred to as stuck-HIGH or stuck-LOW). Figure A-2(a) shows a NAND gate with a stuck-LOW input and a stuck-HIGH output. The stuck-HIGH condition may be the result of an internal short in input A, an internal short at output X, or both.

Connections to output X are also forced HIGH; connections to input A are forced LOW. Shorts of this type in emitter-coupled logic (ECL) devices result in neither a HIGH nor a LOW.

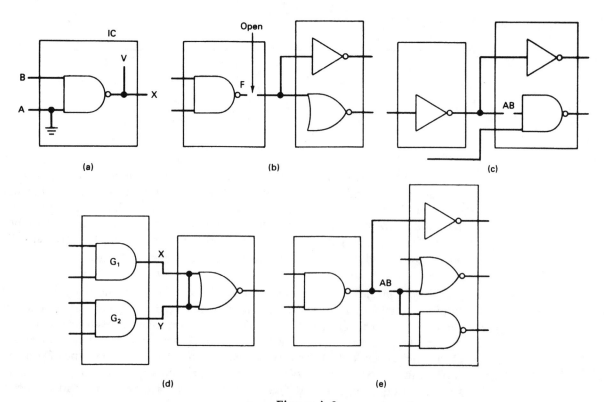

Figure A-2

In troubleshooting this type of failure, the student should be aware that signals may not change beyond the point where the short is located.

Open inputs or outputs: An open output will result in an open input for all inputs driven by the output.   Open inputs in TTL logic devices generally act as HIGHs, causing inputs that are tied to open outputs to resemble a stuck-HIGH input, though not always.   Open CMOS inputs do not generally act as a HIGH or a LOW.   This being the case, inputs tied to an open TTL or CMOS output will resemble a stuck-LOW or stuck-HIGH input or may even oscillate between HIGH and LOW. Open inputs for ECL devices, with inputs pulled down by a resistor, are LOW.

Figure A-2(b) illustrates an open output in a NAND gate.   Figure A-2(c) shows an open input. In the latter diagram, the student should note that all signals before point A are unaffected.

Short between two pins: Figure A-2(d) shows two input pins shorted together.   This means that the outputs of the two driver gates are also shorted.   This condition will cause a fault in TTL and CMOS devices only if the two driver outputs try to go to opposite levels, say, X to HIGH and Y to LOW.   In this case, if the device is TTL, X will be stuck-LOW.   In other words, if one output is LOW, both will be LOW.   However, if the device is CMOS, this condition typically produces an intermediate level (see Figure A-3).   There is obviously no fault which occurs when both outputs are supposed to be at the same level. ECL device outputs can normally be connected together, so no logic faults will occur unless the driver gates are damaged by excessive currents.

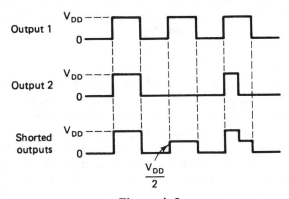

Figure A-3

Internal circuitry failure: Failure in the circuits within a digital IC can cause its inputs and outputs to be stuck-HIGH or stuck-LOW.

External digital IC faults: In addition to the four types of internal failure, there are four types of external failures that can occur:

1) line shorted to ground or power supply
2) open signal line
3) short between signal lines
4) failure of a discrete component

To discover these faults, look for poor soldering joints, solder bridges, open wires or traces, or test components such as capacitors and resistors for opens, shorts, and/or values that are out of tolerance.

Line shorted to ground or power supply: This type of failure will appear like an internal short and can't be distinguished from it. Perform a careful visual inspection to isolate this fault.

Open signal line: Figure A.2(e) shows an open signal line that results in an open input only for points beyond point B. All inputs before A are unaffected by the open line. Signal tracing and/or continuity checks are useful techniques for discovering this type of fault.

Short between two signal lines: This type of fault cannot be distinguished from an internal short. Often, poor soldering on PC boards results in solder bridges across the signal lines. On prototype boards, look for bare connecting wires (poorly dressed) too close together. In either case, a visual inspection is necessary to locate this fault.

Shorted signal lines in TTL will appear different from shorts in CMOS circuits. In TTL, if one signal is trying to go HIGH and the other is going LOW, the level at the short will be about 0 V. This is because resistance at TTL outputs is lower in the LOW state than in the HIGH state. For CMOS and MOS devices, the level at the short will be about midway between 0 V and 5 V for this same situation, because their output resistance is about the same in both states. See Figure A-3 for an example of how waveforms would look for shorted signal lines in CMOS and MOS circuits. Note the 2.5 V levels. These levels would not normally appear on the waveforms.

Failure of discrete components: While most digital components are ICs, there is still circuitry that requires discrete components such as resistors, capacitors, transistors, and diodes. These components can be tested either completely out of the circuit or by unsoldering one or more of their leads and checking them with an appropriate test instrument such as an ohmmeter, capacitance checker, or transistor checker. Faulty discrete components could mean another circuit caused the failure. Be sure and check around for other faults because, in the long run, this avoids repeated failures in the device replaced.

Common test equipment used in digital troubleshooting: Besides the usual analog test equipment, such as VOMs, oscilloscopes, and the like, digital troubleshooting requires some specialized equipment. A list of these specialized instruments would include the following:

1) logic probe
2) logic pulser
3) current tracer
4) logic analyzer

Of the four, the logic probe is the most useful in general troubleshooting. The pulser is useful when it is necessary to trigger gates, flip-flops, counters, or other types of circuits to check for proper operation. Both the logic probe and pulser are described in Experiment 3.

The current tracer is a more specialized test probe used in locating shorts in digital circuits. Whenever a short circuit is suspected, the current tracer can assist the troubleshooter in pinpointing the exact location of the short.

The logic analyzer is a complex instrument used to compare many different logic signals at one time. However, it is expensive and is used mostly in complex systems to solve the more difficult problems that occur in digital systems. The operation of a typical logic analyzer, the Tektronix Model 7D01, is discussed in Appendix B of this manual.

The experiments in this manual provide opportunities to gain experience with the logic probe, logic pulser, and the logic analyzer. It is recommended that you become acquainted with the logic probe you will be using by reading the user manual that should accompany the probe. If your laboratory has a logic analyzer, it would also be to your advantage to learn as much as possible about the instrument before you attempt to use it. If there is an operator's manual for the analyzer, get it and read it.

CLUDING REMARKS

The material in this appendix will be of more use to you if you review it from time to time. There is too much information relating to troubleshooting to include all of it in a short appendix. Your learning resource center or library may have some video tapes, journals, or books on the subject.

Appendix B

LOGIC ANALYZERS

A logic analyzer is a device that can store and display several channels of digital data. Although it resembles a multitrace oscilloscope, the logic analyzer differs from the oscilloscope in several ways:

- The logic analyzer displays only digital data; it cannot display both analog and digital signals like the oscilloscope can.

- The logic analyzer stores its data in memory first, then causes this data to be continually displayed on its CRT screen. Thus, the data that the analyzer displays has already occurred and is not real-time like that displayed by the oscilloscope.

- The logic analyzer is capable of displaying several channels of data simultaneously. A multitrace oscilloscope either chops or alternates between traces (channels) and thus cannot display the channels simultaneously.

- The logic analyzer can display its data in tabular format, using binary, octal, or hexadecimal characters, as well as in timing diagram format. The oscilloscope uses the timing diagram format only.

PART 1—LOGIC ANALYZER FUNDAMENTALS

In this section, we will describe the principles of operation of a typical logic analyzer. The model to be described is the Tektronix 7D01/7D01F. You should consult the operator's manual for your particular logic analyzer and/or ask your instructor for assistance in applying the information covered here to your analyzer.

B.1 Basic Block Diagram

Figure B-1 shows a block diagram for a simple logic analyzer. The probes are connected to a bus that carries the signals you wish to examine. The examination begins when the control block causes the trigger circuitry to issue a write enable to memory. The data on the bus is then clocked into memory, where it is stored. When enough data is stored, the write enable to memory is removed and replaced with a read enable. This permits the data that was stored to be read and displayed on the multitrace oscilloscope.

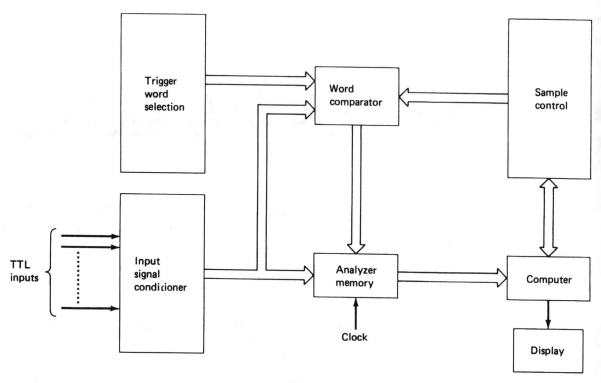

Figure B-1

The logic analyzer described here could be modified to display tabular data. What is needed is a computer to control the probes and display. The probes would be connected to the computer via a peripheral interface adapter (PIA), and the computer would be programmed to clock in the data, store it, and then display the data in the format desired.

B.2 Operating Principles

At the heart of the logic analyzer is its capability to store data in its memory. The memory is organized as serial shift registers, one per channel. Each channel's register size depends on the number of channels being used. For example, the Tektronix 7D01 has three possibilities:

No.data channels		No.bits/channel
4	(Ch. 0-3)	1024
8	(Ch. 0-7)	508
16	(Ch. 0-15)	254

In each case, the memory capacity is 4064 bits (about 4K).

Figure B-2 shows the basic structure for a single data channel. This structure is the same for all of the other channels (up to 16 channels). The input signal that is to be examined is connected to the probe for that channel and delivered to a comparator. Regardless of whether the signal is digital or analog, the comparator

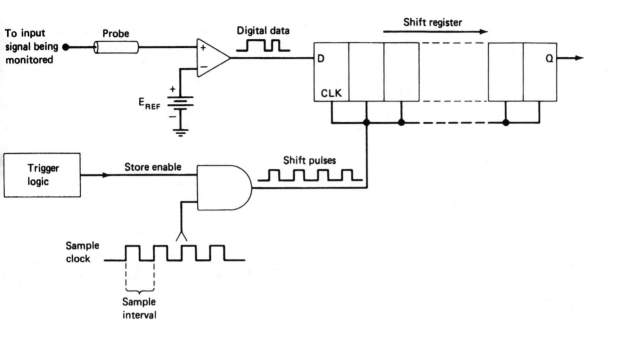

Figure B-2

compares the input to a reference (threshold) voltage, converting the input signal to a pure digital signal. For TTL logic, the threshold voltage is set to +1.4 volts.

Figures B-3 and B-4 show two cases of input signals. In Figure B-3, the input signal is digital, and the output of the comparator is the same as its input. Figure B-4 shows that in the case of a nondigital input, the comparator output will be a digitized version of the input.

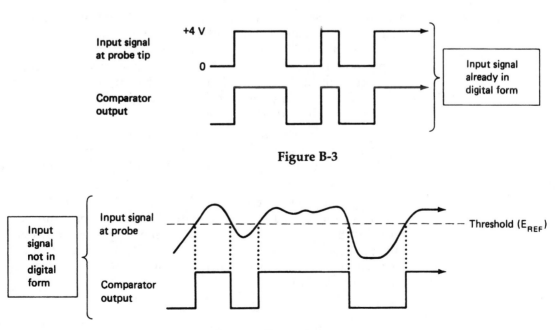

Figure B-3

Figure B-4

B.3 Storing Data (Store Mode)

After the comparator converts the input data to digital, the data is sent to the input of a shift register, where it is clocked into the shift register by the SAMPLE CLOCK for as long as the STORE ENABLE is HIGH. The shift register stores the data until it is needed for display. Figure B-5 shows the timing relationship between the output of the comparator, the STORE ENABLE signal, SAMPLE CLOCK, and the data shifted into the shift register. Note that while the STORE ENABLE is HIGH, the level of the comparator's output at each positive-going transition of the SAMPLE

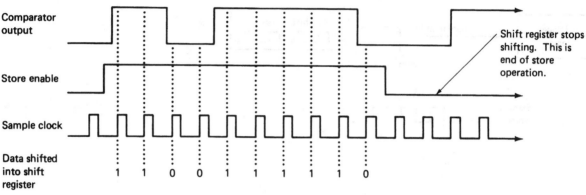

Figure B-5

CLOCK is shifted into the shift register from left to right, and that when the STORE ENABLE goes LOW, the shifting stops. Even though the data at the comparator output is changing, the data currently in the shift register does not change. In other words, the SAMPLE CLOCK periodically samples the data and shifts it into the register for storage. The period between samples is called the SAMPLE INTERVAL. As new data is shifted into the shift register, the old data is shifted out.

B.4 Displaying Data (Display Mode)

After the logic analyzer has completed the STORE operation, its memory contains a digital representation of the input signals that are connected to its inputs. As soon as the STORE ENABLE goes LOW, the logic analyzer goes into its DISPLAY mode of operation. In this mode, the logic analyzer displays the contents of each channel's shift register on the CRT as a serial digital waveform. It does this by applying clock pulses to each shift register to shift the stored data out of the last flip-flop of the register and to the vertical amplifier of the CRT to be displayed.

   As mentioned earlier, the 7D01 can be used to display 4, 8, or 16 channels. It is possible that the actual number of channels being monitored is fewer than the number of channels being displayed. If this is the case, the unused channels are simply ignored.

   Figure B-6 illustrates how the 7D01 can be used to display four channels of stored data on the CRT screen. Note that the channels are numbered from 0 to 3 starting at the top of the display. Each waveform represents the complete contents of the channel memory register. For the 7D01, this means that each waveform represents the 1016 bits that were shifted into the register during the STORE mode, one bit per SAMPLE INTERVAL.

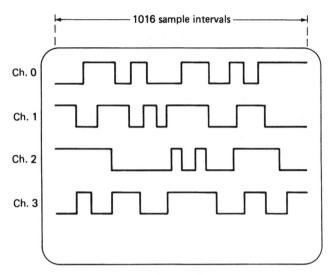

Figure B-6

If the logical analyzer were to be used in the 8-channel display mode, there would be eight channels, numbered 0 through 7, displayed on the screen. Each channel waveform would represent 508 bits of stored data on the screen. In the 16-channel display mode, there would be 16 waveforms displayed on the screen, each one representing 254 bits of data. Thus, as mentioned earlier, the total number of displayed bits is constant at about 4K, but the number per channel depends on how many channels are used.

EXAMPLE 1:

The data displayed in Figure B-6 was obtained using a SAMPLE INTERVAL of 5 microseconds during the STORE operation. What is the total time duration of each waveform?

SOLUTION:

Each waveform consists of 1016 bits, which were shifted into the memory register at the rate of one every 5 microseconds. Thus, the waveform duration is 1016 x 5 microseconds = 5080 microseconds.

EXAMPLE 2:

Repeat Example 1 for a 16-channel display.

SOLUTION:

For a 16-channel display, each waveform consists of 254 sample intervals or 254 x 5 microseconds = 1270 microseconds.

B.5 Types of Sampling

The 7D01 logic analyzer permits input signals to be sampled either *synchronously*, using the clock signal from the system under test, or *asynchronously*, using the 7D01's internal clock (refer to Figure B-7).

B.5.A Synchronous

Most digital systems, and all digital computers, operate from a master clock signal that synchronizes all of the system operations. The logic states of all the system

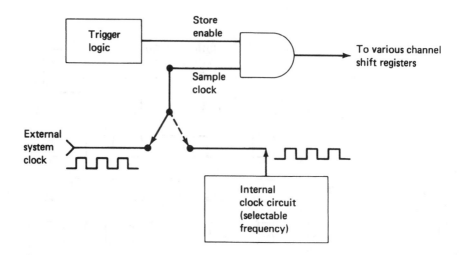

Figure B-7

signals can change only on the appropriate clock edge. The logic analyzer can use synchronous sampling to examine the system's data signals at the precise time that system clock edges occur. Figure B-8 illustrates the use of the negative-going edge of the system clock. The 7D01 permits either clock edge to be selected. Note that the stored data represents data on the input signal line when the negative clock edges occur. Any glitches that occur in the intervals between clock edges are ignored.

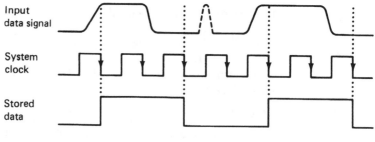

Figure B-8

B.5.B Asynchronous

Asynchronous sampling uses the 7D01's internal clock, which allows selectable sampling intervals from 10 nanoseconds to 5 milliseconds. The smaller sampling intervals permit you to acquire more information about the data signals over a shorter time duration. In other words, for a given number of samples, the use of a shorter sampling interval provides a more detailed look at the data signals. Figure B-9 shows the data signal used in Figure B-8 being sampled at a much higher rate (shorter interval between samples) using the 7D01's internal (asynchronous) clock.

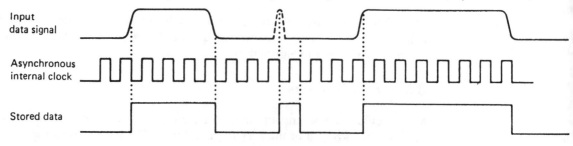

Figure B-9

Note that the shorter sample interval will store a more accurate picture of the input data signal, including glitches or erroneous pulses that occur in the intervals between system clock edges.

In troubleshooting, the synchronous sampling mode is often used to locate the general problem area; then, the asynchronous mode is used to take a closer look at the suspected signals for detection of glitches or erroneous pulses.

B.6 Triggering

In our previous discussion, we stated that the TRIGGER LOGIC circuit (see Figure B-2) generates the STORE ENABLE to control the store and display operations. If the STORE ENABLE is HIGH, the input data is sampled and stored; if the STORE ENABLE is LOW, the stored data is displayed on the CRT.

B.6.A Data Storage Relative to Trigger Event

The TRIGGER LOGIC controls STORE ENABLE in accordance with the occurrence of a selected TRIGGER EVENT. (We will describe the different TRIGGER EVENTS later.) When the TRIGGER EVENT occurs, the TRIGGER LOGIC decides when to make the STORE ENABLE go LOW to end the STORE operation and begin the DISPLAY operation. The 7D01 permits three different possibilities:

1) *Pre-trigger*: In this mode, STORE ENABLE will go LOW right after the TRIGGER EVENT occurs. Thus, the data that is stored in the different channel shift registers represents data that occurred prior to the TRIGGER EVENT. When the data is displayed on the CRT, the display will show those portions of the input waveforms that occurred before the TRIGGER EVENT.

Figure B-10 illustrates how the pre-trigger display appears for the 7D01 logic analyzer. The intensified dots on the display show when the TRIGGER EVENT occurred relative to the various channel waveforms. The greater part of the waveforms occurs prior to the TRIGGER EVENT. The 7D01 also displays a small portion of the waveforms that occur after the TRIGGER EVENT.

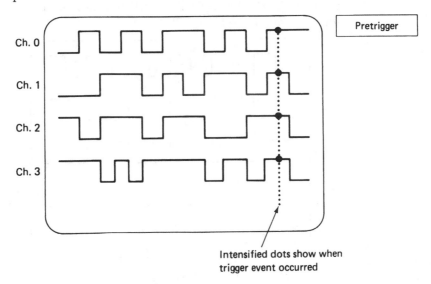

Intensified dots show when
trigger event occurred

Figure B-10

2) *Post-trigger*: In this mode, the logic analyzer stores and displays data that occurs after the TRIGGER EVENT. Figure B-11 shows how the post-trigger appears for the 7D01 and shows that the greater part of the displayed waveforms occurs after the TRIGGER EVENT. The 7D01 also displays a small portion of the waveforms that occur before the TRIGGER EVENT.

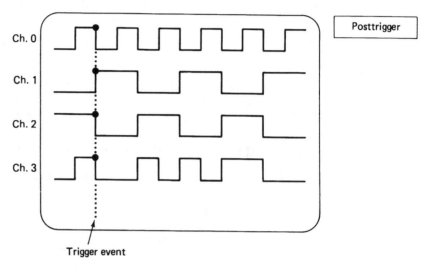

Figure B-11

3) *Center-trigger*: In this mode, the logic analyzer stores and displays data that occur both before and after the TRIGGER EVENT. This is illustrated in Figure B-12, which shows that the TRIGGER EVENT, indicated by the intensified dots, is in the center of the displayed waveforms.

Each of these three trigger modes is useful in different situations, depending on what portion of the waveforms you are interested in examining relative to a particular TRIGGER EVENT. We will now describe the possible TRIGGER EVENT sources that are used in the 7D01.

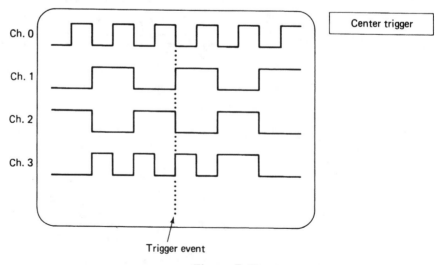

Figure B-12

B.6.B Sources of Trigger Events

The 7D01 allows you to select one of four different sources to produce the TRIGGER EVENT. They are described below:

1) *Manual.* The TRIGGER EVENT occurs when the operator presses the manual trigger button. This is used for the initial setting-up and positioning of the display or for getting a display of stored data when the expected TRIGGER EVENT has failed to occur.

2) *Channel 0 (Ch. 0).* The TRIGGER EVENT is the positive-going transition of the signal on Channel 0.

3) *External.* The TRIGGER EVENT occurs on the selected transition of the signal applied to the external trigger input. This signal is not one of the signals being displayed.

4) *Word Recognizer (WR).* When the WR is selected as the source of the TRIGGER EVENT, the WR unit generates a TRIGGER EVENT pulse when the logic levels present at the 16-channel inputs match a specific 16-bit word. The operator can select any 16-bit word using the WR channel switches on the 7D01 front panel.

B.7 Examining and Interpreting the Display

The logic analyzer has no time scale for measuring time intervals like that of an oscilloscope. Time is measured in units of one SAMPLE INTERVAL and is referenced to the TRIGGER EVENT. The examples in Figures B-13–B-15 show how this is done for the 7D01 4-channel display; the same idea may be extended to the 8- and 16-channel displays.

In Figure B-13, the post-trigger mode is used. The intensified dots on the left indicate when the TRIGGER EVENT occurred. The other set of dots is called the CURSOR and can be positioned anywhere along the waveforms using the CURSOR controls on the 7D01 front panel. The position of the CURSOR relative to the TRIGGER EVENT is displayed on the upper right-hand portion of the CRT screen. Here it is given as TRIG +45, which means that the CURSOR is 45 SAMPLE

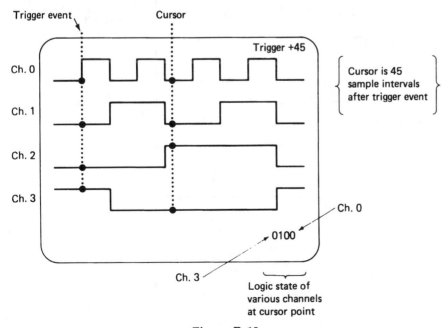

Figure B-13

INTERVALS after the TRIGGER EVENT. The data levels that are present on the various channel waveforms at the CURSOR point are displayed on the bottom of the CRT screen, with Channel 0 being the rightmost bit. Here it is given as 0100, which can be verified by looking at the waveform levels at the CURSOR position.

Figure B-14 illustrates the pre-trigger mode. Here the CURSOR is at -30 SAMPLE INTERVALS before the TRIGGER. The data levels at the CURSOR point are given as 0101.

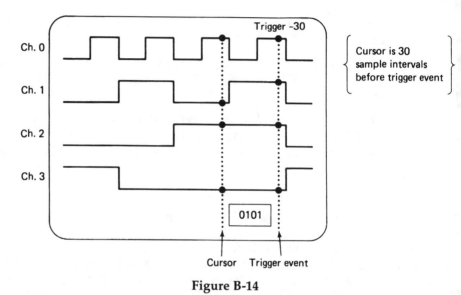

Figure B-14

Figure B-15 shows the CURSOR positioned right at the TRIGGER point, indicated by TRIG +0. The data levels at this point are 0111.

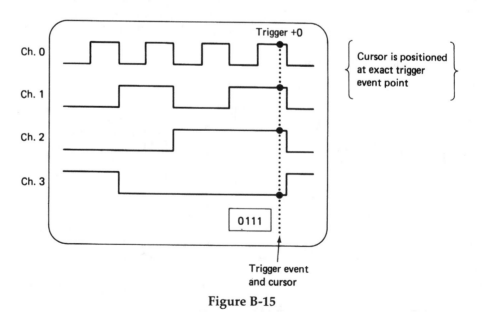

Figure B-15

EXAMPLE:

The waveforms in Figure B-15 were obtained using a SAMPLE INTERVAL of 50 nanoseconds. What is the time duration between the CURSOR and the TRIGGER EVENT?

SOLUTION:

The cursor is 30 SAMPLE INTERVALS before the TRIGGER or 30×50 n sec = 1500 n sec.

PART 2—USING THE STATE TABLE MODE

In Part 1, you saw how the 7D01 logic analyzer was used to sample, store, and display the logic levels present on up to 16 different signals simultaneously. The mode of display used was the TIMING DIAGRAM mode. Although this mode is very useful in many applications, it is not suitable for handling the large amounts of data present in the microprocessor and memory systems.

In Part 2, we will describe the STATE TABLE mode of operation. In this mode, all of the data in the logic analyzer's memory is displayed on the CRT in *tabular* form. Recall that the logic analyzer memory consists of shift registers, one per channel. These registers store the logic levels that were present on the data lines at each SAMPLE CLOCK edge during the STORE cycle.

The STATE TABLE mode is just another way the logic analyzer can display its memory data. The STORE cycle and TRIGGER operation are exactly the same as described in Part 1. Once the STORE cycle ends and the DISPLAY cycle begins, the logic analyzer will display the data in a table instead of as timing diagrams.

B.8 State Table Format

Figure B-16 shows a typical display in the TIMING DIAGRAM mode for four channels. The intensified dots on the left end of each waveform indicate the TRIGGER POINT. These dots also represent the CURSOR position, because the CURSOR is positioned at TRIG +0 as indicated.

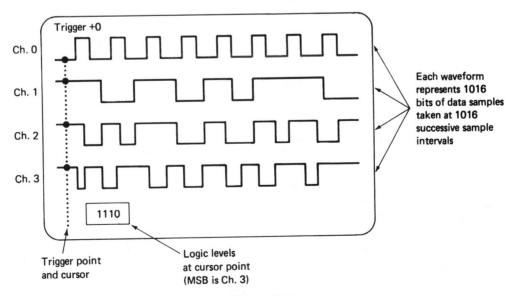

Figure B-16

You may recall that each channel waveform represents 1016 bits of data. These data correspond to samples that were taken at 1016 successive SAMPLE INTERVALS during the STORE cycle. The binary word shown at the lower part of the display tells us what the channel logic levels are at the CURSOR POINT, starting with channel 3 as the MSB. Since the CURSOR has been positioned at the TRIGGER POINT, this binary word also indicates the channel logic levels at the TRIGGER POINT.

Of course, the operator can move the CURSOR along the waveforms in steps of one SAMPLE INTERVAL. As this is done, the binary word will change to indicate the change in channel logic levels. If you were to record the binary words each time you moved the CURSOR one step, you would get a table of 4-bit words corresponding to the channel logic levels at the various sample intervals after the TRIGGER POINT. This is precisely what the logic analyzer does if you use it in the STATE TABLE mode.

B.8.A Binary Table

Figure B-17 shows what the display will look like when the operator selects the BINARY STATE TABLE display instead of the TIMING DIAGRAM display. The display is a table of *eighteen* 4-bit words. The top word in the table is *always* the CURSOR WORD. That is, it represents the logic levels present on the waveforms at the CURSOR POINT. The position of the CURSOR relative to the TRIGGER POINT is given as TRIG + 0 in this example.

The next 16 entries in the table show the logic levels present for the next 16 SAMPLE INTERVALS past the CURSOR POINT. Thus, the second table entry would be the data at TRIG + 1, the third entry would be at TRIG + 2, and so on, until the 17th entry, which is at TRIG + 16.

The 18th word (at the bottom of the display) is the TRIGGER WORD representing the logic levels that are present at the TRIGGER POINT. This TRIGGER WORD is *not* part of the data table; it is simply there as a reminder for the operator.

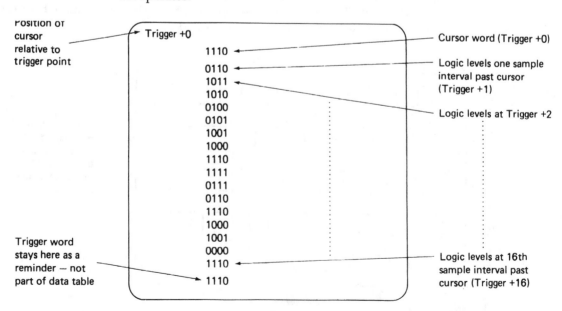

Figure B-17

B.8.B Blinking Trigger Word

Whenever the TRIGGER WORD appears as one of the 17 entries in the displayed data table, it will be blinking. For the example in Figure B-17, the TRIGGER WORD is the top entry in the table, since the CURSOR POINT is TRIG + 0. Thus, this 4-bit word will be blinking on the display

B.8.C 8- or 16-Channel Operation

The same binary table format can be used for 8- or 16-channel operation. The only difference is in the number of bits per word. We are using the 4-channel case here simply for convenience.

B.8.D Examining the Rest of the Data

The display contains only 17 data words, corresponding to the CURSOR WORD and the 16 following SAMPLE INTERVALS. The logic analyzer memory, however, holds a total of 1016 data words (508 for 8-channel operation, 254 for 16-channel operation). The operator can change the displayed data table by using the CURSOR position control. This is illustrated in the two tables of Figure B-18.

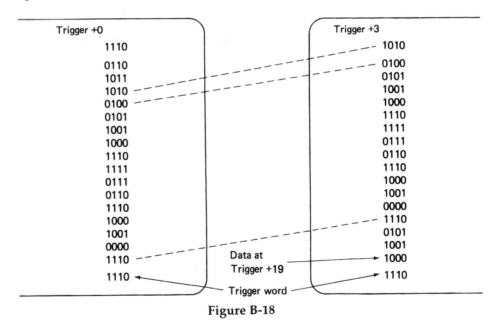

Figure B-18

The table on the left is the same as that in Figure B-17, where the CURSOR has been set at TRIG +0. The table on the right corresponds to a CURSOR position of TRIG +3. This means that the top word in this table is at TRIG +19. Thus, this new table contains three new entries at the bottom which were not contained in the original table. Of course, the new table has lost three of the entries from the top of the original table.

The operator can move the CURSOR to other positions relative to the TRIGGER POINT by using the logic analyzer CURSOR controls. In this manner, the operator can examine all of the data in the logic analyzer memory.

Note that the TRIG WORD at the bottom of both table displays is the same. This will not change with the CURSOR position because it is not part of the data tables. It is there to remind the operator what the TRIG WORD is.

B.8.E Octal and Hex Tables

In many applications, it is more convenient to have the data tables displayed in octal or hexadecimal rather than in binary. The operator can select either octal or hex tables, and the logic analyzer will convert the binary data to the selected format.

PART 3—USING THE REFERENCE TABLE

The REF TABLE is used whenever the operator wishes to save the complete data table taken during a STORE operation so that it can be used as a reference to which subsequent new data can be compared. The following steps will illustrate the basic use of the REF TABLE.

B.8.F Transferring 7D01 Data to the REF TABLE

After the logic analyzer has executed a STORE cycle, it will automatically display the data table in the manner described earlier. This data table will be referred to as the 7D01 data table to distinguish it from the REF TABLE. The 7D01 data table can be transferred to the REF TABLE memory by actuating the 7D01 REF control on the front panel. When this is done, there will be *two* tables displayed on the CRT, as shown in Figure B-19.

The 7D01 data table is on the left, and the REF TABLE is on the right. The two tables are identical because the 7D01 data table was just transferred to the REF TABLE memory.

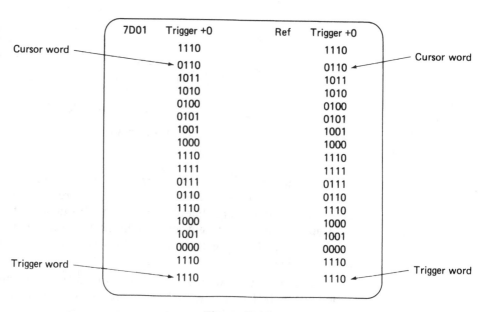

Figure B-19

B.8.G Executing a New STORE Cycle

Once the data has been transferred to the REF TABLE, the operator can have the logic analyzer execute a STORE cycle to obtain a new set of data *without* affecting the REF TABLE. In other words, the REF TABLE will retain its current data while the logic analyzer fills the 7D01 data memory with new data. When the STORE cycle is completed, the logic analyzer will again display both tables. The 7D01 table will have the new set of data while the REF TABLE will have the old set of data.

B.8.H Comparing the 7D01 Data Table and the REF TABLE

The operator can now compare the new data table with the REF TABLE to see if and where any differences occur. This is extremely valuable in testing and troubleshooting situations where data from a known good circuit can be placed in the REF TABLE. The 7D01 helps the operator to see any differences in the two tables by intensifying any part of the 7D01 data table that is different from the REF TABLE. This is illustrated in Figure B-20.

Note that two bits in the 7D01 data table are intensified because they are different from the corresponding bits in the REF TABLE. The operator can use this information to help troubleshoot the circuit from which the new data was taken.

7D01	Trigger +0	Ref	Trigger +0
	1110		1110
	0110		0110
	1011		1011
	1010		1010
	0101		0100
	1001		1001
	1000		1000
	1110		1110
	0111		1111
	0111		0111
	0110		0110
	1110		1110
	1000		1000
	1001		1001
	0000		0000
	1110		1110
	1110		1110

Figure B-20

MANUFACTURERS' DATA SHEETS

- **Wide Range of Supply Voltages**
  Single Supply . . . 3 V to 30 V
  or Dual Supplies

- **Low Supply Current Drain**
  Independent of Supply Voltage
  . . . 0.8 mA Typ

- **Common-Mode Input Voltage
  Range Includes Ground Allowing
  Direct Sensing near Ground**

- **Low Input Bias and Offset Parameters**
  Input Offset Voltage . . . 2 mV Typ
  Input Offset Current . . . 3 nA Typ (LM124)
  Input Bias Current . . . 45 nA Typ

- **Differential Input Voltage Range
  Equal to Maximum-Rated
  Supply Voltage . . . ±32 V**

- **Open-Loop Differential Voltage
  Amplification . . . 100 V/mV Typ**

- **Internal Frequency Compensation**

schematic (each amplifier)

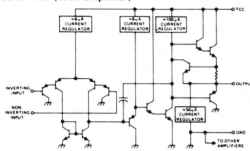

J OR N DUAL-IN-LINE OR
W FLAT PACKAGE (TOP VIEW)

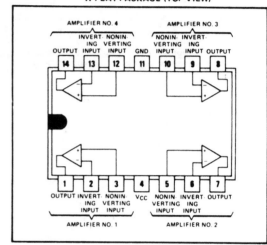

description

These devices consist of four independent, high-gain, frequency-compensated operational amplifiers that were designed specifically to operate from a single supply over a wide range of voltages. Operation from split supplies is also possible so long as the difference between the two supplies is 3 volts to 30 volts and Pin 4 is at least 1.5 volts more positive than the input common-mode voltage. The low supply current drain is independent of the magnitude of the supply voltage.

Applications include transducer amplifiers, d-c amplification blocks, and all the conventional operational amplifier circuits that now can be more easily implemented in single-supply-voltage systems. For example, the LM124 can be operated directly off of the standard five-volt supply that is used in digital systems and will easily provide the required interface electronics without requiring additional ± 15-volt supplies.

absolute maximum ratings over operating free-air temperature range (unless otherwise noted)

Supply voltage, V_{CC} (see Note 1) . . . . 32 V
Differential input voltage (see Note 2) . . . . ±32 V
Input voltage range (either input) . . . . −0.3 V to 32 V
Duration of output short-circuit (one amplifier) to ground at (or below) 25°C
   free-air temperature ($V_{CC} \leqslant 15$ V) (see Note 3) . . . . unlimited
Continuous total dissipation at (or below) 25°C free-air temperature (see Note 4) . . . . 900 mW
Operating free-air temperature range: LM124 . . . . −55°C to 125°C
                                        LM224 . . . . −25°C to 85°C
                                        LM324 . . . . 0°C to 70°C
Storage temperature range . . . . −65°C to 150°C
Lead temperature 1/16 inch (1,6 mm) from case for 60 seconds: J or W package . . . . 300°C
Lead temperature 1/16 inch (1,6 mm) from case for 10 seconds: N package . . . . 260°C

NOTES: 1. All voltage values, except differential voltages, are with respect to the network ground terminal.
   2. Differential voltages are at the noninverting input terminal with respect to the inverting input terminal.
   3. Short circuits from outputs to V_{CC} can cause excessive heating and eventual destruction.
   4. For operation above 25°C free-air temperature, refer to Dissipation Derating Table. In the J package, LM124 chips are alloy-mounted; LM224 and LM324 chips are glass-mounted.

TEXAS INSTRUMENTS
INCORPORATED

POST OFFICE BOX 225012 • DALLAS, TEXAS 75265

electrical characteristics at specified free-air temperature, V_{CC} = 5 V (unless otherwise noted)

PARAMETER		TEST CONDITIONS[†]		LM124, LM224 MIN	TYP	MAX	LM324 MIN	TYP	MAX	UNIT
V_{IO}	Input offset voltage	V_O = 1.4 V, V_{CC} = 5 V to 30 V	25°C		2	5		2	7	mV
			Full range			7			9	
I_{IO}	Input offset current	V_O = 1.4 V	25°C		3	30		5	50	nA
			Full range			100			150	
I_{IB}	Input bias current	V_O = 1.4 V, See Note 5	25°C		−45	−150		−45	−250	nA
			Full range			−300			−500	
V_{ICR}	Common-mode input voltage range	V_{CC} = 30 V	25°C	0 to V_{CC}−1.5			0 to V_{CC}−1.5			V
			Full range	0 to V_{CC}−2			0 to V_{CC}−2			
V_{OH}	High-level output voltage	V_{CC} = 30 V, R_L = 2 kΩ	Full range	26			26			V
		V_{CC} = 30 V, $R_L \geqslant$ 10 kΩ	Full range	27	28		27	28		
V_{OL}	Low-level output voltage	$R_L \leqslant$ 10 kΩ	Full range		5	20		5	20	mV
A_{VD}	Large-signal differential voltage amplification	V_{CC} = 15 V, V_O = 1 V to 11 V, $R_L \geqslant$ 2 kΩ	25°C	50	100		25	100		V/mV
			Full range	25			15			
CMRR	Common-mode rejection ratio	$R_S \leqslant$ 10 kΩ	25°C	70	85		65	85		dB
k_{SVR}*	Supply voltage rejection ratio	$R_S \leqslant$ 10 kΩ	25°C	65	100		65	100		dB
V_{o1}/V_{o2}	Channel separation	f = 1 kHz to 20 kHz	25°C		120			120		dB
I_O	Output current	V_{CC} = 15 V, V_{ID} = 1 V, V_O = 0 V	25°C	−20	−40		−20	−40		mA
			Full range	−10	−20		−10	−20		
		V_{CC} = 15 V, V_{ID} = −1 V, V_O = 5 V	25°C	10	20		10	20		
			Full range	5	8		5	8		
		V_{ID} = −1 V, V_O = 200 mV	25°C	12	50		12	50		µA
I_{CC}	Supply current (four amplifiers)	No load, No signal	25°C		0.8			0.8		mA
			Full range			1.2			1.2	

*$k_{SVR} = \Delta V_{CC}/\Delta V_{IO}$

[†]All characteristics are specified under open-loop conditions. Full range is −55°C to 125°C for LM124, −25°C to 85°C for LM224, and 0°C to 70°C for LM324.

NOTE 5: The direction of the bias current is out of the device due to the P-N-P input stage. This current is essentially constant, regardless of the state of the output, so no loading change is presented to the input lines.

TYPICAL APPLICATION DATA

AUDIO DISTRIBUTION AMPLIFIER

THERMAL INFORMATION

DISSIPATION DERATING TABLE

PACKAGE	POWER RATING	DERATING FACTOR	ABOVE T_A
J (Alloy-Mounted Chip)	900 mW	11.0 mW/°C	68°C
J (Glass-Mounted Chip)	900 mW	8.2 mW/°C	40°C
N	900 mW	9.2 mW/°C	52°C
W	900 mW	8.0 mW/°C	37°C

Also see Dissipation Derating Curves, Section 2.

TEXAS INSTRUMENTS
INCORPORATED
POST OFFICE BOX 225012 • DALLAS, TEXAS 75265

- Timing from Microseconds to Hours
- Astable or Monostable Operation
- Adjustable Duty Cycle
- TTL-Compatible Output Can Sink or Source Up to 200 mA
- Functionally Interchangeable with the Signetics SE555, SE555C, SA555, NE555; Have Same Pinout

SE555C FROM TI IS NOT RECOMMENDED FOR NEW DESIGNS

description

These devices are monolithic timing circuits capable of producing accurate time delays or oscillation. In the time-delay or monostable mode of operation, the timed interval is controlled by a single external resistor and capacitor network. In the astable mode of operation, the frequency and duty cycle may be independently controlled with two external resistors and a single external capacitor.

The threshold and trigger levels are normally two-thirds and one-third, respectively, of V_{CC}. These levels can be altered by use of the control voltage terminal. When the trigger input falls below the trigger level, the flip-flop is set and the output goes high. If the trigger input is above the trigger level and the threshold input is above the threshold level, the flip-flop is reset and the output is low. The reset input can override all other inputs and can be used to initiate a new timing cycle. When the reset input goes low, the flip-flop is reset and the output goes low. Whenever the output is low, a low-impedance path is provided between the discharge terminal and ground.

The output circuit is capable of sinking or sourcing current up to 200 mA. Operation is specified for supplies of 5 to 15 V. With a 5-V supply, output levels are compatible with TTL inputs.

The SE555 and SE555C are characterized for operation over the full military range of −55°C to 125°C. The SA555 is characterized for operation from −40°C to 85°C, and the NE555 is characterized for operation from 0°C to 70°C.

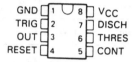

SE555, SE555C . . . JG PACKAGE
SA555, NE555 . . . D, JG, OR P PACKAGE
(TOP VIEW)

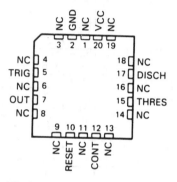

SE555, SE555C . . . FK PACKAGE
(TOP VIEW)

NC—No internal connection

functional block diagram

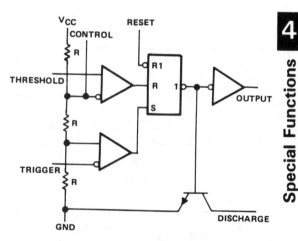

Reset can override Trigger, which can override Threshold.

4

Special Functions

POST OFFICE BOX 655012 • DALLAS, TEXAS 75265

Copyright © 1983, Texas Instruments Incorporated

4-37

electrical characteristics at 25 °C free-air temperature, V_{CC} = 5 V to 15 V (unless otherwise noted)

PARAMETER	TEST CONDITIONS		SE555 MIN	SE555 TYP	SE555 MAX	SE555C, SA555, NE555 MIN	SE555C, SA555, NE555 TYP	SE555C, SA555, NE555 MAX	UNIT
Threshold voltage level	V_{CC} = 15 V		9.4	10	10.6	8.8	10	11.2	V
	V_{CC} = 5 V		2.7	3.3	4	2.4	3.3	4.2	
Threshold current (see Note 2)				30	250		30	250	nA
Trigger voltage level	V_{CC} = 15 V		4.8	5	5.2	4.5	5	5.6	V
	V_{CC} = 5 V		1.45	1.67	1.9	1.1	1.67	2.2	
Trigger current	Trigger at 0 V			0.5	0.9		0.5	2	µA
Reset voltage level			0.3	0.7	1	0.3	0.7	1	V
Reset current	Reset at V_{CC}			0.1	0.4		0.1	0.4	mA
	Reset at 0 V			−0.4	−1		−0.4	−1.5	
Discharge switch off-state current				20	100		20	100	nA
Control voltage (open circuit)	V_{CC} = 15 V		9.6	10	10.4	9	10	11	V
	V_{CC} = 5 V		2.9	3.3	3.8	2.6	3.3	4	
Low-level output voltage	V_{CC} = 15 V	I_{OL} = 10 mA		0.1	0.15		0.1	0.25	V
		I_{OL} = 50 mA		0.4	0.5		0.4	0.75	
		I_{OL} = 100 mA		2	2.2		2	2.5	
		I_{OL} = 200 mA		2.5			2.5		
	V_{CC} = 5 V	I_{OL} = 5 mA		0.1	0.2		0.1	0.35	
		I_{OL} = 8 mA		0.15	0.25		0.15	0.4	
High-level output voltage	V_{CC} = 15 V	I_{OH} = −100 mA	13	13.3		12.75	13.3		V
		I_{OH} = −200 mA		12.5			12.5		
	V_{CC} = 5 V	I_{OH} = −100 mA	3	3.3		2.75	3.3		
Supply current	Output low, No load	V_{CC} = 15 V		10	12		10	15	mA
		V_{CC} = 5 V		3	5		3	6	
	Output high, No load	V_{CC} = 15 V		9	10		9	13	
		V_{CC} = 5 V		2	4		2	5	

NOTE 2: This parameter influences the maximum value of the timing resistors R_A and R_B in the circuit of Figure 12. For example, when V_{CC} = 5 V, the maximum value is $R = R_A + R_B \approx 3.4$ MΩ, and for V_{CC} = 15 V, the maximum value is 10 MΩ.

operating characteristics, V_{CC} = 5 V and 15 V

PARAMETER		TEST CONDITIONS[†]	SE555 MIN	SE555 TYP	SE555 MAX	SE555C, SA555, NE555 MIN	SE555C, SA555, NE555 TYP	SE555C, SA555, NE555 MAX	UNIT
Initial error of timing interval[‡]	Each timer, monostable[§]	T_A = 25 °C		0.5	1.5		1	3	%
	Each timer, astable[¶]			1.5			2.25		
Temperature coefficient of timing interval	Each timer, monostable[§]	T_A = MIN to MAX		30	100		50		ppm/°C
	Each timer, astable[¶]			90			150		
Supply voltage sensitivity of timing interval	Each timer, monostable[§]	T_A = 25 °C		0.05	0.2		0.1	0.5	%/V
	Each timer, astable[¶]			0.15			0.3		
Output pulse rise time		C_L = 15 pF, T_A = 25 °C		100	200		100	300	ns
Output pulse fall time				100	200		100	300	

[†] For conditions shown as MIN or MAX, use the appropriate value specified under recommended operating conditions.

[‡] Timing interval error is defined as the difference between the measured value and the average value of a random sample from each process run.

[§] Values specified are for a device in a monostable circuit similar to Figure 9, with component values as follow: R_A = 2 kΩ to 100 kΩ, C = 0.1 µF.

[¶] Values specified are for a device in an astable circuit similar to Figure 12, with component values as follow: R_A = 1 kΩ to 100 kΩ, C = 0.1 µF.

4 Special Functions

TEXAS INSTRUMENTS
POST OFFICE BOX 655012 • DALLAS, TEXAS 75265

TYPICAL APPLICATION DATA

monostable operation

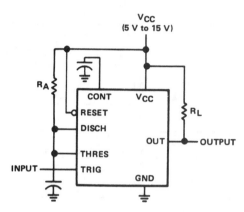

FIGURE 9. CIRCUIT FOR MONOSTABLE OPERATION

$R_A = 9.1\ k\Omega$
$C_L = 0.01\ \mu F$
$R_L = 1\ k\Omega$
See Figure 9

INPUT VOLTAGE

OUTPUT VOLTAGE

CAPACITOR VOLTAGE

Time—0.1 ms/div

FIGURE 10. TYPICAL MONOSTABLE WAVEFORMS

For monostable operation, any of these timers may be connected as shown in Figure 9. If the output is low, application of a negative-going pulse to the trigger input sets the flip-flop ($\overline{Q}$ goes low), drives the output high, and turns off Q1. Capacitor C is then charged through R_A until the voltage across the capacitor reaches the threshold voltage of the threshold input. If the trigger input has returned to a high level, the output of the threshold comparator will reset the flip-flop ($\overline{Q}$ goes high), drive the output low, and discharge C through Q1.

Monostable operation is initiated when the trigger input voltage falls below the trigger threshold. Once initiated, the sequence ends only if the trigger input is high at the end of the timing interval. Because of the threshold level and saturation voltage of Q1, the output pulse duration is approximately $t_W = 1.1\ R_A C$. Figure 11 is a plot of the time constant for various values of R_A and C. The threshold levels and charge rates are both directly proportional to the supply voltage, V_{CC}. The timing interval is therefore independent of the supply voltage, so long as the supply voltage is constant during the time interval.

Applying a negative-going trigger pulse simultaneously to the reset and trigger terminals during the timing interval discharges C and re-initiates the cycle, commencing on the positive edge of the reset pulse. The output is held low as long as the reset pulse is low. To prevent false triggering, when the reset input is not used, it should be connected to V_{CC}.

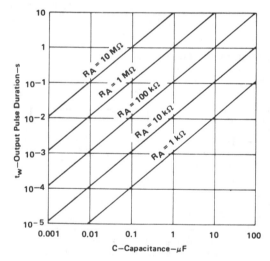

**FIGURE 11. OUTPUT PULSE
DURATION vs CAPACITANCE**

TEXAS
INSTRUMENTS
POST OFFICE BOX 655012 • DALLAS, TEXAS 75265

TYPICAL APPLICATION DATA

astable operation

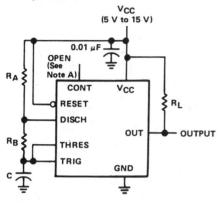

NOTE A: Decoupling the control voltage input to ground with a capacitor may improve operation. This should be evaluated for individual applications.

FIGURE 12. CIRCUIT FOR ASTABLE OPERATION

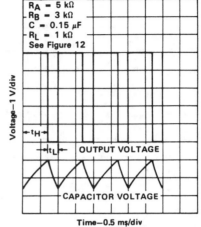

FIGURE 13. TYPICAL ASTABLE WAVEFORMS

As shown in Figure 12, adding a second resistor, R_B, to the circuit of Figure 9 and connecting the trigger input to the threshold input causes the timer to self-trigger and run as a multivibrator. The capacitor C will charge through R_A and R_B and then discharge through R_B only. The duty cycle may be controlled, therefore, by the values of R_A and R_B.

This astable connection results in capacitor C charging and discharging between the threshold-voltage level ($\approx 0.67 \cdot V_{CC}$) and the trigger-voltage level ($\approx 0.33 \cdot V_{CC}$). As in the monostable circuit, charge and discharge times (and therefore the frequency and duty cycle) are independent of the supply voltage.

Figure 13 shows typical waveforms generated during astable operation. The output high-level duration t_H and low-level duration t_L may be calculated as follows:

$$t_H = 0.693 (R_A + R_B) C$$

$$t_L = 0.693 (R_B) C$$

Other useful relationships are shown below.

$$\text{period} = t_H + t_L = 0.693 (R_A + 2R_B) C$$

$$\text{frequency} \approx \frac{1.44}{(R_A + 2R_B) C}$$

$$\text{Output driver duty cycle} = \frac{t_L}{t_H + t_L} = \frac{R_B}{R_A + 2R_B}$$

$$\text{Output waveform duty cycle} = \frac{t_H}{t_H + t_L} = 1 - \frac{R_B}{R_A + 2R_B}$$

$$\text{Low-to-high ratio} = \frac{t_L}{t_H} = \frac{R_B}{R_A + R_B}$$

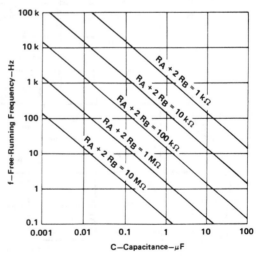

FIGURE 14. FREE-RUNNING FREQUENCY

Special Functions

4

TEXAS
INSTRUMENTS

POST OFFICE BOX 655012 • DALLAS, TEXAS 75265

TYPICAL APPLICATION DATA

sequential timer

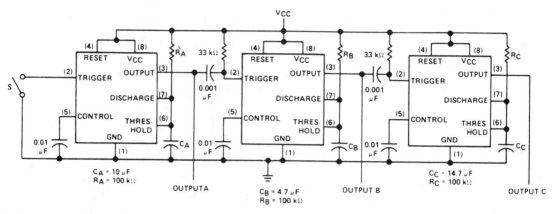

S closes momentarily at t = 0.

FIGURE 22. SEQUENTIAL TIMER CIRCUIT

Many applications, such as computers, require signals for initializing conditions during start-up. Other applications, such as test equipment, require activation of test signals in sequence. These timing circuits may be connected to provide such sequential control. The timers may be used in various combinations of astable or monostable circuit connections, with or without modulation, for extremely flexible waveform control. Figure 22 illustrates a sequencer circuit with possible applications in many systems, and Figure 23 shows the output waveforms.

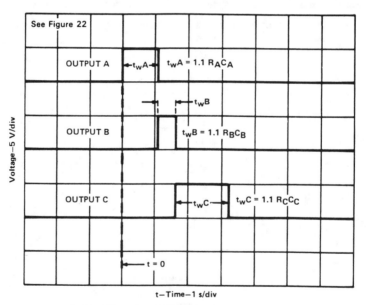

FIGURE 23. SEQUENTIAL TIMER WAVEFORMS

Special Functions 4

MOTOROLA

MC1408
MC1508

Specifications and Applications Information

EIGHT-BIT MULTIPLYING
DIGITAL-TO-ANALOG CONVERTER

SILICON MONOLITHIC
INTEGRATED CIRCUIT

EIGHT-BIT MULTIPLYING DIGITAL-TO-ANALOG CONVERTER

. . . designed for use where the output current is a linear product of an eight-bit digital word and an analog input voltage.

- Eight-Bit Accuracy Available in Both Temperature Ranges
  - Relative Accuracy: ±0.19% Error maximum (MC1408L8, MC1408P8, MC1508L8)
- Seven and Six-Bit Accuracy Available with MC1408 Designated by 7 or 6 Suffix after Package Suffix
- Fast Settling Time – 300 ns typical
- Noninverting Digital Inputs are MTTL and CMOS Compatible
- Output Voltage Swing – +0.4 V to -5.0 V
- High-Speed Multiplying Input
  Slew Rate 4.0 mA/μs
- Standard Supply Voltages: +5.0 V and -5.0 V to -15 V

L SUFFIX
CERAMIC PACKAGE
CASE 620

P SUFFIX
PLASTIC PACKAGE
CASE 648

FIGURE 1 – D-to-A TRANSFER CHARACTERISTICS

I₀, OUTPUT CURRENT (mA)

0

1.0

2.0

(00000000) INPUT DIGITAL WORD (11111111)

FIGURE 2 – BLOCK DIAGRAM

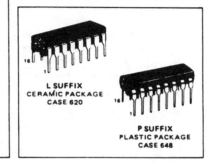

TYPICAL APPLICATIONS

- Tracking A-to-D Converters
- Successive Approximation A-to-D Converters
- 2 1/2 Digit Panel Meters and DVM's
- Waveform Synthesis
- Sample and Hold
- Peak Detector
- Programmable Gain and Attenuation
- CRT Character Generation

- Audio Digitizing and Decoding
- Programmable Power Supplies
- Analog-Digital Multiplication
- Digital-Digital Multiplication
- Analog-Digital Division
- Digital Addition and Subtraction
- Speech Compression and Expansion
- Stepping Motor Drive

MAXIMUM RATINGS (T$_A$ = +25°C unless otherwise noted.)

Rating	Symbol	Value	Unit
Power Supply Voltage	V$_{CC}$ V$_{EE}$	+5.5 -16.5	Vdc
Digital Input Voltage	V$_5$ thru V$_{12}$	0 to +5.5	Vdc
Applied Output Voltage	V$_O$	+0.5, -5.2	Vdc
Reference Current	I$_{14}$	5.0	mA
Reference Amplifier Inputs	V$_{14}$, V$_{15}$	V$_{CC}$, V$_{EE}$	Vdc

Operating Temperature Range
          MC1508
          MC1408 Series
	T$_A$	
		
		-55 to +125
		0 to +75
			°C

Storage Temperature Range	T$_{stg}$	-65 to +150	°C

ELECTRICAL CHARACTERISTICS (V$_{CC}$ = +5.0 Vdc, V$_{EE}$ = -15 Vdc, $\frac{V_{ref}}{R14}$ = 2.0 mA, MC1508L8: T$_A$ = -55°C to +125°C. MC1408L Series: T$_A$ = 0 to +75°C unless otherwise noted. All digital inputs at high logic level.)

Characteristic	Figure	Symbol	Min	Typ	Max	Unit

Relative Accuracy (Error relative to full scale I$_O$)
  MC1508L8, MC1408L8, MC1408P8
  MC1408P7, MC1408L7, See Note 1
  MC1408P6, MC1408L6, See Note 1
	4	E$_r$	
			–
			–
			–
				
				–
				–
				–
					
					±0.19
					±0.39
					±0.78
						%

Settling Time to within ±1/2 LSB [includes tp$_{LH}$] (T$_A$ = +25°C) See Note 2	5	t$_S$	–	300	–	ns
Propagation Delay Time T$_A$ = +25°C	5	t$_{PLH}$, t$_{PHL}$	–	30	100	ns
Output Full Scale Current Drift		TCI$_O$	–	-20	–	PPM/°C

Digital Input Logic Levels (MSB)
  High Level, Logic "1"
  Low Level, Logic "0"
	3	
		V$_{IH}$
		V$_{IL}$
			
			2.0
			–
				
				–
				–
					
					–
					0.8
						Vdc

Digital Input Current (MSB)
  High Level, V$_{IH}$ = 5.0 V
  Low Level, V$_{IL}$ = 0.8 V
	3	
		I$_{IH}$
		I$_{IL}$
			
			–
			–
				
				0
				-0.4
					
					0.04
					-0.8
						mA

Reference Input Bias Current (Pin 15)	3	I$_{15}$	–	-1.0	-5.0	µA

Output Current Range
  V$_{EE}$ = -5.0 V
  V$_{EE}$ = -15 V, T$_A$ = 25°C
	3	I$_{OR}$	
			0
			0
				
				2.0
				2.0
					
					2.1
					4.2
						mA

Output Current V$_{ref}$ = 2.000 V, R14 = 1000 Ω	3	I$_O$	 1.9	 1.99	 2.1	mA
Output Current (All bits low)	3	I$_{O(min)}$	–	0	4.0	µA

Output Voltage Compliance (E$_r$ ≤ 0.19% at T$_A$ = +25°C)
  Pin 1 grounded
  Pin 1 open, V$_{EE}$ below -10 V
	3	V$_O$	
			–
			
				–
				
					-0.55, +0.4
					-5.0, +0.4
						Vdc

Reference Current Slew Rate	6	SR I$_{ref}$		4.0		mA/µs
Output Current Power Supply Sensitivity		PSRR(-)	–	0.5	2.7	µA/V
Power Supply Current (All bits low)	3	I$_{CC}$ I$_{EE}$	– 	+13.5 -7.5	+22 -13	mA
Power Supply Voltage Range (T$_A$ = +25°C)	3	V$_{CCR}$ V$_{EER}$	+4.5 -4.5	+5.0 -15	+5.5 -16.5	Vdc

Power Dissipation
  All bits low
    V$_{EE}$ = -5.0 Vdc
    V$_{EE}$ = -15 Vdc
  All bits high
    V$_{EE}$ = -5.0 Vdc
    V$_{EE}$ = -15 Vdc
	3	P$_D$	
			
			–
			
			–
			–
				
				105
				190
				
				90
				160
					
					170
					305
					
					–
					–
						mW

Note 1   All current switches are tested to guarantee at least 50% of rated output current.
Note 2.   All bits switched.

2114
1024 X 4 BIT STATIC RAM

	2114-2	2114-3	2114	2114L3	2114L
Max. Access Time (ns)	200	300	450	300	450
Max. Power Dissipation (mw)	710mw	710mw	710mw	370mw	370mw

- **High Density 18 Pin Package**
- **Identical Cycle and Access Times**
- **Single +5V Supply**
- **No Clock or Timing Strobe Required**
- **Completely Static Memory**

- **Directly TTL Compatible: All Inputs and Outputs**
- **Common Data Input and Output Using Three-State Outputs**
- **Pin-Out Compatible with 3605 and 3625 Bipolar PROMs**

The Intel® 2114 is a 4096-bit static Random Access Memory organized as 1024 words by 4-bits using N-channel Silicon-Gate MOS technology. It uses fully DC stable (static) circuitry throughout — in both the array and the decoding — and therefore requires no clocks or refreshing to operate. Data access is particularly simple since address setup times are not required. The data is read out nondestructively and has the same polarity as the input data. Common input/output pins are provided.

The 2114 is designed for memory applications where high performance, low cost, large bit storage, and simple interfacing are important design objectives. The 2114 is placed in an 18-pin package for the highest possible density.

It is directly TTL compatible in all respects: inputs, outputs, and a single +5V supply. A separate Chip Select ($\overline{CS}$) lead allows easy selection of an individual package when outputs are or-tied.

The 2114 is fabricated with Intel's N-channel Silicon-Gate technology — a technology providing excellent protection against contamination permitting the use of low cost plastic packaging.

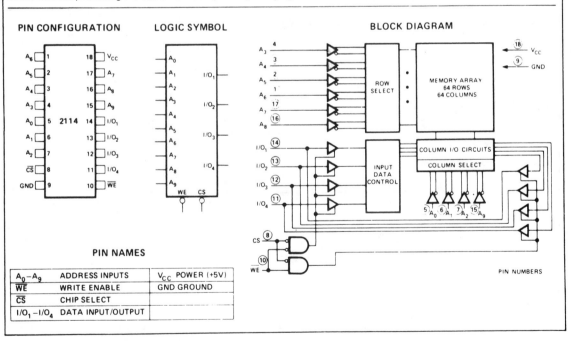

PIN CONFIGURATION

A_6	1		18	V_{CC}
A_5	2		17	A_7
A_4	3		16	A_8
A_3	4	2114	15	A_9
A_0	5		14	I/O_1
A_1	6		13	I/O_2
A_2	7		12	I/O_3
$\overline{CS}$	8		11	I/O_4
GND	9		10	$\overline{WE}$

LOGIC SYMBOL

BLOCK DIAGRAM

PIN NAMES

A_0–A_9	ADDRESS INPUTS	V_{CC}	POWER (+5V)
$\overline{WE}$	WRITE ENABLE	GND	GROUND
$\overline{CS}$	CHIP SELECT		
I/O_1 –I/O_4	DATA INPUT/OUTPUT		

(Courtesy of Intel Corporation)

A.C. CHARACTERISTICS $T_A = 0°C$ to $70°C$, $V_{CC} = 5V \pm 5\%$, unless otherwise noted.

READ CYCLE [1]

SYMBOL	PARAMETER	2114-2 Min.	2114-2 Max.	2114-3, 2114L3 Min.	2114-3, 2114L3 Max.	2114, 2114L Min.	2114, 2114L Max.	UNIT
t_{RC}	Read Cycle Time	200		300		450		ns
t_A	Access Time		200		300		450	ns
t_{CO}	Chip Selection to Output Valid		70		100		100	ns
t_{CX}	Chip Selection to Output Active	0		0		0		ns
t_{OTD}	Output 3-state from Deselection	0	40	0	80	0	100	ns
t_{OHA}	Output Hold from Address Change	10		10		10		ns

WRITE CYCLE [2]

SYMBOL	PARAMETER	2114-2 Min.	2114-2 Max.	2114-3, 2114L3 Min.	2114-3, 2114L3 Max.	2114, 2114L Min.	2114, 2114L Max.	UNIT
t_{WC}	Write Cycle Time	200		300		450		ns
t_W	Write Time	100		150		200		ns
t_{WR}	Write Release Time	20		0		0		ns
t_{OTW}	Output 3-state from Write	0	40	0	80	0	100	ns
t_{DW}	Data to Write Time Overlap	100		150		200		ns
t_{DH}	Data Hold From Write Time	0		0		0		ns

NOTES 1. A Read occurs during the overlap of a low $\overline{CS}$ and a high $\overline{WE}$.
2. A Write occurs during the overlap of a low $\overline{CS}$ and a low $\overline{WE}$.

A.C. CONDITIONS OF TEST

Input Pulse Levels . . . . 0.8 Volt to 2.4 Volt

Input Rise and Fall Times . . . . 10 nsec

Input and Output Timing Levels . . . . 1.5 Volts

Output Load . . . . 1 TTL Gate and $C_L = 50$ pF

National Semiconductor

CD4016BM/CD4016BC Quad Bilateral Switch

General Description

The CD4016BM/CD4016BC is a quad bilateral switch intended for the transmission or multiplexing of analog or digital signals. It is pin-for-pin compatible with CD4066BM/CD4066BC.

Features

- Wide supply voltage range   3V to 15V
- Wide range of digital and analog switching $\pm 7.5\ V_{PEAK}$
- "ON" resistance for 15V operation 400Ω (typ.)
- Matched "ON" resistance over 15V signal input $\Delta R_{ON} = 10\Omega$ (typ.)
- High degree of linearity   0.4% distortion (typ.)

    @ $f_{IS} = 1$ kHz, $V_{IS} = 5\ V_{p-p}$,

    $V_{DD} - V_{SS} = 10V$, $R_L = 10\ k\Omega$

- Extremely low "OFF" switch leakage   0.1 nA (typ.)

    @ $V_{DD} - V_{SS} = 10V$

    $T_A = 25°C$

- Extremely high control input impedance $10^{12}\Omega$ (typ.)
- Low crosstalk between switches -50 dB (typ.)

    @ $f_{IS} = 0.9$ MHz, $R_L = 1$ kΩ

- Frequency response, switch "ON"   40 MHz (typ.)

Applications

- Analog signal switching/multiplexing
  - Signal gating
  - Squelch control
  - Chopper
  - Modulator/Demodulator
  - Commutating switch
- Digital signal switching/multiplexing
- CMOS logic implementation
- Analog-to-digital/digital-to-analog conversion
- Digital control of frequency, impedance, phase, and analog-signal gain

Schematic and Connection Diagrams

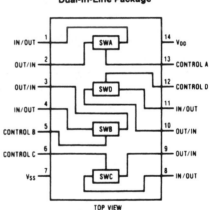

Dual-In-Line Package

TOP VIEW

TL/F/5661–1

Order Number CD4016BMJ or CD4016BCJ
NS Package J14A

Order Number CD4016BMN or CD4016BCN
NS Package N14A

AC Electrical Characteristics

$T_A = 25\,°C$, $C_L = 50\,pF$, $R_L = 200\,K$, $t_r = t_f = 20\,ns$, unless otherwise specified.

Symbol	Parameter	Conditions	Min	Typ	Max	Units
Clocked Operation						
t_{PHL}, t_{PLH}	Propagation Delay Time	$V_{DD} = 5V$		230	350	ns
		$V_{DD} = 10V$		80	160	ns
		$V_{DD} = 15V$		60	120	ns
t_{THL}, t_{TLH}	Transition Time	$V_{DD} = 5V$		100	200	ns
		$V_{DD} = 10V$		50	100	ns
		$V_{DD} = 15V$		40	80	ns
t_{WL}, t_{WM}	Minimum Clock Pulse-Width	$V_{DD} = 5V$		160	250	ns
		$V_{DD} = 10V$		60	110	ns
		$V_{DD} = 15V$		50	85	ns
t_{rCL}, t_{fCL}	Clock Rise and Fall Time	$V_{DD} = 5V$			15	μS
		$V_{DD} = 10V$			15	μS
		$V_{DD} = 15V$			15	μS
t_{SU}	Minimum Data Set-Up Time	$V_{DD} = 5V$		50	100	ns
		$V_{DD} = 10V$		20	40	ns
		$V_{DD} = 15V$		15	30	ns
f_{CL}	Maximum Clock Frequency	$V_{DD} = 5V$	2	3.5		MHz
		$V_{DD} = 10V$	4.5	8		MHz
		$V_{DD} = 15V$	6	11		MHz
C_{IN}	Input Capacitance	Clock Input		7.5	10	pF
		Other Inputs		5	7.5	pF
Reset Operation						
$t_{PHL(R)}$	Propagation Delay Time	$V_{DD} = 5V$		200	400	ns
		$V_{DD} = 10V$		100	200	ns
		$V_{DD} = 15V$		80	160	ns
$t_{WH(R)}$	Minimum Reset Pulse Width	$V_{DD} = 5V$		135	250	ns
		$V_{DD} = 10V$		40	80	ns
		$V_{DD} = 15V$		30	60	ns

Absolute Maximum Ratings

(Notes 1 and 2)

V_{DD} Supply Voltage	-0.5V to $+18$V
V_{IN} Input Voltage	-0.5V to $V_{DD} + 0.5$V
T_S Storage Temperature Range	$-65°C$ to $+150°C$
P_D Package Dissipation	500 mW
Lead Temperature (Soldering, 10 seconds)	260°C

Recommended Operating Conditions (Note 2)

V_{DD} Supply Voltage	3V to 15V
V_{IN} Input Voltage	0V to V_{DD}
T_A Operating Temperature Range	
CD4016BM	$-55°C$ to $+125°C$
CD4016BC	$-40°C$ to $+85°C$

DC Electrical Characteristics CD4016BM (Note 2)

Symbol	Parameter	Conditions	$-55°C$ Min	$-55°C$ Max	25°C Min	25°C Typ	25°C Max	125°C Min	125°C Max	Units
I_{DD}	Quiescent Device Current	$V_{DD} = 5$V, $V_{IN} = V_{DD}$ or V_{SS}		0.25		0.01	0.25		7.5	μA
		$V_{DD} = 10$V, $V_{IN} = V_{DD}$ or V_{SS}		0.5		0.01	0.5		15	μA
		$V_{DD} = 15$V, $V_{IN} = V_{DD}$ or V_{SS}		1.0		0.01	1.0		30	μA

Signal Inputs and Outputs

Symbol	Parameter	Conditions	$-55°C$ Min	$-55°C$ Max	25°C Min	25°C Typ	25°C Max	125°C Min	125°C Max	Units
R_{ON}	"ON" Resistance	$R_L = 10$ kΩ to $\frac{V_{DD}-V_{SS}}{2}$ $V_C = V_{DD}$, $V_{IS} = V_{SS}$ or V_{DD}								
		$V_{DD} = 10$V		600		250	660		960	Ω
		$V_{DD} = 15$V		360		200	400		600	Ω
		$R_L = 10$ kΩ to $\frac{V_{DD}-V_{SS}}{2}$ $V_C = V_{DD}$								
		$V_{DD} = 10$V, $V_{IS} = 4.75$ to 5.25V		1870		850	2000		2600	Ω
		$V_{DD} = 15$V, $V_{IS} = 7.25$ to 7.75V		775		400	850		1230	Ω
ΔR_{ON}	Δ"ON" Resistance Between any 2 of 4 Switches (In Same Package)	$R_L = 10$ kΩ to $\frac{V_{DD}-V_{SS}}{2}$ $V_C = V_{DD}$, $V_{IS} = V_{SS}$ to V_{DD}								
		$V_{DD} = 10$V				15				Ω
		$V_{DD} = 15$V				10				Ω
I_{IS}	Input or Output Leakage Switch "OFF"	$V_C = 0$, $V_{DD} = 15$V $V_{IS} = 15$V and 0V, $V_{OS} = 0$V and 15V		± 50		± 0.1	± 50		± 500	nA

Control Inputs

Symbol	Parameter	Conditions	$-55°C$ Min	$-55°C$ Max	25°C Min	25°C Typ	25°C Max	125°C Min	125°C Max	Units
V_{ILC}	Low Level Input Voltage	$V_{IS} = V_{SS}$ and V_{DD} $V_{OS} = V_{DD}$ and V_{SS} $I_{IS} = \pm 10$ μA								
		$V_{DD} = 5$V		0.9			0.7		0.5	V
		$V_{DD} = 10$V		0.9			0.7		0.5	V
		$V_{DD} = 15$V		0.9			0.7		0.5	V
V_{IHC}	High Level Input Voltage	$V_{DD} = 5$V	3.5		3.5			3.5		V
		$V_{DD} = 10$V (see Note 6 and	7.0		7.0			7.0		V
		$V_{DD} = 15$V Figure 8)	11.0		11.0			11.0		V
I_{IN}	Input Current	$V_{DD} - V_{SS} = 15$V $V_{DD} \geq V_{IS} \geq V_{SS}$ $V_{DD} \geq V_C \geq V_{SS}$		± 0.1		$\pm 10^{-5}$	± 0.1		± 1.0	μA

DC Electrical Characteristics CD4016BC (Note 2) (Continued)

Symbol	Parameter	Conditions	−40°C		25°C			85°C		Units
			Min	Max	Min	Typ	Max	Min	Max	
I_{DD}	Quiescent Device Current	$V_{DD} = 5V$, $V_{IN} = V_{DD}$ or V_{SS}		1.0		0.01	1.0		7.5	μA
		$V_{DD} = 10V$, $V_{IN} = V_{DD}$ or V_{SS}		2.0		0.01	2.0		15	μA
		$V_{DD} = 15V$, $V_{IN} = V_{DD}$ or V_{SS}		4.0		0.01	4.0		'30	μA

Signal Inputs and Outputs

Symbol	Parameter	Conditions	−40°C		25°C			85°C		Units
			Min	Max	Min	Typ	Max	Min	Max	
R_{ON}	"ON" Resistance	$R_L = 10\ k\Omega$ to $\frac{V_{DD} - V_{SS}}{2}$								
		$V_C = V_{DD}$, $V_{IS} = V_{SS}$ or V_{DD}								
		$V_{DD} = 10V$		610		275	660		840	Ω
		$V_{DD} = 15V$		370		200	400		520	Ω
		$R_L = 10\ k\Omega$ to $\frac{V_{DD} - V_{SS}}{2}$								
		$V_C = V_{DD}$								
		$V_{DD} = 10V$, $V_{IS} = 4.75$ to $5.25V$		1900		850	2000		2380	Ω
		$V_{DD} = 15V$, $V_{IS} = 7.25$ to $7.75V$		790		400	850		1080	Ω
ΔR_{ON}	Δ"ON" Resistance Between any 2 of 4 Switches (In Same Package)	$R_L = 10\ k\Omega$ to $\frac{V_{DD} - V_{SS}}{2}$ $V_C = V_{DD}$, $V_{IS} = V_{SS}$ to V_{DD}								
		$V_{DD} = 10V$				15				Ω
		$V_{DD} = 15V$				10				Ω
I_{IS}	Input or Output Leakage Switch "OFF"	$V_C = 0$, $V_{DD} = 15V$ $V_{IS} = 0V$ or $15V$, $V_{OS} = 15V$ or $0V$		±50		±0.1	±50		±200	nA

Control Inputs

Symbol	Parameter	Conditions	−40°C		25°C			85°C		Units
			Min	Max	Min	Typ	Max	Min	Max	
V_{ILC}	Low Level Input Voltage	$V_{IS} = V_{SS}$ and V_{DD} $V_{OS} = V_{DD}$ and V_{SS} $I_{IS} = ±10\ \mu A$								
		$V_{DD} = 5V$		0.9			0.7		0.4	V
		$V_{DD} = 10V$		0.9			0.7		0.4	V
		$V_{DD} = 15V$		0.9			0.7		0.4	V
V_{IHC}	High Level Input Voltage	$V_{DD} = 5V$	3.5		3.5			3.5		V
		$V_{DD} = 10V$ (see Note 6 and	7.0		7.0			7.0		V
		$V_{DD} = 15V$ Figure 8)	11.0		11.0			11.0		V
I_{IN}	Input Current	$V_{CC} - V_{SS} = 15V$ $V_{DD} \geq V_{IS} \geq V_{SS}$ $V_{DD} \geq V_C \geq V_{SS}$		±0.3		$±10^{-5}$	±0.3		±1.0	μA

AC Electrical Characteristics $T_A = 25°C$, $t_r = t_f = 20$ ns and $V_{SS} = 0V$ unless otherwise specified

Symbol	Parameter	Conditions	Min	Typ	Max	Units
t_{PHL}, t_{PLH}	Propagation Delay Time Signal Input to Signal Output	$V_C = V_{DD}$, $C_L = 50$ pF, (Figure 1) $R_L = 200k$				
		$V_{DD} = 5V$		58	100	ns
		$V_{DD} = 10V$		27	50	ns
		$V_{DD} = 15V$		20	40	ns
t_{PZH}, t_{PZL}	Propagation Delay Time Control Input to Signal Output High Impedance to Logical Level	$R_L = 1.0\ k\Omega$, $C_L = 50$ pF, (Figures 2 and 3)				
		$V_{DD} = 5V$		20	50	ns
		$V_{DD} = 10V$		18	40	ns
		$V_{DD} = 15V$		17	35	ns
t_{PHZ}, t_{PLZ}	Propagation Delay Time Control Input to Signal Output Logical Level to High Impedance	$R_L = 1.0\ k\Omega$, $C_L = 50$ pF, (Figures 2 and 3)				
		$V_{DD} = 5V$		15	40	ns
		$V_{DD} = 10V$		11	25	ns
		$V_{DD} = 15V$		10	22	ns
	Sine Wave Distortion	$V_C = V_{DD} = 5V$, $V_{SS} = -5$ $R_L = 10\ k\Omega$, $V_{IS} = 5\ V_{P\text{-}P}$, $f = 1$ kHz, (Figure 4)		0.4		%

AC Electrical Characteristics (Continued)

$T_A = 25°C$, $t_r = t_f = 20$ ns and $V_{SS} = 0V$ unless otherwise specified

Symbol	Parameter	Conditions	Min	Typ	Max	Units
	Frequency Response — Switch "ON" (Frequency at −3 dB)	$V_C = V_{DD} = 5V$, $V_{SS} = -5V$, $R_L = 1$ kΩ, $V_{IS} = 5$ V_{P-P}, 20 Log_{10} V_{OS}/V_{OS} (1 kHz) −dB, (*Figure 4*)		40		MHz
	Feedthrough — Switch "OFF" (Frequency at −50 dB)	$V_{DD} = 5V$, $V_C = V_{SS} = -5V$, $R_L = 1$ kΩ, $V_{IS} = 5$ V_{P-P}, 20 Log_{10} (V_{OS}/V_{IS}) = −50 dB, (*Figure 4*)		1.25		MHz
	Crosstalk Between Any Two Switches (Frequency at −50 dB)	$V_{DD} = V_{C(A)} = 5V$; $V_{SS} = V_{C(B)} = -5V$, $R_L = 1$ kΩ $V_{IS(A)} = 5$ V_{P-P}, 20 Log_{10} ($V_{OS(B)}/V_{OS(A)}$) = −50 dB, (*Figure 5*)		0.9		MHz
	Crosstalk; Control Input to Signal Output	$V_{DD} = 10V$, $R_L = 10$ kΩ $R_{IN} = 1$ kΩ, $V_{CC} = 10V$ Square Wave, $C_L = 50$ pF (*Figure 6*)		150		mV$_{P-P}$
	Maximum Control Input	$R_L = 1$ kΩ, $C_L = 50$ pF, (*Figure 7*) $V_{OS(f)} = \frac{1}{2}$ V_{OS}(1 kHz)				
		$V_{DD} = 5V$		6.5		MHz
		$V_{DD} = 10V$		8.0		MHz
		$V_{DD} = 15V$		9.0		MHz
C_{IS}	Signal Input Capacitance			4		pF
C_{OS}	Signal Output Capacitance	$V_{DD} = 10V$		4		pF
C_{IOS}	Feedthrough Capacitance	$V_C = 0V$		0.2		pF
C_{IN}	Control Input Capacitance			5	7.5	pF

Note 1: "Absolute Maximum Ratings" are those values beyond which the safety of the device cannot be guaranteed. They are not meant to imply that the devices should be operated at these limits. The tables of "Recommended Operating Conditions" and "Electrical Characteristics" provide conditions for actual device operation.

Note 2: $V_{SS} = 0V$ unless otherwise specified.

Note 3: These devices should not be connected to circuits with the power "ON".

Note 4: In all cases, there is approximately 5 pF of probe and jig capacitance on the output; however, this capacitance is included in C_L wherever it is specified.

Note 5: V_{IS} is the voltage at the in/out pin and V_{OS} is the voltage at the out/in pin. V_C is the voltage at the control input.

Note 6: If the switch input is held at V_{DD}, V_{IHC} is the control input level that will cause the switch output to meet the standard "B" series V_{OH} and I_{OH} output levels. If the analog switch input is connected to V_{SS}, V_{IHC} is the control input level — which allows the switch to *sink* standard "B" series $|I_{OH}|$, high level current, and still maintain a $V_{OL} \leq$ "B" series. These currents are shown in *Figure 8*.

AC Test Circuits and Switching Time Waveforms

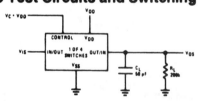 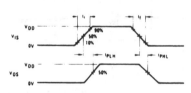

Figure 1. t_{PLH}, t_{PLH} Propagation Delay Time Signal Input to Signal Output

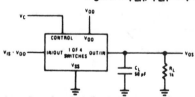 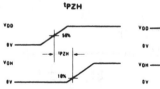 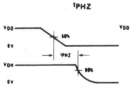

TL/H/5661-2

FIGURE 2. t_{PZH}, t_{PHZ} Propagation Delay Time Control to Signal Output

AC Test Circuits and Switching Time Waveforms (Continued)

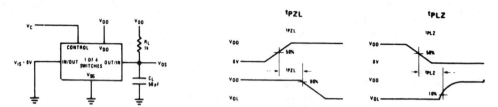

FIGURE 3. t$_{PZH}$, t$_{PHZ}$ Propagation Delay Time Control to Signal Output

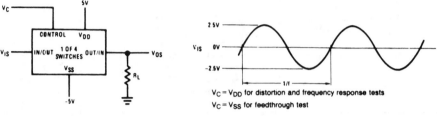

V$_C$ = V$_{DD}$ for distortion and frequency response tests

V$_C$ = V$_{SS}$ for feedthrough test

FIGURE 4. Sine Wave Distortion, Frequency Response and Feedthrough

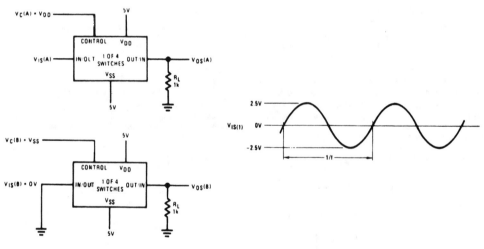

FIGURE 5. Crosstalk Between Any Two Switches

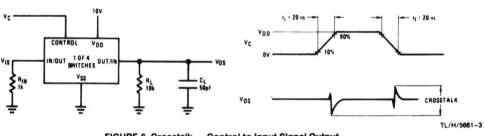

TL/H/5661–3

FIGURE 6. Crosstalk — Control to Input Signal Output

282

4023B
TRIPLE 3-INPUT NAND GATE

DESCRIPTION — This CMOS logic element provides a 3-input positive NAND function. The outputs are fully buffered for highest noise immunity and pattern insensitivity of output impedance.

LOGIC AND CONNECTION DIAGRAM
DIP (TOP VIEW)

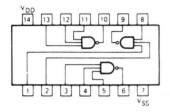

NOTE:
The Flatpak version has the same pinouts (Connection Diagram) as the Dual In-line Package.

DC CHARACTERISTICS: V_{DD} as shown, V_{SS} = 0 V (See Note 1)

SYMBOL	PARAMETER		V_{DD} = 5 V			V_{DD} = 10 V			V_{DD} = 15 V			UNITS	TEMP	TEST CONDITIONS
			MIN	TYP	MAX	MIN	TYP	MAX	MIN	TYP	MAX			
I_{DD}	Quiescent Power Supply Current	XC			1			2			4	μA	MIN, 25°C	All inputs at 0 V or V_{DD}
					7.5			15			30		MAX	
		XM			0.25			0.5			1	μA	MIN, 25°C	
					7.5			15			30		MAX	

AC CHARACTERISTICS: V_{DD} as shown, V_{SS} = 0 V, T_A = 25°C (See Note 2)

SYMBOL	PARAMETER	V_{DD} = 5 V			V_{DD} = 10 V			V_{DD} = 15V			UNITS	TEST CONDITIONS
		MIN	TYP	MAX	MIN	TYP	MAX	MIN	TYP	MAX		
t_{PLH}	Propagation Delay		45	110		25	60		19	48	ns	C_L = 50 pF,
t_{PHL}			51	110		25	60		12	48	ns	R_L = 200 kΩ
t_{TLH}	Output Transition Time		45	135		18	70		17	45	ns	Input Transition
t_{THL}			45	135		18	70		12	45	ns	Times ≤ 20 ns

NOTES:
1. Additional DC Characteristics are listed in this section under 4000B Series CMOS Family Characteristics.
2. Propagation Delays and Output Transition Times are graphically described in this section under 4000B Series CMOS Family Characteristics.

TYPICAL ELECTRICAL CHARACTERISTICS

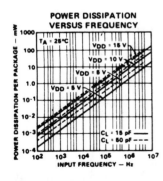

POWER DISSIPATION VERSUS FREQUENCY

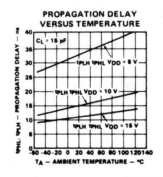

PROPAGATION DELAY VERSUS TEMPERATURE

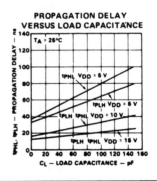

PROPAGATION DELAY VERSUS LOAD CAPACITANCE

(Courtesy of Fairchild – A Schlumberger Company)

- Package Options Include Plastic "Small Outline" Packages, Ceramic Chip Carriers and Flat Packages, and Plastic and Ceramic DIPs

- Dependable Texas Instruments Quality and Reliability

description

These devices contain four independent 2-input-NAND gates.

The SN5400, SN54LS00, and SN54S00 are characterized for operation over the full military temperature range of −55°C to 125°C. The SN7400, SN74LS00, and SN74S00 are characterized for operation from 0°C to 70°C.

FUNCTION TABLE (each gate)

INPUTS		OUTPUT
A	B	Y
H	H	L
L	X	H
X	L	H

logic symbol†

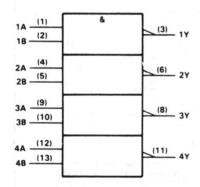

†This symbol is in accordance with ANSI/IEEE Std. 91-1984 and IEC Publication 617-12.
Pin numbers shown are for D, J, and N packages.

SN5400 . . . J PACKAGE
SN54LS00, SN54S00 . . . J OR W PACKAGE
SN7400 . . . N PACKAGE
SN74LS00, SN74S00 . . . D OR N PACKAGE
(TOP VIEW)

```
1A  [1    14]  VCC
1B  [2    13]  4B
1Y  [3    12]  4A
2A  [4    11]  4Y
2B  [5    10]  3B
2Y  [6     9]  3A
GND [7     8]  3Y
```

SN5400 . . . W PACKAGE
(TOP VIEW)

```
1A  [1    14]  4Y
1B  [2    13]  4B
1Y  [3    12]  4A
VCC [4    11]  GND
2Y  [5    10]  3B
2A  [6     9]  3A
2B  [7     8]  3Y
```

SN54LS00, SN54S00 . . . FK PACKAGE
(TOP VIEW)

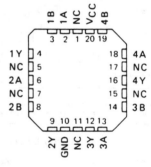

NC - No internal connection

logic diagram (positive logic)

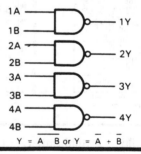

$$Y = \overline{A \cdot B} \text{ or } Y = \overline{A} + \overline{B}$$

TEXAS
INSTRUMENTS

POST OFFICE BOX 655012 • DALLAS, TEXAS 75265

2
TTL Devices

SN5400, SN54LS00, SN54S00,
SN7400, SN74LS00, SN74S00
QUADRUPLE 2-INPUT POSITIVE-NAND GATES

schematics (each gate)

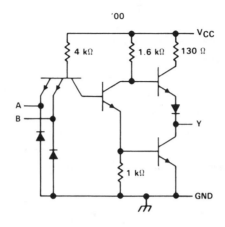

'00

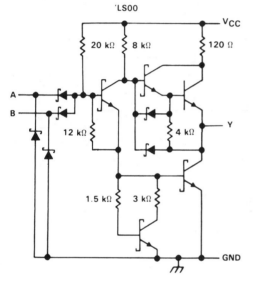

'LS00

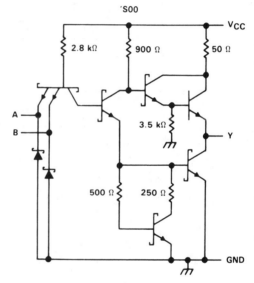

'S00

Resistor values shown are nominal.

absolute maximum ratings over operating free-air temperature range (unless otherwise noted)

Supply voltage, V_{CC} (see Note 1) . . . . 7 V
Input voltage: '00, 'S00 . . . . 5.5 V
              'LS00 . . . . 7 V
Operating free-air temperature range: SN54' . . . . −55 °C to 125 °C
                              SN74' . . . . 0 °C to 70 °C
Storage temperature range . . . . −65 °C to 150 °C

NOTE 1: Voltage values are with respect to network ground terminal.

TEXAS
INSTRUMENTS

POST OFFICE BOX 655012 • DALLAS, TEXAS 75265

2

TTL Devices

recommended operating conditions

		SN5400 MIN	SN5400 NOM	SN5400 MAX	SN7400 MIN	SN7400 NOM	SN7400 MAX	UNIT
V_{CC}	Supply voltage	4.5	5	5.5	4.75	5	5.25	V
V_{IH}	High-level input voltage	2			2			V
V_{IL}	Low-level input voltage			0.8			0.8	V
I_{OH}	High-level output current			− 0.4			− 0.4	mA
I_{OL}	Low-level output current			16			16	mA
T_A	Operating free-air temperature	− 55		125	0		70	°C

electrical characteristics over recommended operating free-air temperature range (unless otherwise noted)

PARAMETER	TEST CONDITIONS†	SN5400 MIN	SN5400 TYP‡	SN5400 MAX	SN7400 MIN	SN7400 TYP‡	SN7400 MAX	UNIT
V_{IK}	V_{CC} = MIN, I_I = − 12 mA			− 1.5			− 1.5	V
V_{OH}	V_{CC} = MIN, V_{IL} = 0.8 V, I_{OH} = − 0.4 mA	2.4	3.4		2.4	3.4		V
V_{OL}	V_{CC} = MIN, V_{IH} = 2 V, I_{OL} = 16 mA		0.2	0.4		0.2	0.4	V
I_I	V_{CC} = MAX, V_I = 5.5 V			1			1	mA
I_{IH}	V_{CC} = MAX, V_I = 2.4 V			40			40	μA
I_{IL}	V_{CC} = MAX, V_I = 0.4 V			− 1.6			− 1.6	mA
I_{OS}§	V_{CC} = MAX	− 20		− 55	− 18		− 55	mA
I_{CCH}	V_{CC} = MAX, V_I = 0 V		4	8		4	8	mA
I_{CCL}	V_{CC} = MAX, V_I = 4.5 V		12	22		12	22	mA

† For conditions shown as MIN or MAX, use the appropriate value specified under recommended operating conditions.
‡ All typical values are at V_{CC} = 5 V, T_A = 25°C.
§ Not more than one output should be shorted at a time.

switching characteristics, V_{CC} = 5 V, T_A = 25°C (see note 2)

PARAMETER	FROM (INPUT)	TO (OUTPUT)	TEST CONDITIONS	MIN	TYP	MAX	UNIT
t_{PLH}	A or B	Y	R_L = 400 Ω, C_L = 15 pF		11	22	ns
t_{PHL}					7	15	ns

NOTE 2: Load circuits and voltage waveforms are shown in Section 1.

TEXAS INSTRUMENTS
POST OFFICE BOX 655012 • DALLAS, TEXAS 75265

2-5

286

SN54LS00, SN74LS00
QUADRUPLE 2-INPUT POSITIVE-NAND GATES

recommended operating conditions

		SN54LS00			SN74LS00			UNIT
		MIN	NOM	MAX	MIN	NOM	MAX	
V_{CC}	Supply voltage	4.5	5	5.5	4.75	5	5.25	V
V_{IH}	High-level input voltage	2			2			V
V_{IL}	Low-level input voltage			0.7			0.8	V
I_{OH}	High-level output current			− 0.4			− 0.4	mA
I_{OL}	Low-level output current			4			8	mA
T_A	Operating free-air temperature	−55		125	0		70	°C

electrical characteristics over recommended operating free-air temperature range (unless otherwise noted)

PARAMETER	TEST CONDITIONS †	SN54LS00			SN74LS00			UNIT
		MIN	TYP‡	MAX	MIN	TYP‡	MAX	
V_{IK}	V_{CC} = MIN, I_I = − 18 mA			− 1.5			− 1.5	V
V_{OH}	V_{CC} = MIN, V_{IL} = MAX, I_{OH} = − 0.4 mA	2.5	3.4		2.7	3.4		V
V_{OL}	V_{CC} = MIN, V_{IH} = 2 V, I_{OL} = 4 mA		0.25	0.4		0.25	0.4	V
	V_{CC} = MIN, V_{IH} = 2 V, I_{OL} = 8 mA					0.35	0.5	
I_I	V_{CC} = MAX, V_I = 7 V			0.1			0.1	mA
I_{IH}	V_{CC} = MAX, V_I = 2.7 V			20			20	µA
I_{IL}	V_{CC} = MAX, V_I = 0.4 V			− 0.4			− 0.4	mA
I_{OS} §	V_{CC} = MAX	− 20		− 100	− 20		− 100	mA
I_{CCH}	V_{CC} = MAX, V_I = 0 V		0.8	1.6		0.8	1.6	mA
I_{CCL}	V_{CC} = MAX, V_I = 4.5 V		2.4	4.4		2.4	4.4	mA

† For conditions shown as MIN or MAX, use the appropriate value specified under recommended operating conditions.
‡ All typical values are at V_{CC} = 5 V, T_A = 25°C
§ Not more than one output should be shorted at a time, and the duration of the short-circuit should not exceed one second.

switching characteristics, V_{CC} = 5 V, T_A = 25°C (see note 2)

PARAMETER	FROM (INPUT)	TO (OUTPUT)	TEST CONDITIONS	MIN	TYP	MAX	UNIT
t_{PLH}	A or B	Y	R_L = 2 kΩ, C_L = 15 pF		9	15	ns
t_{PHL}					10	15	ns

NOTE 2: Load circuits and voltage waveforms are shown in Section 1.

TEXAS
INSTRUMENTS
POST OFFICE BOX 655012 • DALLAS, TEXAS 75265

D2684, DECEMBER 1982—REVISED MARCH 1984

- Package Options Include Plastic ''Small Outline'' Packages, Ceramic Chip Carriers, and Standard Plastic and Ceramic 300-mil DIPs

- Dependable Texas Instruments Quality and Reliability

description

These devices contain four independent 2-input NAND gates. They perform the Boolean functions $Y = \overline{A \cdot B}$ or $Y = \overline{A} + \overline{B}$ in positive logic.

The SN54HC00 is characterized for operation over the full military temperature range of $-55\,°C$ to $125\,°C$. The SN74HC00 is characterized for operation from $-40\,°C$ to $85\,°C$.

FUNCTION TABLE (each gate)

INPUTS		OUTPUT
A	B	Y
H	H	L
L	X	H
X	L	H

logic symbol†

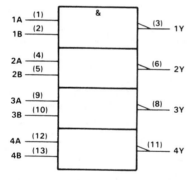

† This symbol is in accordance with ANSI/IEEE Std 91-1984 and IEC Publication 617-12.
Pin numbers shown are for D, J, or N packages.

SN54HC00 . . . J PACKAGE
SN74HC00 . . . D OR N PACKAGE
(TOP VIEW)

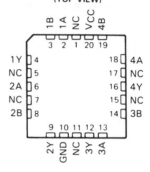

SN54HC00 . . . FK PACKAGE
(TOP VIEW)

NC – No internal connection

logic diagram (each gate)

HCMOS Devices

2

Copyright © 1982, Texas Instruments Incorporated

TEXAS INSTRUMENTS
POST OFFICE BOX 655012 • DALLAS, TEXAS 75265

2-3

SN54HC00, SN74HC00
QUADRUPLE 2-INPUT POSITIVE-NAND GATES

absolute maximum ratings over operating free-air temperature range[†]

Supply voltage, V_{CC} .... −0.5 V to 7 V
Input clamp current, I_{IK} (V_I < 0 or V_I > V_{CC}) .... ±20 mA
Output clamp current, I_{OK} (V_O < 0 or V_O > V_{CC}) .... ±20 mA
Continuous output current, I_O (V_O = 0 to V_{CC}) .... ±25 mA
Continuous current through V_{CC} or GND pins .... ±50 mA
Lead temperature 1,6 mm (1/16 in) from case for 60 s: FK or J package .... 300°C
Lead temperature 1,6 mm (1/16 in) from case for 10 s: D or N package .... 260°C
Storage temperature range .... −65°C to 150°C

[†] Stresses beyond those listed under "absolute maximum ratings" may cause permanent damage to the device. These are stress ratings only, and functional operation of the device at these or any other conditions beyond those indicated under "recommended operating conditions" is not implied. Exposure to absolute-maximum-rated conditions for extended periods may affect device reliability.

recommended operating conditions

			SN54HC00			SN74HC00			UNIT
			MIN	NOM	MAX	MIN	NOM	MAX	
V_{CC}	Supply voltage		2	5	6	2	5	6	V
V_{IH}	High-level input voltage	V_{CC} = 2 V	1.5			1.5			V
		V_{CC} = 4.5 V	3.15			3.15			
		V_{CC} = 6 V	4.2			4.2			
V_{IL}	Low-level input voltage	V_{CC} = 2 V	0		0.3	0		0.3	V
		V_{CC} = 4.5 V	0		0.9	0		0.9	
		V_{CC} = 6 V	0		1.2	0		1.2	
V_I	Input voltage		0		V_{CC}	0		V_{CC}	V
V_O	Output voltage		0		V_{CC}	0		V_{CC}	V
t_t	Input transition (rise and fall) times	V_{CC} = 2 V	0		1000	0		1000	ns
		V_{CC} = 4.5 V	0		500	0		500	
		V_{CC} = 6 V	0		400	0		400	
T_A	Operating free-air temperature		−55		125	−40		85	°C

electrical characteristics over recommended operating free-air temperature range (unless otherwise noted)

PARAMETER	TEST CONDITIONS	V_{CC}	T_A = 25°C			SN54HC00		SN74HC00		UNIT
			MIN	TYP	MAX	MIN	MAX	MIN	MAX	
V_{OH}	V_I = V_{IH} or V_{IL}, I_{OH} = −20 μA	2 V	1.9	1.998		1.9		1.9		V
		4.5 V	4.4	4.499		4.4		4.4		
		6 V	5.9	5.999		5.9		5.9		
	V_I = V_{IH} or V_{IL}, I_{OH} = −4 mA	4.5 V	3.98	4.30		3.7		3.84		
	V_I = V_{IH} or V_{IL}, I_{OH} = −5.2 mA	6 V	5.48	5.80		5.2		5.34		
V_{OL}	V_I = V_{IH} or V_{IL}, I_{OL} = 20 μA	2 V		0.002	0.1		0.1		0.1	V
		4.5 V		0.001	0.1		0.1		0.1	
		6 V		0.001	0.1		0.1		0.1	
	V_I = V_{IH} or V_{IL}, I_{OL} = 4 mA	4.5 V		0.17	0.26		0.4		0.33	
	V_I = V_{IH} or V_{IL}, I_{OL} = 5.2 mA	6 V		0.15	0.26		0.4		0.33	
I_I	V_I = V_{CC} or 0	6 V		±0.1	±100		±1000		±1000	nA
I_{CC}	V_I = V_{CC} or 0, I_O = 0	6 V			2		40		20	μA
C_i		2 to 6 V		3	10		10		10	pF

TEXAS
INSTRUMENTS

POST OFFICE BOX 655012 • DALLAS, TEXAS 75265

switching characteristics over recommended operating free-air temperature range (unless otherwise noted), C_L = 50 pF (see Note 1)

PARAMETER	FROM (INPUT)	TO (OUTPUT)	V_{CC}	T_A = 25°C			SN54HC00		SN74HC00		UNIT
				MIN	TYP	MAX	MIN	MAX	MIN	MAX	
t_{pd}	A or B	Y	2 V		45	90		135		115	ns
			4.5 V		9	18		27		23	
			6 V		8	15		23		20	
t_t		Y	2 V		38	75		110		95	ns
			4.5 V		8	15		22		19	
			6 V		6	13		19		16	

C_{pd}	Power dissipation capacitance per gate	No load, T_A = 25°C	20 pF typ

NOTE 1: Load circuit and voltage waveforms are shown in Section 1.

2

HCMOS Devices

TEXAS INSTRUMENTS

POST OFFICE BOX 655012 • DALLAS, TEXAS 75265

2-5

- Package Options Include Plastic "Small Outline" Packages, Ceramic Chip Carriers and Flat Packages, and Plastic and Ceramic DIPs

- Dependable Texas Instruments Quality and Reliability

description

These devices contain four independent 2-input-NOR gates.

The SN5402, SN54LS02, and SN54S02 are characterized for operation over the full military temperature range of −55°C to 125°C. The SN7402, SN74LS02, and SN74S02 are characterized for operation from 0°C to 70°C.

FUNCTION TABLE (each gate)

INPUTS		OUTPUT
A	B	Y
H	X	L
X	H	L
L	L	H

logic symbol[†]

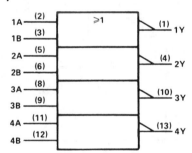

```
1A  (2)          ≥1
1B  (3)                    (1)  1Y

2A  (5)
2B  (6)                    (4)  2Y

3A  (8)
3B  (9)                    (10) 3Y

4A  (11)
4B  (12)                   (13) 4Y
```

[†]This symbol is in accordance with ANSI/IEEE Std. 91-1984 and IEC Publication 617-12.
Pin numbers shown are for D, J, and N packages.

logic diagram (positive logic)

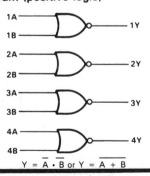

```
1A
1B          1Y

2A
2B          2Y

3A
3B          3Y

4A
4B          4Y
```

$Y = \overline{A} \cdot \overline{B}$ or $Y = \overline{A + B}$

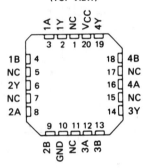

SN5402 . . . J PACKAGE
SN54LS02, SN54S02 . . . J OR W PACKAGE
SN7402 . . . N PACKAGE
SN74LS02, SN74S02 . . . D OR N PACKAGE
(TOP VIEW)

```
1Y  [1    14] VCC
1A  [2    13] 4Y
1B  [3    12] 4B
2Y  [4    11] 4A
2A  [5    10] 3Y
2B  [6     9] 3B
GND [7     8] 3A
```

SN5402 . . . W PACKAGE
(TOP VIEW)

```
1A  [1    14] 4Y
1B  [2    13] 4B
1Y  [3    12] 4A
VCC [4    11] GND
2Y  [5    10] 3B
2A  [6     9] 3A
2B  [7     8] 3Y
```

SN54LS02, SN54S02 . . . FK PACKAGE
(TOP VIEW)

```
        1A 1Y NC VCC 4Y
         3  2  1 20 19
1B  [4              18] 4B
NC  [5              17] NC
2Y  [6              16] 4A
NC  [7              15] NC
2A  [8              14] 3Y
         9 10 11 12 13
        2B GND NC 3A 3B
```

NC - No internal connection

2

TTL Devices

TEXAS
INSTRUMENTS

POST OFFICE BOX 655012 • DALLAS, TEXAS 75265

schematics (each gate)

'02

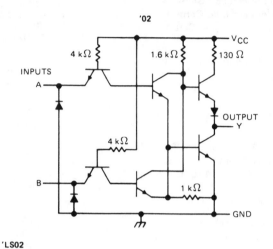

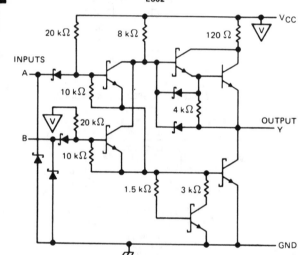

'LS02

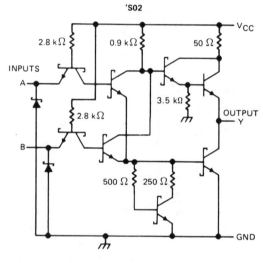

'S02

Resistor values shown are nominal.

absolute maximum ratings over operating free-air temperature range (unless otherwise noted)

Supply voltage, V_{CC} (see Note 1) . . . . 7 V
Input voltage: '02, 'S02 . . . . 5.5 V
             'LS02 . . . . 7 V
Off-state output voltage . . . . 7 V
Operating free-air temperature range: SN54' . . . . −55°C to 125°C
                                  SN74' . . . . 0°C to 70°C
Storage temperature range . . . . −65°C to 150°C

NOTE 1. Voltage values are with respect to network ground terminal.

TEXAS
INSTRUMENTS

POST OFFICE BOX 655012 • DALLAS, TEXAS 75265

2

TTL Devices

SN54LS02, SN74LS02
QUADRUPLE 2-INPUT POSITIVE-NOR GATES

recommended operating conditions

		SN54LS02			SN74LS02			UNIT
		MIN	NOM	MAX	MIN	NOM	MAX	
V_{CC}	Supply voltage	4.5	5	5.5	4.75	5	5.25	V
V_{IH}	High-level input voltage	2			2			V
V_{IL}	Low-level input voltage			0.7			0.8	V
I_{OH}	High-level output current			−0.4			−0.4	mA
I_{OL}	Low-level output current			4			8	mA
T_A	Operating free-air temperature	−55		125	0		70	°C

electrical characteristics over recommended operating free-air temperature range (unless otherwise noted)

PARAMETER	TEST CONDITIONS †			SN54LS02			SN74LS02			UNIT
				MIN	TYP‡	MAX	MIN	TYP‡	MAX	
V_{IK}	V_{CC} = MIN,	I_I = −18 mA				−1.5			−1.5	V
V_{OH}	V_{CC} = MIN,	V_{IL} = MAX,	I_{OH} = −0.4 mA	2.5	3.4		2.7	3.4		V
V_{OL}	V_{CC} = MIN,	V_{IH} = 2 V,	I_{OL} = 4 mA		0.25	0.4		0.25	0.4	V
	V_{CC} = MIN,	V_{IH} = 2 V,	I_{OL} = 8 mA					0.35	0.5	
I_I	V_{CC} = MAX,	V_I = 7 V				0.1			0.1	mA
I_{IH}	V_{CC} = MAX,	V_I = 2.7 V				20			20	µA
I_{IL}	V_{CC} = MAX,	V_I = 0.4 V				−0.4			−0.4	mA
I_{OS}§	V_{CC} = MAX			−20		−100	−20		−100	mA
I_{CCH}	V_{CC} = MAX,	V_I = 0 V			1.6	3.2		1.6	3.2	mA
I_{CCL}	V_{CC} = MAX,	See Note 2			2.8	5.4		2.8	5.4	mA

† For conditions shown as MIN or MAX, use the appropriate value specified under recommended operating conditions.
‡ All typical values are at V_{CC} = 5 V, T_A = 25°C
§ Not more than one output should be shorted at a time, and the duration of the short-circuit should not exceed one second.
NOTE 2: One input at 4.5 V, all others at GND.

switching characteristics, V_{CC} = 5 V, T_A = 25°C (see note 3)

PARAMETER	FROM (INPUT)	TO (OUTPUT)	TEST CONDITIONS		MIN	TYP	MAX	UNIT
t_{PLH}	A or B	Y	R_L = 2 kΩ,	C_L = 15 pF		10	15	ns
t_{PHL}						10	15	ns

NOTE 3: Load circuits and voltage waveforms are shown in Section 1.

TEXAS
INSTRUMENTS
POST OFFICE BOX 655012 • DALLAS, TEXAS 75265

2

TTL Devices

- Package Options Include Plastic "Small Outline" Packages, Ceramic Chip Carriers and Flat Packages, and Plastic and Ceramic DIPs

- Dependable Texas Instruments Quality and Reliability

description

These devices contain six independent inverters.

The SN5404, SN54LS04, and SN54S04 are characterized for operation over the full military temperature range of $-55\,°C$ to $125\,°C$. The SN7404, SN74LS04, and SN74S04 are characterized for operation from $0\,°C$ to $70\,°C$.

FUNCTION TABLE (each inverter)

INPUTS A	OUTPUT Y
H	L
L	H

logic symbol†

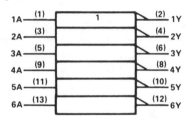

† This symbol is in accordance with ANSI/IEEE Std. 91-1984 and IEC Publication 617-12.

Pin numbers shown are for D, J, and N packages.

logic diagram (positive logic)

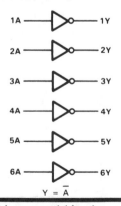

$Y = \overline{A}$

SN5404 . . . J PACKAGE
SN54LS04, SN54S04 . . . J OR W PACKAGE
SN7404 . . . N PACKAGE
SN74LS04, SN74S04 . . . D OR N PACKAGE
(TOP VIEW)

```
1A  [1    14] VCC
1Y  [2    13] 6A
2A  [3    12] 6Y
2Y  [4    11] 5A
3A  [5    10] 5Y
3Y  [6     9] 4A
GND [7     8] 4Y
```

SN5404 . . . W PACKAGE
(TOP VIEW)

```
1A  [1    14] 1Y
2Y  [2    13] 6A
2A  [3    12] 6Y
VCC [4    11] GND
3A  [5    10] 5Y
3Y  [6     9] 5A
4A  [7     8] 4Y
```

SN54LS04, SN54S04 . . . FK PACKAGE
(TOP VIEW)

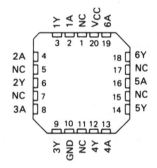

NC - No internal connection

TEXAS INSTRUMENTS

POST OFFICE BOX 655012 • DALLAS, TEXAS 75265

2

TTL Devices

2-25

SN5404, SN54LS04, SN54S04,
SN7404, SN74LS04, SN74S04
HEX INVERTERS

schematics (each gate)

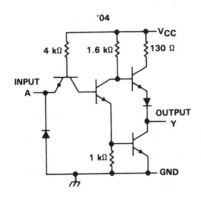

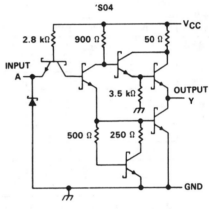

Resistor values shown are nominal.

absolute maximum ratings over operating free-air temperature range (unless otherwise noted)

Supply voltage, V_{CC} (see Note 1) . . . . 7 V
Input voltage: '04, 'S04 . . . . 5.5 V
            'LS04 . . . . 7 V
Operating free-air temperature range: SN54' . . . . −55°C to 125°C
                                 SN74' . . . . 0°C to 70°C
Storage temperature range . . . . −65°C to 150°C

NOTE 1: Voltage values are with respect to network ground terminal.

TEXAS
INSTRUMENTS

POST OFFICE BOX 655012 • DALLAS, TEXAS 75265

SN54LS04, SN74LS04
HEX INVERTERS

recommended operating conditions

		SN54LS04			SN74LS04			UNIT
		MIN	NOM	MAX	MIN	NOM	MAX	
V_{CC}	Supply voltage	4.5	5	5.5	4.75	5	5.25	V
V_{IH}	High-level input voltage	2			2			V
V_{IL}	Low-level input voltage			0.7			0.8	V
I_{OH}	High-level output current			−0.4			−0.4	mA
I_{OL}	Low-level output current			4			8	mA
T_A	Operating free-air temperature	−55		125	0		70	°C

electrical characteristics over recommended operating free-air temperature range (unless otherwise noted)

PARAMETER	TEST CONDITIONS †			SN54LS04			SN74LS04			UNIT
			MIN	TYP‡	MAX	MIN	TYP‡	MAX	
V_{IK}	V_{CC} = MIN,	I_I = −18 mA			−1.5			−1.5	V
V_{OH}	V_{CC} = MIN,	V_{IL} = MAX, I_{OH} = −0.4 mA	2.5	3.4		2.7	3.4		V
V_{OL}	V_{CC} = MIN,	V_{IH} = 2 V, I_{OL} = 4 mA		0.25	0.4			0.4	V
	V_{CC} = MIN,	V_{IH} = 2 V, I_{OL} = 8 mA					0.25	0.5	
I_I	V_{CC} = MAX,	V_I = 7 V			0.1			0.1	mA
I_{IH}	V_{CC} = MAX,	V_I = 2.7 V			20			20	µA
I_{IL}	V_{CC} = MAX,	V_I = 0.4 V			−0.4			−0.4	mA
I_{OS} §	V_{CC} = MAX		−20		−100	−20		−100	mA
I_{CCH}	V_{CC} = MAX,	V_I = 0 V		1.2	2.4		1.2	2.4	mA
I_{CCL}	V_{CC} = MAX,	V_I = 4.5 V		3.6	6.6		3.6	6.6	mA

† For conditions shown as MIN or MAX, use the appropriate value specified under recommended operating conditions.
‡ All typical values are at V_{CC} = 5 V, T_A = 25°C.
§ Not more than one output should be shorted at a time, and the duration of the short-circuit should not exceed one second.

switching characteristics, V_{CC} = 5 V, T_A = 25°C (see note 2)

PARAMETER	FROM (INPUT)	TO (OUTPUT)	TEST CONDITIONS		MIN	TYP	MAX	UNIT
t_{PLH}	A	Y	R_L = 2 kΩ,	C_L = 15 pF		9	15	ns
t_{PHL}						10	15	ns

NOTE 2: Load circuits and voltage waveforms are shown in Section 1.

TEXAS
INSTRUMENTS
POST OFFICE BOX 655012 • DALLAS, TEXAS 75265

- **Package Options Include Both Plastic and Ceramic Chip Carriers in Addition to Plastic and Ceramic DIPs**

- **Dependable Texas Instruments Quality and Reliability**

description

These devices contain six independent inverters. The open-collector outputs require pull-up resistors to perform correctly. They may be connected to other open-collector outputs to implement active-low wired-OR or active-high wired-AND functions. Open collector devices are often used to generate high V_{OH} levels.

The SN5405, SN54H05, SN54LS05 and SN54S05 are characterized for operation over the full military temperature range of $-55°C$ to $125°C$. The SN7405, SN74H05, SN74LS05 and SN74S05 are characterized for operation from 0°C to 70°C.

FUNCTION TABLE (each inverter)

INPUT	OUTPUT
A	**Y**
H	L
L	H

logic diagram (each inverter)

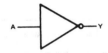

positive logic

$$Y = \overline{A}$$

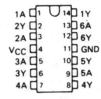

SN5405, SN54H05 . . . J PACKAGE
SN54LS05, SN54S05 . . . J OR W PACKAGE
SN7405, SN74H05 . . . J OR N PACKAGE
SN74LS05, SN74S05 . . . D, J OR N PACKAGE
(TOP VIEW)

1A	1	14 VCC
1Y	2	13 6A
2A	3	12 6Y
2Y	4	11 5A
3A	5	10 5Y
3Y	6	9 4A
GND	7	8 4Y

SN5405, SN54H05 . . . W PACKAGE
(TOP VIEW)

1A	1	14 1Y
2Y	2	13 6A
2A	3	12 6Y
VCC	4	11 GND
3A	5	10 5Y
3Y	6	9 5A
4A	7	8 4Y

SN54LS05, SN54S05 . . . FK PACKAGE
SN74LS05, SN74S05 . . . FN PACKAGE
(TOP VIEW)

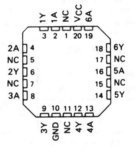

NC - No internal connection

3

TTL DEVICES

TEXAS INSTRUMENTS
POST OFFICE BOX 225012 ● DALLAS, TEXAS 75265

3-37

297

recommended operating conditions

		SN5405			SN7405			UNIT
		MIN	NOM	MAX	MIN	NOM	MAX	
V_{CC}	Supply voltage	4.5	5	5.5	4.75	5	5.25	V
V_{IH}	High-level input voltage	2			2			V
V_{IL}	Low-level input voltage			0.8			0.8	V
V_{OH}	High-level output voltage			5.5			5.5	V
I_{OL}	Low-level output current			16			16	mA
T_A	Operating free-air temperature	-55		125	0		70	°C

electrical characteristics over recommended operating free-air temperature range (unless otherwise noted)

PARAMETER	TEST CONDITIONS†		MIN	TYP‡	MAX	UNIT
V_{IK}	V_{CC} = MIN,	I_I = -12 mA			-1.5	V
I_{OH}	V_{CC} = MIN,	V_{IL} = 0.8 V, V_{OH} = 5.5 V			0.25	mA
V_{OL}	V_{CC} = MIN, ··	V_{IH} = 2 V, I_{OL} = 16 mA		0.2	0.4	V
I_I	V_{CC} = MAX,	V_I = 5.5 V			1	mA
I_{IH}	V_{CC} = MAX,	V_I = 2.4 V			40	µA
I_{IL}	V_{CC} = MAX,	V_I = 0.4 V			-1.6	mA
I_{CCH}	V_{CC} = MAX,	V_I = 0 V		6	12	mA
I_{CCL}	V_{CC} = MAX,	V_I = 4.5 V		18	33	mA

† For conditions shown as MIN or MAX, use the appropriate value specified under recommended operating conditions.
‡ All typical values are at V_{CC} = 5 V, T_A = 25°C.

switching characteristics, V_{CC} = 5 V, T_A = 25°C (see note 2)

PARAMETER	FROM (INPUT)	TO (OUTPUT)	TEST CONDITIONS		MIN	TYP	MAX	UNIT
t_{PLH}	A	Y	R_L = 4 kΩ,	C_L = 15 pF		40	55	ns
t_{PHL}			R_L = 400 Ω,	C_L = 15 pF		8	15	ns

NOTE 2: See General Information Section for load circuits and voltage waveforms.

TEXAS
INSTRUMENTS
POST OFFICE BOX 225012 ● DALLAS, TEXAS-75265

3

TTL DEVICES

recommended operating conditions

	SN54H05 MIN	NOM	MAX	SN74H05 MIN	NOM	MAX	UNIT
V_{CC} Supply voltage	4.5	5	5.5	4.75	5	5.25	V
V_{IH} High-level input voltage	2			2			V
V_{IL} Low-level input voltage			0.8			0.8	V
V_{OH} High-level output voltage			5.5			5.5	V
I_{OL} Low-level output current			20			20	mA
T_A Operating free-air temperature	−55		125	0		70	°C

electrical characteristics over recommended operating free-air temperature range (unless otherwise noted)

PARAMETER	TEST CONDITIONS†	MIN	TYP‡	MAX	UNIT
V_{IK}	V_{CC} = MIN, I_I = −8 mA			−1.5	V
I_{OH}	V_{CC} = MIN, V_{IL} = 0.8 V, V_{OH} = 5.5 V			0.25	mA
V_{OL}	V_{CC} = MIN, V_{IH} = 2 V, I_{OL} = 20 mA		0.2	0.4	V
I_I	V_{CC} = MAX, V_I = 5.5 V			1	mA
I_{IH}	V_{CC} = MAX, V_I = 2.4 V			50	µA
I_{IL}	V_{CC} = MAX, V_I = 0.4 V			−2	mA
I_{CCH}	V_{CC} = MAX, V_I = 0 V		16	26	mA
I_{CCL}	V_{CC} = MAX, V_I = 4.5 V		40	58	mA

† For conditions shown as MIN or MAX, use the appropriate value specified under recommended operating conditions.
‡ All typical values are at V_{CC} = 5 V, T_A = 25°C.

switching characteristics, V_{CC} = 5 V, T_A = 25°C (see note 2)

PARAMETER	FROM (INPUT)	TO (OUTPUT)	TEST CONDITIONS	MIN	TYP	MAX	UNIT
t_{PLH}	A	Y	R_L = 280 Ω, C_L = 25 pF		10	15	ns
t_{PHL}					7.5	12	ns

NOTE 2: See General Information Section for load circuits and voltage waveforms.

TEXAS
INSTRUMENTS
POST OFFICE BOX 225012 ● DALLAS, TEXAS 75265

3

TTL DEVICES

- Package Options Include Plastic "Small Outline" Packages, Ceramic Chip Carriers and Flat Packages, and Plastic and Ceramic DIPs

- Dependable Texas Instruments Quality and Reliability

description

These devices contain three independent 3-input NAND gates.

The SN5410, SN54LS10, and SN54S10 are characterized for operation over the full military temperature range of −55°C to 125°C. The SN7410, SN74LS10, and SN74S10 are characterized for operation from 0°C to 70°C.

FUNCTION TABLE (each gate)

INPUTS			OUTPUT
A	B	C	Y
H	H	H	L
L	X	X	H
X	L	X	H
X	X	L	H

logic symbol†

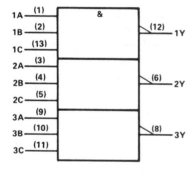

†This symbol is in accordance with ANSI/IEEE Std. 91-1984 and IEC Publication 617-12.
Pin numbers shown are for D, J, and N packages.

positive logic

$$Y = \overline{A \cdot B \cdot C} \text{ or } Y = \overline{A} + \overline{B} + \overline{C}$$

SN5410 . . . J PACKAGE
SN54LS10, SN54S10 . . . J OR W PACKAGE
SN7410 . . . N PACKAGE
SN74LS10, SN74S10 . . . D OR N PACKAGE
(TOP VIEW)

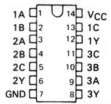

SN5410 . . . W PACKAGE
(TOP VIEW)

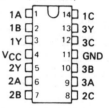

SN54LS10, SN54S10 . . . . FK PACKAGE
(TOP VIEW)

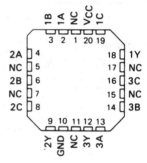

NC - No internal connection

logic diagram (positive logic)

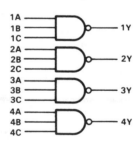

2

TTL Devices

TEXAS INSTRUMENTS
POST OFFICE BOX 655012 • DALLAS, TEXAS 75265

54/7411
54H/74H11
54S/74S11
54LS/74LS11

TRIPLE 3-INPUT AND GATE

CONNECTION DIAGRAMS
PINOUT A

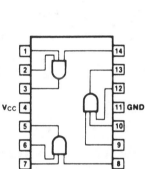

ORDERING CODE: See Section 9

PKGS	PIN OUT	COMMERCIAL GRADE Vcc = +5.0 V ±5%, TA = 0°C to +70°C	MILITARY GRADE Vcc = +5.0 V ±10%, TA = -55°C to +125°C	PKG TYPE
Plastic DIP (P)	A	7411PC, 74H11PC 74S11PC, 74LS11PC		9A
Ceramic DIP (D)	A	7411DC, 74H11DC 74S11DC, 74LS11DC	5411DM, 54H11DM 54S11DM, 54LS11DM	6A
Flatpak (F)	A	74S11FC, 74LS11FC	54S11FM, 54LS11FM	3I
	B	7411FC, 74H11FC	5411FM, 54H11FM	

PINOUT B

INPUT LOADING/FAN-OUT: See Section 3 for U.L definitions

PINS	54/74 (U.L.) HIGH/LOW	54/74H (U.L.) HIGH/LOW	54/74S (U.L.) HIGH/LOW	54/74LS (U.L.) HIGH/LOW
Inputs	1.0/1.0	1.25/1.25	1.25/1.25	0.5/0.25
Outputs	20/10	12.5/12.5	25/12.5	10/5.0 (2.5)

DC AND AC CHARACTERISTICS: See Section 3*

SYMBOL	PARAMETER	54/74 Min	54/74 Max	54/74H Min	54/74H Max	54/74S Min	54/74S Max	54/74LS Min	54/74LS Max	UNITS	CONDITIONS
I_{CCH}	Power Supply		15		30		24		3.6	mA	V_{IN} = Open, V_{CC} = Max
I_{CCL}	Current		24		48		42		6.6		V_{IN} = Gnd
t_{PLH}	Propagation Delay		27		12	2.5	7.0		13	ns	Figs. 3-1, 3-5
t_{PHL}			19		12	2.5	7.5		11		

*DC limits apply over operating temperature range; AC limits apply at T_A = +25°C and V_{CC} = +5.0 V.

54/7413
54LS/74LS13
DUAL 4-INPUT SCHMITT TRIGGER

ORDERING CODE: See Section 9

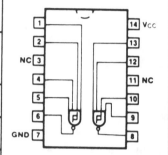

PKGS	PIN OUT	COMMERCIAL GRADE V_{CC} = +5.0 V ±5%, T_A = 0°C to +70°C	MILITARY GRADE V_{CC} = +5.0 V ±10%, T_A = -55°C to +125°C	PKG TYPE
Plastic DIP (P)	A	7413PC, 74LS13PC		9A
Ceramic DIP (D)	A	7413DC, 74LS13DC	5413DM, 54LS13DM	6A
Flatpak (F)	A	7413FC, 74LS13FC	5413FM, 54LS13FM	3I

INPUT LOADING/FAN-OUT: See Section 3 for U.L. definitions

PINS	54/74 (U.L.) HIGH/LOW	54/74LS (U.L.) HIGH/LOW
Inputs	1.0/1.0	0.5/0.25
Outputs	20/10	10/5.0 (2.5)

DC AND AC CHARACTERISTICS: See Section 3*

SYMBOL	PARAMETER	54/74 Min	54/74 Max	54/74LS Min	54/74LS Max	UNITS	CONDITIONS	
V_{T+}	Positive-going Threshold Voltage	1.5	2.0	1.5	2.0	V	V_{CC} = +5.0 V	
V_{T-}	Negative-going Threshold Voltage	0.6	1.1	0.6	1.1	V	V_{CC} = +5.0 V	
$V_{T+} - V_{T-}$	Hysteresis Voltage	0.4		0.4		V	V_{CC} = +5.0 V	
I_{T+}	Input Current at Positive-going Threshold	-0.65**		-0.14**		mA	V_{CC} = +5.0 V, V_{IN} = V_{T+}	
I_{T-}	Input Current at Negative-going Threshold	-0.85**		-0.18**		mA	V_{CC} = +5.0 V, V_{IN} = V_{T-}	
I_{OS}	Output Short Circuit Current	-18	-55	-20	-100	mA	V_{CC} = Max	
I_{CCH}	Power Supply Current		23		6.0	mA	V_{IN} = Gnd	V_{CC} = Max
I_{CCL}			32		7.0		V_{IN} = Open	
t_{PLH}	Propagation Delay		27		22	ns	Fig. 3-1, 3-15	
t_{PHL}			22		27			

*DC limits apply over operating temperature range, AC limits apply at T_A = +25°C and V_{CC} = +5.0 V. **Typical Value

- **Operation from Very Slow Edges**

- **Improved Line-Receiving Characteristics**

- **High Noise Immunity**

description

Each circuit functions as an inverter, but because of the Schmitt action, it has different input threshold levels for positive (V_{T+}) and for negative going (V_{T-}) signals.

These circuits are temperature-compensated and can be triggered from the slowest of input ramps and still give clean, jitter-free output signals.

The SN5414 and SN54LS14 are characterized for operation over the full military temperature range of –55°C to 125°C. The SN7414 and the SN74LS14 are characterized for operation from 0° C to 70° C.

logic symbol†

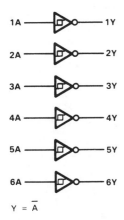

1A — (1) (2) — 1Y
2A — (3) (4) — 2Y
3A — (5) (6) — 3Y
4A — (9) (8) — 4Y
5A — (11) (10) — 5Y
6A — (13) (12) — 6Y

† This symbol is in accordance with ANSI/IEEE Std 91-1984 and IEC Publication 617-12.
Pin numbers shown are for D, J, N, and W packages.

logic diagram (positive logic)

1A —▷∘— 1Y

2A —▷∘— 2Y

3A —▷∘— 3Y

4A —▷∘— 4Y

5A —▷∘— 5Y

6A —▷∘— 6Y

$Y = \overline{A}$

SN5414, SN54LS14 . . . J OR W PACKAGE
SN7414 . . . N PACKAGE
SN74LS14 . . . D OR N PACKAGE
(TOP VIEW)

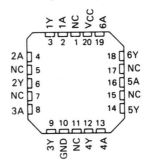

1A [1		14] V_CC
1Y [2		13] 6A
2A [3		12] 6Y
2Y [4		11] 5A
3A [5		10] 5Y
3Y [6		9] 4A
GND [7		8] 4Y

SN54LS14 . . . FK PACKAGE
(TOP VIEW)

Top pins: 1Y(3) 1A(2) NC(1) VCC(20) 6A(19)

2A [4 — 18] 6Y
NC [5 — 17] NC
2Y [6 — 16] 5A
NC [7 — 15] NC
3A [8 — 14] 5Y

Bottom pins: 3Y(9) GND(10) NC(11) 4Y(12) 4A(13)

NC—No internal connection

2

TTL Devices

TEXAS
INSTRUMENTS
POST OFFICE BOX 655012 • DALLAS, TEXAS 75265

2-77

schematics

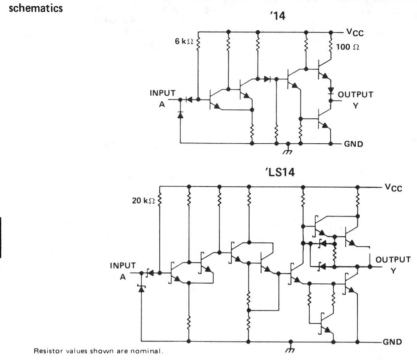

Resistor values shown are nominal.

absolute maximum ratings over operating free-air temperature range (unless otherwise noted)

Supply voltage, V_{CC} (see Note 1) . . . . 7 V
Input voltage: '14 . . . . 5.5 V
           'LS14 . . . . 7 V
Operating free-air temperature: SN54' . . . . -55°C to 125°C
                              SN74' . . . . 0°C to 70°C
Storage temperature range . . . . -65°C to 150°C

NOTE 1: Voltage values are with respect to network ground terminal.

2

TTL Devices

TEXAS
INSTRUMENTS

POST OFFICE BOX 655012 • DALLAS, TEXAS 75265

SN54LS14, SN74LS14
HEX SCHMITT-TRIGGER INVERTERS

recommended operating conditions

		SN54LS14			SN74LS14			UNIT
		MIN	NOM	MAX	MIN	NOM	MAX	
V_{CC}	Supply voltage	4.5	5	5.5	4.75	5	5.25	V
I_{OH}	High-level output current			−0.4			−0.4	mA
I_{OL}	Low-level output current			4			8	mA
T_A	Operating free-air temperature	−55		125	0		70	C

electrical characteristics over recommended operating free-air temperature range (unless otherwise noted)

PARAMETER	TEST CONDITIONS†		SN54LS14			SN74LS14			UNIT
			MIN	TYP‡	MAX	MIN	TYP‡	MAX	
V_{T+}	V_{CC} = 5 V		1.4	1.6	1.9	1.4	1.6	1.9	V
V_{T-}	V_{CC} = 5 V		0.5	0.8	1	0.5	0.8	1	V
Hysteresis ($V_{T+} - V_{T-}$)	V_{CC} = 5 V		0.4	0.8		0.4	0.8		V
V_{IK}	V_{CC} = MIN, I_I = −18 mA				−1.5			−1.5	V
V_{OH}	V_{CC} = MIN, V_I = 0.5 V, I_{OH} = −0.4 mA		2.5	3.4		2.7	3.4		V
V_{OL}	V_{CC} = MIN, V_I = 1.9 V	I_{OL} = 4 mA		0.25	0.4		0.25	0.4	V
		I_{OL} = 8 mA					0.35	0.5	
I_{T+}	V_{CC} = 5 V, V_I = V_{T+}			−0.14			−0.14		mA
I_{T-}	V_{CC} = 5 V, V_I = V_{T-}			−0.18			−0.18		mA
I_I	V_{CC} = MAX, V_I = 7 V				0.1			0.1	mA
I_{IH}	V_{CC} = MAX, V_{IH} = 2.7 V				20			20	μA
I_{IL}	V_{CC} = MAX, V_{IL} = 0.4 V				−0.4			−0.4	mA
I_{OS} §	V_{CC} = MAX		−20		−100	−20		−100	mA
I_{CCH}	V_{CC} = MAX			8.6	16		8.6	16	mA
I_{CCL}	V_{CC} = MAX			12	21		12	21	mA

† For conditions shown as MIN or MAX, use the appropriate value specified under recommended operating conditions.
‡ All typical values are at V_{CC} = 5 V, T_A = 25°C.
§ Not more than one output should be shorted at a time, and duration of the short-circuit should not exceed one second.

switching characteristics, V_{CC} = 5 V, T_A = 25°C

PARAMETER	FROM (INPUT)	TO (OUTPUT)	TEST CONDITIONS		MIN	TYP	MAX	UNIT
t_{PLH}	A	Y	R_L = 2 kΩ,	C_L = 15 pF		15	22	ns
t_{PHL}						15	22	ns

TEXAS
INSTRUMENTS
POST OFFICE BOX 655012 • DALLAS, TEXAS 75265

2

TTL Devices

TYPICAL CHARACTERISTICS OF 'LS14 CIRCUITS

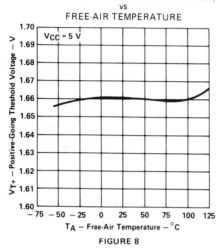

POSITIVE-GOING THRESHOLD VOLTAGE
vs
FREE-AIR TEMPERATURE

FIGURE 8

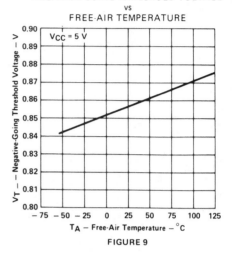

NEGATIVE-GOING THRESHOLD VOLTAGE
vs
FREE-AIR TEMPERATURE

FIGURE 9

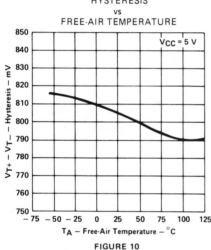

HYSTERESIS
vs
FREE-AIR TEMPERATURE

FIGURE 10

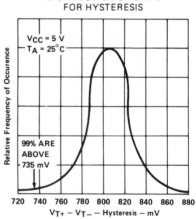

DISTRIBUTION OF UNITS
FOR HYSTERESIS

FIGURE 11

Data for temperatures below 0°C and above 70°C and supply voltages below 4.75 V and above 5.25 V are applicable for SN54LS14 only.

TEXAS
INSTRUMENTS
POST OFFICE BOX 655012 • DALLAS, TEXAS 75265

TTL Devices

2

2-83

TYPICAL CHARACTERISTICS OF 'LS14 CIRCUITS

THRESHOLD VOLTAGES AND HYSTERESIS
vs
SUPPLY VOLTAGE

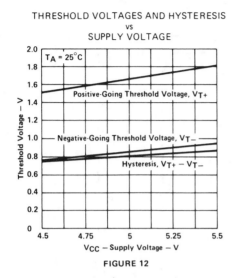

FIGURE 12

OUTPUT VOLTAGE
vs
INPUT VOLTAGE

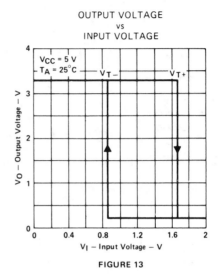

FIGURE 13

Data for temperatures below 0°C and above 70°C and supply voltages below 4.75 V and above 5.25 V are applicable for SN54LS14 only.

TEXAS
INSTRUMENTS

POST OFFICE BOX 655012 • DALLAS, TEXAS 75265

TYPICAL APPLICATION DATA

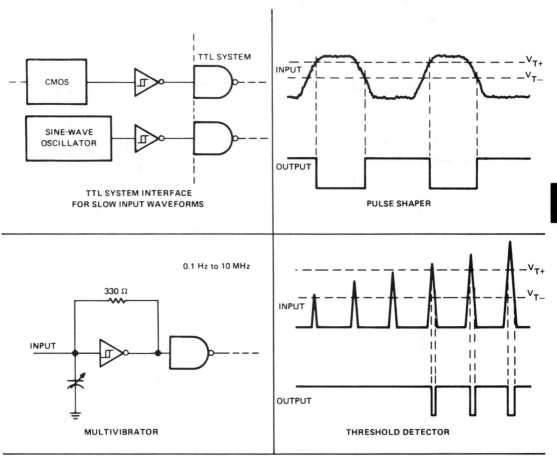

TTL SYSTEM INTERFACE
FOR SLOW INPUT WAVEFORMS

PULSE SHAPER

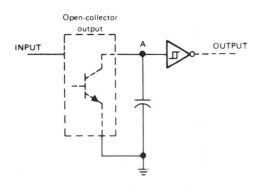

0.1 Hz to 10 MHz

330 Ω

MULTIVIBRATOR

THRESHOLD DETECTOR

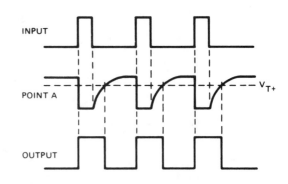

Open-collector output

PULSE STRETCHER

TEXAS INSTRUMENTS

POST OFFICE BOX 655012 • DALLAS, TEXAS 75265

2-85

2

TTL Devices

- **Package Options Include Plastic "Small Outline" Packages, Ceramic Chip Carriers and Flat Packages, and Plastic and Ceramic DIPs**

- **Dependable Texas Instruments Quality and Reliability**

description

These devices contain three independent 3-input NOR gates.

The SN5427 and SN54LS27 are characterized for operation over the full military temperature range of −55°C to 125°C. The SN7427 and SN74LS27 are characterized for operation from 0°C to 70°C.

FUNCTION TABLE (each gate)

INPUTS			OUTPUT
A	B	C	Y
H	X	X	L
X	H	X	L
X	X	H	L
L	L	L	H

logic symbol†

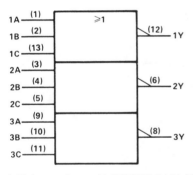

1A (1)
1B (2)
1C (13)
≥1
(12) 1Y

2A (3)
2B (4)
2C (5)
(6) 2Y

3A (9)
3B (10)
3C (11)
(8) 3Y

This symbol is in accordance with ANSI/IEEE Std 91-1984 and IEC Publication 617-12.

Pin numbers shown are for D, J, N, and W packages

SN5427, SN54LS27 . . . J OR W PACKAGE
SN7427 . . . N PACKAGE
SN74LS27 . . . D OR N PACKAGE
(TOP VIEW)

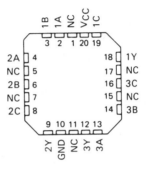

1A	1	14	V$_{CC}$
1B	2	13	1C
2A	3	12	1Y
2B	4	11	3C
2C	5	10	3B
2Y	6	9	3A
GND	7	8	3Y

SN54LS27 . . . FK PACKAGE
(TOP VIEW)

1B 1A NC V$_{CC}$ 1C
3 2 1 20 19

2A 4   18 1Y
NC 5   17 NC
2B 6   16 3C
NC 7   15 NC
2C 8   14 3B

9 10 11 12 13
2Y GND NC 3Y 3A

NC - No internal connection

logic diagram

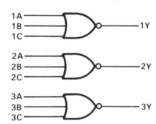

1A
1B   1Y
1C

2A
2B   2Y
2C

3A
3B   3Y
3C

positive logic

$$Y = \overline{A + B + C} \text{ or } Y = \overline{A} \cdot \overline{B} \cdot \overline{C}$$

TTL Devices

2

![Texas Instruments logo]

TEXAS INSTRUMENTS
POST OFFICE BOX 225012 • DALLAS, TEXAS 75265

2-119

- Package Options Include Plastic "Small Outline" Packages, Ceramic Chip Carriers and Flat Packages, and Plastic and Ceramic DIPs

- Dependable Texas Instruments Quality and Reliability

description

These devices contain four independent 2-input OR gates.

The SN5432, SN54LS32 and SN54S32 are characterized for operation over the full military range of −55°C to 125°C. The SN7432, SN74LS32 and SN74S32 are characterized for operation from 0°C to 70°C.

FUNCTION TABLE (each gate)

INPUTS		OUTPUT
A	**B**	**Y**
H	X	H
X	H	H
L	L	L

logic symbol†

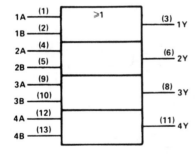

† This symbol is in accordance with ANSI IEEE Std 91 1984 and IEC Publication 617 12.
Pin numbers shown are for D, J, N, or W packages.

SN5432, SN54LS32, SN54S32 . . . J OR W PACKAGE
SN7432 . . . N PACKAGE
SN74LS32, SN74S32 . . . D OR N PACKAGE
(TOP VIEW)

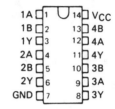

SN54LS32, SN54S32 . . . FK PACKAGE
(TOP VIEW)

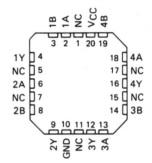

NC – No internal connection

logic diagram

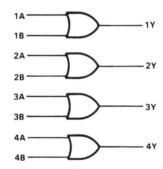

positive logic

$$Y = A + B \text{ or } Y = \overline{\overline{A} \cdot \overline{B}}$$

2

TTL Devices

TEXAS
INSTRUMENTS

POST OFFICE BOX 655012 • DALLAS, TEXAS 75265

2-137

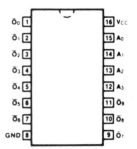

54/7442A • 54LS/74LS42
54/7443A • 54/7444A
1-of-10 DECODER

DESCRIPTION - The '42, '43 and '44 are multipurpose decoders. For any valid input combination, one and only one output is LOW. For all invalid input combinations all outputs are HIGH. The '42 accepts four BCD inputs and provides ten mutually exclusive outputs; the '43 accepts four lines of EXCESS-3 encoded data and provides ten mutually exclusive outputs; the '44 accepts four lines of EXCESS-3 Gray encoded data and provides ten mutually exclusive totem pole outputs.

- **MULTIFUNCTION CAPABILITY**
- **MUTUALLY EXCLUSIVE OUTPUTS**
- **DEMULTIPLEXING CAPABILITY**
- **FULLY TTL AND CMOS COMPATIBLE**

ORDERING CODE: See Section 9

PKGS	PIN OUT	COMMERCIAL GRADE $V_{CC} = +5.0$ V $\pm5\%$, $T_A = 0°$ C to $+70°$ C	MILITARY GRADE $V_{CC} = +5.0$ V $\pm10\%$, $T_A = -55°$ C to $+125°$ C	PKG TYPE
Plastic DIP (P)	A	7442APC, 74LS42PC 7443APC, 7444APC		9B
Ceramic DIP (D)	A	7442ADC, 74LS42DC 7443ADC, 7444ADC	5442ADM, 54LS42DM 5443ADM, 5444ADM	6B
Flatpak (F)	A	7442AFC, 74LS42FC 7443AFC, 7444AFC	5442AFM, 54LS42FM 5443AFM, 5444AFM	4L

LOGIC SYMBOL

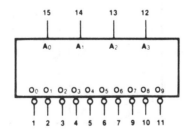

V_{CC} = Pin 16
GND = Pin 8

INPUT LOADING/FAN-OUT: See Section 3 for U.L. definitions

PIN NAMES	DESCRIPTION	54/74 (U.L.) HIGH/LOW	54/74LS (U.L.) HIGH/LOW
$A_0 - A_3$	BCD Inputs ('42)	1.0/1.0	0.5/0.25
$A_0 - A_3$	EXCESS-3 Inputs ('43)	1.0/1.0	
$A_0 - A_3$	EXCESS-3 GRAY Inputs ('44)	1.0/1.0	
$\overline{O}_0 - \overline{O}_0$	Decimal Outputs (Active LOW)	20/10	10/5.0 (2.5)

FUNCTIONAL DESCRIPTION — Logically, the '42, '43 and '44 differ only in their input codes. The '42 accepts the standard 8421 BCD code. The '43 accepts the EXCESS-3 decimal code while the '44 accepts the EXCESS-3 Gray code. For any input combination within the assigned ten states, only one output is LOW, as shown in the Truth Table. For all invalid input combinations, all ten outputs are HIGH.

The '42 can be used as a conventional 1-of-8 decoder by treating the most significant input A_3 as an active LOW Enable. Similarly, it can be used as an 8-output demultiplexer by using A_3 as the data input.

TRUTH TABLE

'42A • 'LS42 BCD INPUT				'43A EXCESS-3 INPUT				'44A EXCESS-3 GRAY INPUT				ALL TYPES DECIMAL OUTPUT									
A_3	A_2	A_1	A_0	A_3	A_2	A_1	A_0	A_3	A_2	A_1	A_0	$\overline{O}_0$	$\overline{O}_1$	$\overline{O}_2$	$\overline{O}_3$	$\overline{O}_4$	$\overline{O}_5$	$\overline{O}_6$	$\overline{O}_7$	$\overline{O}_8$	$\overline{O}_9$
L	L	L	L	L	L	H	H	L	L	H	L	L	H	H	H	H	H	H	H	H	H
L	L	L	H	L	H	L	L	L	H	H	L	H	L	H	H	H	H	H	H	H	H
L	L	H	L	L	H	L	H	L	H	H	H	H	H	L	H	H	H	H	H	H	H
L	L	H	H	L	H	H	L	L	H	L	H	H	H	H	L	H	H	H	H	H	H
L	H	L	L	L	H	H	H	L	H	L	L	H	H	H	H	L	H	H	H	H	H
L	H	L	H	H	L	L	L	H	H	L	L	H	H	H	H	H	L	H	H	H	H
L	H	H	L	H	L	L	H	H	H	L	H	H	H	H	H	H	H	L	H	H	H
L	H	H	H	H	L	H	L	H	H	H	H	H	H	H	H	H	H	H	L	H	H
H	L	L	L	H	L	H	H	H	H	H	L	H	H	H	H	H	H	H	H	L	H
H	L	L	H	H	H	L	L	H	L	H	L	H	H	H	H	H	H	H	H	H	L
H	L	H	L	H	H	L	H	H	L	H	H	H	H	H	H	H	H	H	H	H	H
H	L	H	H	H	H	H	L	H	L	L	H	H	H	H	H	H	H	H	H	H	H
H	H	L	L	H	H	H	H	H	L	L	L	H	H	H	H	H	H	H	H	H	H
H	H	L	H	L	L	L	L	L	L	L	L	H	H	H	H	H	H	H	H	H	H
H	H	H	L	L	L	L	H	L	L	L	H	H	H	H	H	H	H	H	H	H	H
H	H	H	H	L	L	H	L	L	L	H	H	H	H	H	H	H	H	H	H	H	H

H = HIGH Voltage Level
L = LOW Voltage Level

(Courtesy Of Fairchild – A Schlumberger Company)

'46A, '47A, 'LS47 feature	'48, 'LS48 feature	'LS49 feature
• **Open-Collector Outputs Drive Indicators Directly** • **Lamp-Test Provision** • **Leading/Trailing Zero Suppression**	• **Internal Pull-Ups Eliminate Need for External Resistors** • **Lamp-Test Provision** • **Leading/Trailing Zero Suppression**	• **Open-Collector Outputs** • **Blanking Input**

SN5446A, SN5447A, SN54LS47, SN5448,
SN54LS48 . . . J PACKAGE
SN7446A, SN7447A,
SN7448 . . . N PACKAGE
SN74LS47, SN74LS48 . . . D OR N PACKAGE
(TOP VIEW)

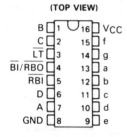

SN54LS47, SN54LS48 . . . FK PACKAGE
(TOP VIEW)

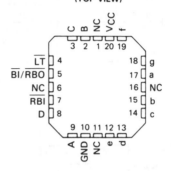

SN54LS49 . . . J OR W PACKAGE
SN74LS49 . . . D OR N PACKAGE
(TOP VIEW)

SN54LS49 . . . FK PACKAGE
(TOP VIEW)

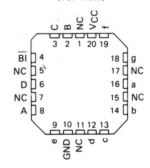

NC – No internal connection

2

TTL Devices

TEXAS
INSTRUMENTS
POST OFFICE BOX 655012 • DALLAS, TEXAS 75265

2-175

SN5446A, '47A, '48, SN54LS47, 'LS48, 'LS49, SN7446A, '47A, '48, SN74LS47, 'LS48, 'LS49 BCD-TO-SEVEN-SEGMENT DECODERS/DRIVERS

- ● All Circuit Types Feature Lamp Intensity Modulation Capability

| TYPE | ACTIVE LEVEL | DRIVER OUTPUTS | | | TYPICAL POWER DISSIPATION | PACKAGES |
		OUTPUT CONFIGURATION	SINK CURRENT	MAX VOLTAGE		
SN5446A	low	open-collector	40 mA	30 V	320 mW	J, W
SN5447A	low	open-collector	40 mA	15 V	320 mW	J, W
SN5448	high	2-kΩ pull-up	6.4 mA	5.5 V	265 mW	J,W
SN54LS47	low	open-collector	12 mA	15 V	35 mW	J, W
SN54LS48	high	2-kΩ pull-up	2 mA	5.5 V	125 mW	J, W
SN54LS49	high	open-collector	4 mA	5.5 V	40 mW	J, W
SN7446A	low	open-collector	40 mA	30 V	320 mW	J, N
SN7447A	low	open-collector	40 mA	15 V	320 mW	J, N
SN7448	high	2-kΩ pull-up	6.4 mA	5.5 V	265 mW	J, N
SN74LS47	low	open-collector	24 mA	15 V	35 mW	J, N
SN74LS48	high	2-kΩ pull-up	6 mA	5.5 V	125 mW	J, N
SN74LS49	high	open-collector	8 mA	5.5 V	40 mW	J, N

logic symbols[†]

'46A, '47A, 'LS47

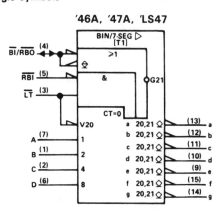

'48, 'LS48

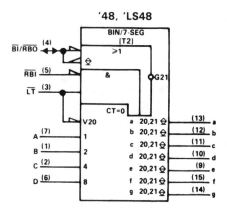

'LS49

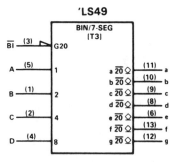

[†]These symbols are in accordance with ANSI/IEEE Std 91-1984 and IEC Publication 617-12.
Pin numbers shown are for D, J, N, and W packages.

TEXAS INSTRUMENTS

POST OFFICE BOX 655012 • DALLAS, TEXAS 75265

logic diagrams (positive logic)

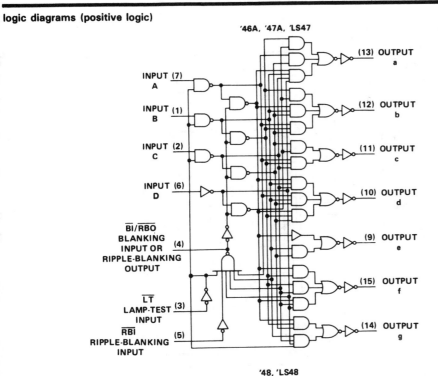

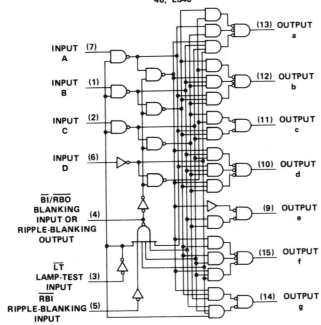

Pin numbers shown are for D, J, N, and W packages.

TEXAS
INSTRUMENTS
POST OFFICE BOX 655012 • DALLAS, TEXAS 75265

2-179

TTL Devices

2

logic diagrams (continued)

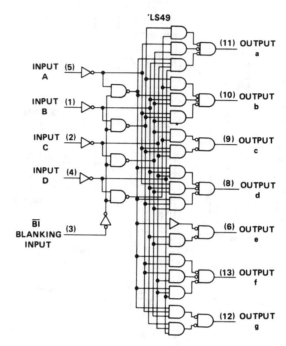

'LS49

INPUT A (5)
INPUT B (1)
INPUT C (2)
INPUT D (4)

$\overline{BI}$ BLANKING INPUT (3)

(11) OUTPUT a
(10) OUTPUT b
(9) OUTPUT c
(8) OUTPUT d
(6) OUTPUT e
(13) OUTPUT f
(12) OUTPUT g

Pin numbers shown are for D, J, N, and W packages.

TEXAS INSTRUMENTS
POST OFFICE BOX 655012 • DALLAS, TEXAS 75265

316

54/7474
54H/74H74
54S/74S74
54LS/74LS74

DUAL D-TYPE POSITIVE EDGE-TRIGGERED FLIP-FLOP

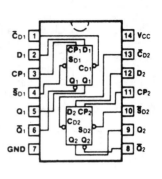

DESCRIPTION — The '74 devices are dual D-type flip-flops with Direct Clear and Set inputs and complementary (Q, $\overline{Q}$) outputs. Information at the input is transferred to the outputs on the positive edge of the clock pulse. Clock triggering occurs at a voltage level of the clock pulse and is not directly related to the transition time of the positive going pulse. After the Clock Pulse input threshold voltage has been passed, the Data input is locked out and information present will not be transferred to the outputs until the next rising edge of the Clock Pulse input.

PINOUT B

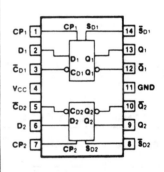

TRUTH TABLE
(Each Half)

INPUT	OUTPUTS	
@ t_n	@ t_{n+1}	
D	Q	$\overline{Q}$
L	L	H
H	H	L

Asynchronous Inputs:
LOW input to $\overline{S}_D$ sets Q to HIGH level
LOW input to $\overline{C}_D$ sets Q to LOW level
Clear and Set are independent of clock
Simultaneous LOW on $\overline{C}_D$ and $\overline{S}_D$
makes both Q and $\overline{Q}$ HIGH

H = HIGH Voltage Level
L = LOW Voltage Level
t_n = Bit time before clock pulse.
t_{n+1} = Bit time after clock pulse.

ORDERING CODE: See Section 9

PKGS	PIN OUT	COMMERCIAL GRADE V_{CC} = +5.0 V ±5%, T_A = 0°C to +70°C	MILITARY GRADE V_{CC} = +5.0 V ±10%, T_A = -55°C to +125°C	PKG TYPE
Plastic DIP (P)	A	7474PC, 74H74PC 74S74PC, 74LS74PC		9A
Ceramic DIP (D)	A	7474DC, 74H74DC 74S74DC, 74LS74DC	5474DM, 54H74DM 54S74DM, 54LS74DM	6A
Flatpak (F)	A	74S74FC, 74LS74FC	54S74FM, 54LS74FM	31
	B	7474FC, 74H74FC	5474FM, 54H74FM	

LOGIC SYMBOL

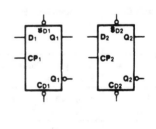

V_{CC} = Pin 14 (4)
GND = Pin 7 (11)

INPUT LOADING/FAN-OUT: See Section 3 for U.L. definitions

PIN NAMES	DESCRIPTION	54/74 (U.L.) HIGH/LOW	54/74H (U.L.) HIGH/LOW	54/74S (U.L.) HIGH/LOW	54/74LS (U.L.) HIGH/LOW
D_1, D_2	Data Inputs	1.0/1.0	1.25/1.25	1.25/1.25	0.5/0.25
CP_1, CP_2	Clock Pulse Inputs (Active Rising Edge)	2.0/2.0	2.5/2.5	2.5/2.5	1.0/0.5
$\overline{C}_{D1}, \overline{C}_{D2}$	Direct Clear Inputs (Active LOW)	3.0/2.0	3.75/2.5	3.75/3.75	1.5/0.75
$\overline{S}_{D1}, \overline{S}_{D2}$	Direct Set Inputs (Active LOW)	2.0/1.0	2.5/1.25	2.5/2.5	1.0/0.5
$Q_1, \overline{Q}_1, Q_2, \overline{Q}_2$	Outputs	20/10	12.5/12.5	25/12.5	10/5.0 (2.5)

LOGIC DIAGRAM (one half shown)

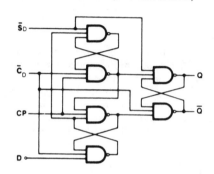

DC CHARACTERISTICS OVER OPERATING TEMPERATURE RANGE (unless otherwise specified)

SYMBOL	PARAMETER		54/74 Min	54/74 Max	54/74H Min	54/74H Max	54/74S Min	54/74S Max	54/74LS Min	54/74LS Max	UNITS	CONDITIONS
I_{CC}	Power Supply Current	XM		30		42		50		8.0	mA	V_{CC} = Max, V_{CP} = 0 V
		XC		30		50		50		8.0		

AC CHARACTERISTICS: V_{CC} = +5.0 V, T_A = +25°C (See Section 3 for waveforms and load configurations)

SYMBOL	PARAMETER	54/74 C_L = 15 pF R_L = 400 Ω Min	Max	54/74H C_L = 25 pF R_L = 280 Ω Min	Max	54/74S C_L = 15 pF R_L = 280 Ω Min	Max	54/74LS C_L = 15 pF Min	Max	UNITS	CONDITIONS
f_{max}	Maximum Clock Frequency	15		35		75		30		MHz	Figs. 3-1, 3-8
t_{PLH}	Propagation Delay CP_n to Q_n or $\overline{Q}_n$		25		15		9.0		25	ns	Figs. 3-1, 3-8
t_{PHL}			40		20		11		35		
t_{PLH}	Propagation Delay $\overline{C}_{Dn}$ or $\overline{S}_{Dn}$ to Q_n or $\overline{Q}_n$		25		20		6.0		15	ns	$V_{CP} \geq 2.0$ V Figs. 3-1, 3-10
t_{PHL}			40		30		13.5		35		
t_{PLH}	Propagation Delay $\overline{C}_{Dn}$ or $\overline{S}_{Dn}$ to Q_n or $\overline{Q}_n$		25		20		6.0		15	ns	$V_{CP} \leq 0.8$ V Figs. 3-1, 3-10
t_{PHL}			40		30		8.0		24		

(Courtesy of Fairchild – A Schlumberger Company)

AC OPERATING REQUIREMENTS: V_{CC} = +5.0 V, T_A = +25°C

SYMBOL	PARAMETER	54/74		54/74H		54/74S		54/74LS		UNITS	CONDITIONS
		Min	Max	Min	Max	Min	Max	Min	Max		
t_s (H)	Setup Time HIGH D_n to CP_n	20		10		3.0		10		ns	Fig. 3-6
t_h (H)	Hold Time HIGH D_n to CP_n	5.0		0		0		5.0		ns	
t_s (L)	Setup Time LOW D_n to CP_n	20		15		3.0		20		ns	Fig. 3-6
t_h (L)	Hold Time LOW D_n to CP_n	5.0		0		0		5.0		ns	
t_w (H) t_w (L)	CP_n Pulse Width	30 37		15 13.5		6.0 7.3		18 15.5		ns	Fig. 3-8
t_w (L)	$\overline{C}_{Dn}$ or $\overline{S}_{Dn}$ Pulse Width LOW	30		25		7.0		15		ns	Fig. 3-10

FUNCTION TABLE
(each latch)

INPUTS		OUTPUTS	
D	C	Q	$\overline{Q}$
L	H	L	H
H	H	H	L
X	L	Q_0	$\overline{Q_0}$

H = high level, L = low level, X = irrelevant

Q_0 = the level of Q before the high-to-low transition of G

description

These latches are ideally suited for use as temporary storage for binary information between processing units and input/output or indicator units. Information present at a data (D) input is transferred to the Q output when the enable (C) is high and the Q output will follow the data input as long as the enable remains high. When the enable goes low, the information (that was present at the data input at the time the transition occurred) is retained at the Q output until the enable is permitted to go high.

The '75 and 'LS75 feature complementary Q and $\overline{Q}$ outputs from a 4-bit latch, and are available in various 16-pin packages. For higher component density applications, the '77 and 'LS77 4-bit latches are available in 14-pin flat packages.

These circuits are completely compatible with all popular TTL families. All inputs are diode-clamped to minimize transmission-line effects and simplify system design. Series 54 and 54LS devices are characterized for operation over the full military temperature range of −55°C to 125°C; Series 74, and 74LS devices are characterized for operation from 0°C to 70°C.

SN5475, SN54LS75 . . . J OR W PACKAGE
SN7475 . . . N PACKAGE
SN74LS75 . . . D OR N PACKAGE
(TOP VIEW)

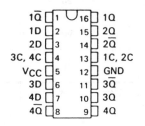

SN5477, SN54LS77 . . . W PACKAGE
(TOP VIEW)

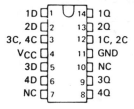

NC - No internal connection

logic symbols†

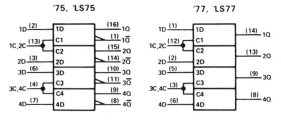

'75, 'LS75   '77, 'LS77

†These symbols are in accordance with ANSI/IEEE Std 91-1984 and IEC Publication 617-12.

absolute maximum ratings over operating free-air temperature range (unless otherwise noted)

Supply voltage, V_{CC} (See Note 1)	7 V
Input voltage: '75, '77	5.5 V
'LS75, 'LS77	7 V
Interemitter voltage (see Note 2)	5.5 V
Operating free-air temperature range: SN54'	−55°C to 125°C
SN74'	0°C to 70°C
Storage temperature range	−65°C to 150°C

NOTES: 1. Voltage values are with respect to network ground terminal.
2. This is the voltage between two emitters of a multiple-emitter input transistor and is not applicable to the 'LS75 and 'LS77.

TEXAS
INSTRUMENTS

POST OFFICE BOX 655012 • DALLAS, TEXAS 75265

2-241

2

TTL Devices

54/7476
54H/74H76
54LS/74LS76

DUAL JK FLIP-FLOP
(With Separate Sets, Clears and Clocks)

DESCRIPTION — The '76 and 'H76 are dual JK master/slave flip-flops with separate Direct Set, Direct Clear and Clock Pulse inputs for each flip-flop. Inputs to the master section are controlled by the clock pulse. The clock pulse also regulates the state of the coupling transistors which connect the master and slave sections. The sequence of operation is as follows: 1) isolate slave from master; 2) enter information from J and K inputs to master; 3) disable J and K inputs; 4) transfer information from master to slave.

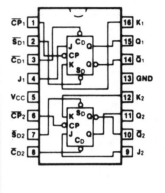

TRUTH TABLE

INPUTS		OUTPUT
@ t_n		@ t_{n+1}
J	K'	Q
L	L	Q_n
L	H	L
H	L	H
H	H	$\bar{Q}_n$

H = HIGH Voltage Level
L = LOW Voltage Level
t_n = Bit time before clock pulse.
t_{n+1} = Bit time after clock pulse.

CLOCK WAVEFORM

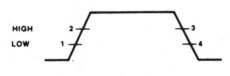

Asynchronous Inputs:
    LOW input to $\bar{S}_D$ sets Q to HIGH level
    LOW input to $\bar{C}_D$ sets Q to LOW level
    Clear and Set are independent of clock
    Simultaneous LOW on $\bar{C}_D$ and $\bar{S}_D$
    makes both Q and $\bar{Q}$ HIGH

LOGIC SYMBOL

The 'LS76 is a dual JK, negative edge-triggered flip-flop also offering individual Direct Set, Direct Clear and Clock Pulse inputs. When the Clock Pulse input is HIGH, the JK inputs are enabled and data is accepted. This data will be transferred to the outputs according to the Truth Table on the HIGH-to-LOW clock transitions.

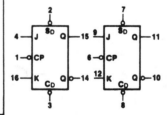

Vcc = Pin 5
GND = Pin 13

ORDERING CODE: See Section 9

PKGS	PIN OUT	COMMERCIAL GRADE Vcc = +5.0 V ±5%, T_A = 0°C to +70°C	MILITARY GRADE Vcc = +5.0 V ±10%, T_A = -55°C to +125°C	PKG TYPE
Plastic DIP (P)	A	7476PC, 74H76PC 74LS76PC		9B
Ceramic DIP (D)	A	7476DC, 74H76DC 74LS76DC	5476DM, 54H76DM 54LS76DM	6B
Flatpak (F)	A	7476FC, 74H76FC 74LS76FC	5476FM, 54H76FM 54LS76FM	4L

(Courtesy of Fairchild – A Schlumberger Company)

INPUT LOADING/FAN-OUT: See Section 3 for U.L. definitions

PIN NAMES	DESCRIPTION	54/74 (U.L.) HIGH/LOW	54/74H (U.L.) HIGH/LOW	54/74LS (U.L.) HIGH/LOW
J_1, J_2, K_1, K_2	Data Inputs	1.0/1.0	1.25/1.25	0.5/0.25
$\overline{CP}_1, \overline{CP}_2$	Clock Pulse Inputs (Active Falling Edge)	2.0/2.0	2.5/2.5	2.0/0.5
$\overline{C}_{D1}, \overline{C}_{D2}$	Direct Clear Inputs (Active LOW)	2.0/2.0	2.5/2.5	1.5/0.5
$\overline{S}_{D1}, \overline{S}_{D2}$	Direct Set Inputs (Active LOW)	2.0/2.0	2.5/2.5	1.5/0.5
$Q_1, \overline{Q}_1, Q_2, \overline{Q}_2$	Outputs	20/10	12.5/12.5	10/5.0 (2.5)

LOGIC DIAGRAMS (one half shown)
'76, 'H76

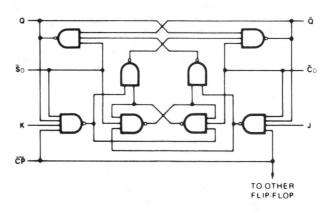

TO OTHER FLIP-FLOP

'LS76

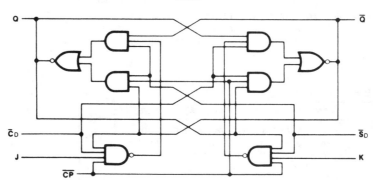

DC CHARACTERISTICS OVER OPERATING TEMPERATURE RANGE (unless otherwise specified)

SYMBOL	PARAMETER	54/74		54/74H		54/74LS		UNITS	CONDITIONS
		Min	Max	Min	Max	Min	Max		
I_{CC}	Power Supply Current		40		50		8.0	mA	V_{CC} = Max, V_{CP} = 0 V

AC CHARACTERISTICS: V_{CC} = +5.0 V, T_A = +25°C (See Section 3 for waveforms and load configurations)

SYMBOL	PARAMETER	54/74 C_L = 15 pF R_L = 400 Ω		54/74H C_L = 25 pF R_L = 280 Ω		54/74LS C_L = 15 pF		UNITS	CONDITIONS
		Min	Max	Min	Max	Min	Max		
f_{max}	Maximum Clock Frequency	15		25		30		MHz	Figs. 3-1, 3-9
t_{PLH} t_{PHL}	Propagation Delay $\overline{CP}_n$ to Q_n or $\overline{Q}_n$		25 40		21 27		20 30	ns	Figs. 3-1, 3-9
t_{PLH} t_{PHL}	Propagation Delay $\overline{C}_{Dn}$ or $\overline{S}_{Dn}$ to Q_n or $\overline{Q}_n$		25 40		13 24		20 30	ns	Figs. 3-1, 3-10

AC OPERATING REQUIREMENTS: V_{CC} = +5.0 V, T_A = +25°C

SYMBOL	PARAMETER	54/74		54/74H		54/74LS		UNITS	CONDITIONS
		Min	Max	Min	Max	Min	Max		
t_s (H)	Setup Time HIGH J_n or K_n to $\overline{CP}_n$	0		0		20		ns	
t_h (H)	Hold Time HIGH J_n or K_n to $\overline{CP}_n$	0		0		0		ns	Fig. 3-18 ('76, 'H76)
t_s (L)	Setup Time LOW J_n or K_n to $\overline{CP}_n$	0		0		20		ns	Fig. 3-7 ('LS76)
t_h (L)	Hold Time LOW J_n or K_n to $\overline{CP}_n$	0		0		0		ns	
t_w (H) t_w (L)	$\overline{CP}_n$ Pulse Width	20 47		12 28		20 13.5		ns	Fig. 3-9
t_w (L)	$\overline{C}_{Dn}$ or $\overline{S}_{Dn}$ Pulse Width LOW	25		16		25		ns	Fig. 3-10

(Courtesy of Fairchild – A Schlumberger Company)

- Full-Carry Look-Ahead across the Four Bits

- Systems Achieve Partial Look-Ahead Performance with the Economy of Ripple Carry

- SN54283/SN74283 and SN54LS283/SN74LS283 Are Recommended For New Designs as They Feature Supply Voltage and Ground on Corner Pins to Simplify Board Layout

| TYPE | TYPICAL ADD TIMES | | TYPICAL POWER DISSIPATION PER 4-BIT ADDER |
	TWO 8-BIT WORDS	TWO 16-BIT WORDS	
'83A	23 ns	43 ns	310 mW
'LS83A	25 ns	45 ns	95 mW

description

These improved full adders perform the addition of two 4-bit binary numbers. The sum (Σ) outputs are provided for each bit and the resultant carry (C4) is obtained from the fourth bit. These adders feature full internal look ahead across all four bits generating the carry term in ten nanoseconds typically. This provides the system designer with partial look-ahead performance at the economy and reduced package count of a ripple-carry implementation.

The adder logic, including the carry, is implemented in its true form meaning that the end-around carry can be accomplished without the need for logic or level inversion.

Designed for medium-speed applications, the circuits utilize transistor-transistor logic that is compatible with most other TTL families and other saturated low-level logic families.

Series 54 and 54LS circuits are characterized for operation over the full military temperature range of $-55°C$ to $125°C$, and Series 74 and 74LS circuits are characterized for operation from $0°C$ to $70°C$.

logic symbol†

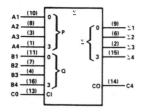

†This symbol is in accordance with ANSI/IEEE Std 91-1984 and IEC Publication 617-12.
Pin numbers are for D, J, N, and W packages.

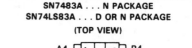

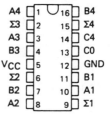

SN54LS83A . . . FK PACKAGE
(TOP VIEW)

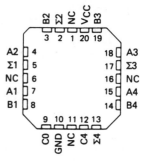

NC - No internal connection

FUNCTION TABLE

INPUT				OUTPUT					
				WHEN C0 = L			WHEN C0 = H		
						WHEN C2 = L			WHEN C2 = H
A1 / A3	B1 / B3	A2 / A4	B2 / B4	$\Sigma1$ / $\Sigma3$	$\Sigma2$ / $\Sigma4$	C2 / C4	$\Sigma1$ / $\Sigma3$	$\Sigma2$ / $\Sigma4$	C2 / C4
L	L	L	L	L	L	L	H	L	L
H	L	L	L	H	L	L	L	H	L
L	H	L	L	H	L	L	L	H	L
H	H	L	L	L	H	L	H	H	L
L	L	H	L	L	H	L	H	H	L
H	L	H	L	H	H	L	L	L	H
L	H	H	L	H	H	L	L	L	H
H	H	H	L	L	L	H	H	L	H
L	L	L	H	L	H	L	H	H	L
H	L	L	H	H	H	L	L	L	H
L	H	L	H	H	H	L	L	L	H
H	H	L	H	L	L	H	H	L	H
L	L	H	H	L	L	H	H	L	H
H	L	H	H	H	L	H	L	H	H
L	H	H	H	H	L	H	L	H	H
H	H	H	H	L	H	H	H	H	H

H = high level, L = low level
NOTE: Input conditions at A1, B1, A2, B2, and C0 are used to determine outputs $\Sigma1$ and $\Sigma2$ and the value of the internal carry C2. The values at C2, A3, B3, A4, and B4 are then used to determine outputs $\Sigma3$, $\Sigma4$, and C4.

TEXAS INSTRUMENTS
POST OFFICE BOX 655012 • DALLAS, TEXAS 75265

2-257

2

TTL Devices

logic diagram (positive logic)

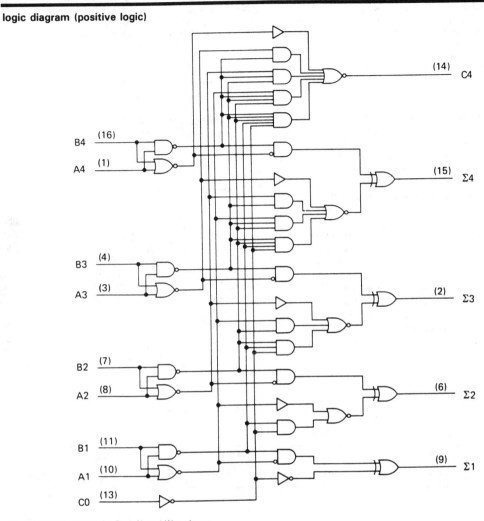

Pin numbers shown are for D, J, N, and W packages.

absolute maximum ratings over operating free-air temperature range (unless otherwise noted)

Supply voltage, V_{CC} (see Note 1)	7 V
Input voltage: '83A	5.5 V
'LS83A	7 V
Interemitter voltage (see Note 2)	5.5 V
Operating free-air temperature range: SN5483A, SN54LS83A	−55°C to 125°C
SN7483A, SN74LS83A	0°C to 70°C
Storage temperature range	−65°C to 150°C

NOTES: 1. Voltage values, except interemitter voltage, are with respect to network ground terminal.
　　　　　2. This is the voltage between two emitters of a multiple-emitter transistor. This rating applies for the '83A only between the following pairs: A1 and B1, A2 and B2, A3 and B3, A4 and B4.

TEXAS INSTRUMENTS
POST OFFICE BOX 555012 • DALLAS, TEXAS 75265

2

TTL Devices

TYPE	TYPICAL POWER DISSIPATION	TYPICAL DELAY (4-BIT WORDS)
'85	275 mW	23 ns
'LS85	52 mW	24 ns
'S85	365 mW	11 ns

description

These four-bit magnitude comparators perform comparison of straight binary and straight BCD (8-4-2-1) codes. Three fully decoded decisions about two 4-bit words (A, B) are made and are externally available at three outputs. These devices are fully expandable to any number of bits without external gates. Words of greater length may be compared by connecting comparators in cascade. The A > B, A < B, and A = B outputs of a stage handling less-significant bits are connected to the corresponding A > B, A < B, and A = B inputs of the next stage handling more-significant bits. The stage handling the least-significant bits must have a high-level voltage applied to the A = B input. The cascading paths of the '85, 'LS85, and 'S85 are implemented with only a two-gate-level delay to reduce overall comparison times for long words. An alternate method of cascading which further reduces the comparison time is shown in the typical application data.

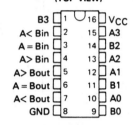

SN5485, SN54LS85, SN54S85 . . . J OR W PACKAGE
SN7485 . . . N PACKAGE
SN74LS85, SN74S85 . . . D OR N PACKAGE
(TOP VIEW)

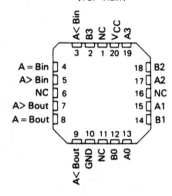

SN54LS85, SN54S85 . . . FK PACKAGE
(TOP VIEW)

NC - No internal connection

FUNCTION TABLE

COMPARING INPUTS				CASCADING INPUTS			OUTPUTS		
A3, B3	A2, B2	A1, B1	A0, B0	A > B	A < B	A = B	A > B	A < B	A = B
A3 > B3	X	X	X	X	X	X	H	L	L
A3 < B3	X	X	X	X	X	X	L	H	L
A3 = B3	A2 > B2	X	X	X	X	X	H	L	L
A3 = B3	A2 < B2	X	X	X	X	X	L	H	L
A3 = B2	A2 = B2	A1 > B1	X	X	X	X	H	L	L
A3 = B3	A2 = B2	A1 < B1	X	X	X	X	L	H	L
A2 = B3	A2 = B2	A1 = B1	A0 > B0	X	X	X	H	L	L
A3 = B3	A2 = B2	A1 = B1	A0 < B0	X	X	X	L	H	L
A3 = B3	A2 = B2	A1 = B1	A0 = B0	H	L	L	H	L	L
A3 = B3	A2 = B2	A1 = B1	A0 = B0	L	H	L	L	H	L
A3 = B3	A2 = B2	A1 = B1	A0 = B0	X	X	H	L	L	H
A3 = B3	A2 = B2	A1 = B1	A0 = B0	H	H	L	L	L	L
A3 = B3	A2 = B2	A1 = B1	A0 = B0	L	L	L	H	H	L

TEXAS INSTRUMENTS

POST OFFICE BOX 655012 • DALLAS, TEXAS 75265

2-263

2

TTL Devices

logic diagrams (positive logic)

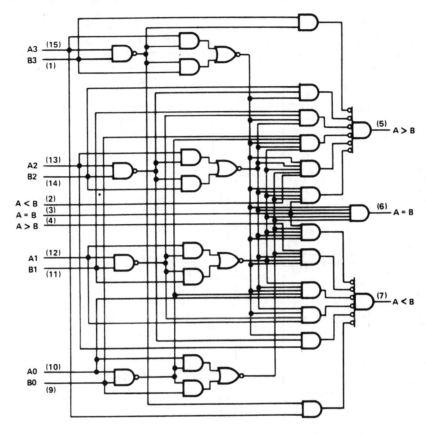

logic symbol†

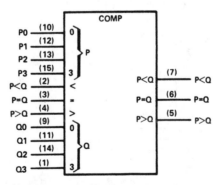

†This symbol is in accordancae with ANSI/IEEE Std 91-1984 and IEC Publication 617-12.
Pin numbers shown are for D, J, N, and W packages.

POST OFFICE BOX 655012 • DALLAS. TEXAS 75265

TYPICAL APPLICATION DATA

COMPARISON OF TWO N-BIT WORDS

This application demonstrates how these magnitude comparators can be cascaded to compare longer words. The example illustrated shows the comparison of two 24-bit words; however, the design is expandable to n-bits. As an example, one comparator can be used with five of the 24-bit comparators illustrated to expand the word length to 120-bits. Typical comparison times for various word lengths using the '85, 'LS85, or 'S85 are:

WORD LENGTH	NUMBER OF PKGS	'85	'LS85	'S85
1-4 bits	1	23 ns	24 ns	11 ns
5-24 bits	2-6	46 ns	48 ns	22 ns
25-120 bits	8-31	69 ns	72 ns	33 ns

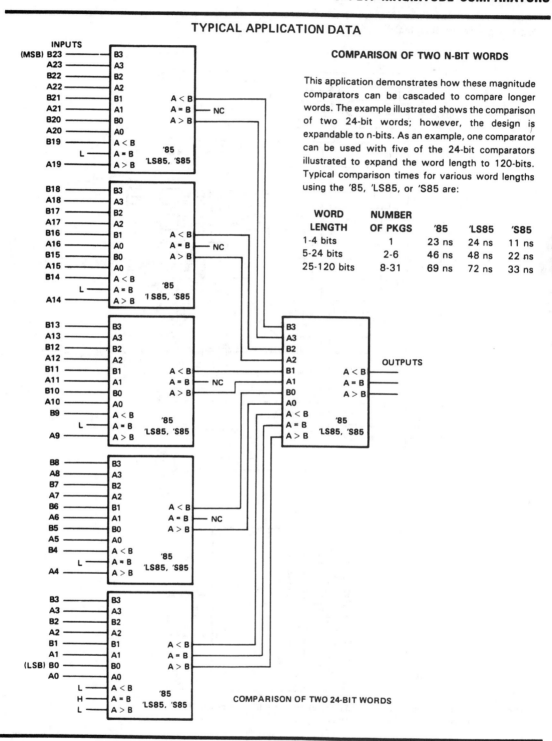

COMPARISON OF TWO 24-BIT WORDS

- Package Options Include Plastic "Small Outline" Packages, Ceramic Chip Carriers and Flat Packages, and Standard Plastic and Ceramic 300-mil DIPs

- Dependable Texas Instruments Quality and Reliability

TYPE	TYPICAL AVERAGE PROPAGATION DELAY TIME	TYPICAL TOTAL POWER DISSIPATION
'86	14 ns	150 mW
'LS86A	10 ns	30.5 mW
'S86	7 ns	250 mW

SN5486, SN54LS86A, SN54S86 . . . J OR W PACKAGE
SN7486 . . . N PACKAGE
SN74LS86A, SN74S86 . . . D OR N PACKAGE
(TOP VIEW)

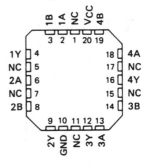

SN54LS86A, SN54S86 . . . FK PACKAGE
(TOP VIEW)

NC - No internal connection

description

These devices contain four independent 2-input Exclusive-OR gates. They perform the Boolean functions $Y = A \oplus B = \overline{A}B + A\overline{B}$ in positive logic.

A common application is as a true/complement element. If one of the inputs is low, the other input will be reproduced in true form at the output. If one of the inputs is high, the signal on the other input will be reproduced inverted at the output.

The SN5486, 54LS86A, and the SN54S86 are characterized for operation over the full military temperature range of −55°C to 125°C. The SN7486, SN74LS86A, and the SN74S86 are characterized for operation from 0°C to 70°C.

exclusive-OR logic

An exclusive-OR gate has many applications, some of which can be represented better by alternative logic symbols.

EXCLUSIVE-OR

These are five equivalent Exclusive-OR symbols valid for an '86 or 'LS86A gate in positive logic; negation may be shown at any two ports.

LOGIC IDENTITY ELEMENT	**EVEN-PARITY**	**ODD-PARITY ELEMENT**
The output is active (low) if all inputs stand at the same logic level (i.e., A = B).	The output is active (low) if an even number of inputs (i.e., 0 or 2) are active.	The output is active (high) if an odd number of inputs (i.e., only 1 of the 2) are active.

TTL Devices 2

TEXAS INSTRUMENTS

POST OFFICE BOX 655012 • DALLAS, TEXAS 75265

2-271

SN5486, SN54LS86A, SN54S86,
SN7486, SN74LS86A, SN74S86
QUADRUPLE 2-INPUT EXCLUSIVE-OR GATES

schematics of inputs and outputs

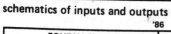

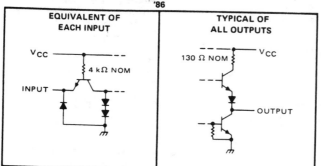

'86

EQUIVALENT OF EACH INPUT	TYPICAL OF ALL OUTPUTS

logic symbol†

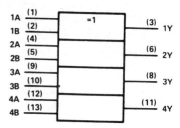

†This symbol is in accordance with
ANSI/IEEE Std. 91-1984 and IEC Publication 617-12.
Pin numbers shown are for D, J, N, and W packages.

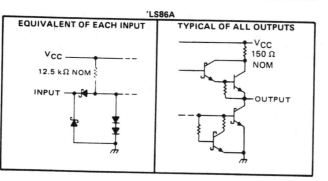

'LS86A

FUNCTION TABLE

INPUTS		OUTPUT
A	B	Y
L	L	L
L	H	H
H	L	H
H	H	L

H = high level, L = low level

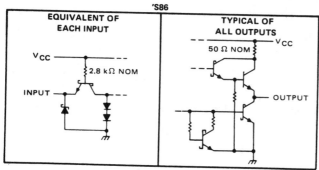

'S86

POST OFFICE BOX 655012 • DALLAS, TEXAS 75265

2

TTL Devices

SN5490A, SN5492A, SN5493A, SN54LS90, SN54LS92, SN54LS93, SN7490A, SN7492A, SN7493A, SN74LS90, SN74LS92, SN74LS93
DECADE, DIVIDE-BY-TWELVE AND BINARY COUNTERS

MARCH 1974—REVISED MARCH 1988

'90A, 'LS90 . . . Decade Counters

'92A, 'LS92 . . . Divide By-Twelve Counters

'93A, 'LS93 . . . 4-Bit Binary Counters

TYPES	TYPICAL POWER DISSIPATION
'90A	145 mW
'92A, '93A	130 mW
'LS90, 'LS92, 'LS93	45 mW

description

Each of these monolithic counters contains four master-slave flip-flops and additional gating to provide a divide-by-two counter and a three-stage binary counter for which the count cycle length is divide-by-five for the '90A and 'LS90, divide-by-six for the '92A and 'LS92, and the divide-by-eight for the '93A and 'LS93.

All of these counters have a gated zero reset and the '90A and 'LS90 also have gated set-to-nine inputs for use in BCD nine's complement applications.

To use their maximum count length (decade, divide-by-twelve, or four-bit binary) of these counters, the CKB input is connected to the Q_A output. The input count pulses are applied to CKA input and the outputs are as described in the appropriate function table. A symmetrical divide-by-ten count can be obtained from the '90A or 'LS90 counters by connecting the Q_D output to the CKA input and applying the input count to the CKB input which gives a divide-by-ten square wave at output Q_A.

SN5490A, SN54LS90 . . . J OR W PACKAGE
SN7490A . . . N PACKAGE
SN74LS90 . . . D OR N PACKAGE
(TOP VIEW)

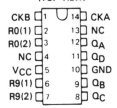

CKB	1	14 CKA
R0(1)	2	13 NC
R0(2)	3	12 Q_A
NC	4	11 Q_D
V_{CC}	5	10 GND
R9(1)	6	9 Q_B
R9(2)	7	8 Q_C

SN5492A, SN54LS92 . . . J OR W PACKAGE
SN7492A . . . N PACKAGE
SN74LS92 . . . D OR N PACKAGE
(TOP VIEW)

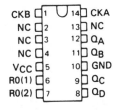

CKB	1	14 CKA
NC	2	13 NC
NC	3	12 Q_A
NC	4	11 Q_B
V_{CC}	5	10 GND
R0(1)	6	9 Q_C
R0(2)	7	8 Q_D

SN5493A, SN54LS93 . . . J OR W PACKAGE
SN7493 . . . N PACKAGE
SN74LS93 . . . D OR N PACKAGE
(TOP VIEW)

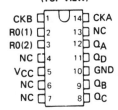

CKB	1	14 CKA
R0(1)	2	13 NC
R0(2)	3	12 Q_A
NC	4	11 Q_D
V_{CC}	5	10 GND
NC	6	9 Q_B
NC	7	8 Q_C

NC—No internal connection

PRODUCTION DATA documents contain information current as of publication date. Products conform to specifications per the terms of Texas Instruments standard warranty. Production processing does not necessarily include testing of all parameters.

TEXAS
INSTRUMENTS

POST OFFICE BOX 655012 • DALLAS, TEXAS 75265

TTL Devices

2

SN5490A, '92A, '93A, SN54LS90, 'LS92, 'LS93, SN7490A, '92A, '93A, SN74LS90, 'LS92, 'LS93
DECADE, DIVIDE-BY-TWELVE, AND BINARY COUNTERS

logic symbols[†]

'90

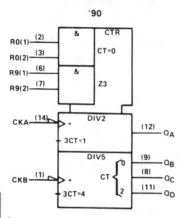

'92

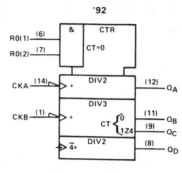

'93A, 'LS93

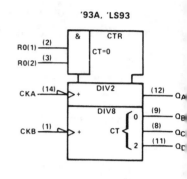

[†]These symbols are in accordance with ANSI/IEEE Std. 91-1984 and IEC Publication 617-12.

2

TTL Devices

TEXAS
INSTRUMENTS
POST OFFICE BOX 655012 • DALLAS, TEXAS 75265

332

'90A, 'LS90 BCD COUNT SEQUENCE
(See Note A)

COUNT	OUTPUT			
	Q_D	Q_C	Q_B	Q_A
0	L	L	L	L
1	L	L	L	H
2	L	L	H	L
3	L	L	H	H
4	L	H	L	L
5	L	H	L	H
6	L	H	H	L
7	L	H	H	H
8	H	L	L	L
9	H	L	L	H

'90A, 'LS90 BI-QUINARY (5-2)
(See Note B)

COUNT	OUTPUT			
	Q_A	Q_D	Q_C	Q_B
0	L	L	L	L
1	L	L	L	H
2	L	L	H	L
3	L	L	H	H
4	L	H	L	L
5	H	L	L	L
6	H	L	L	H
7	H	L	H	L
8	H	L	H	H
9	H	H	L	L

'92A, 'LS92 COUNT SEQUENCE
(See Note C)

COUNT	OUTPUT			
	Q_D	Q_C	Q_B	Q_A
0	L	L	L	L
1	L	L	L	H
2	L	L	H	L
3	L	L	H	H
4	L	H	L	L
5	L	H	L	H
6	H	L	L	L
7	H	L	L	H
8	H	L	H	L
9	H	L	H	H
10	H	H	L	L
11	H	H	L	H

'90A, 'LS90 RESET/COUNT FUNCTION TABLE

RESET INPUTS				OUTPUT			
$R_{0(1)}$	$R_{0(2)}$	$R_{9(1)}$	$R_{9(2)}$	Q_D	Q_C	Q_B	Q_A
H	H	L	X	L	L	L	L
H	H	X	L	L	L	L	L
X	X	H	H	H	L	L	H
X	L	X	L	COUNT			
L	X	L	X	COUNT			
L	X	X	L	COUNT			
X	L	L	X	COUNT			

'92A, 'LS92, '93A, 'LS93 RESET/COUNT FUNCTION TABLE

RESET INPUTS		OUTPUT			
$R_{0(1)}$	$R_{0(2)}$	Q_D	Q_C	Q_B	Q_A
H	H	L	L	L	L
L	X	COUNT			
X	L	COUNT			

'93A, 'LS93 COUNT SEQUENCE
(See Note C)

COUNT	OUTPUT			
	Q_D	Q_C	Q_B	Q_A
0	L	L	L	L
1	L	L	L	H
2	L	L	H	L
3	L	L	H	H
4	L	H	L	L
5	L	H	L	H
6	L	H	H	L
7	L	H	H	H
8	H	L	L	L
9	H	L	L	H
10	H	L	H	L
11	H	L	H	H
12	H	H	L	L
13	H	H	L	H
14	H	H	H	L
15	H	H	H	H

NOTES: A. Output Q_A is connected to input CKB for BCD count.
B. Output Q_D is connected to input CKA for bi-quinary count.
C. Output Q_A is connected to input CKB.
D. H = high level, L = low level, X = irrelevant

2

TTL Devices

TEXAS
INSTRUMENTS
POST OFFICE BOX 655012 • DALLAS, TEXAS 75265

2-279

333

SN5490A, '92A, '93A, SN54LS90, 'LS92, 'LS93, SN7490A, '92A, '93A, SN74LS90, 'LS92, 'LS93 DECADE, DIVIDE-BY-TWELVE, AND BINARY COUNTERS

logic diagrams (positive logic)

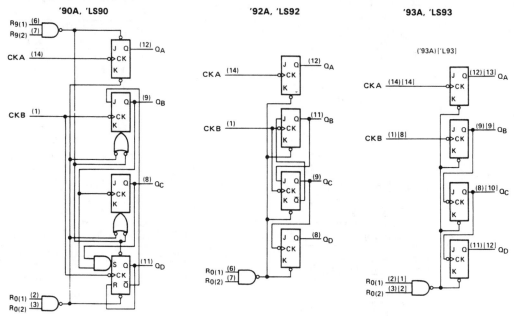

The J and K inputs shown without connection are for reference only and are functionally at a high level.
Pin numbers shown in ( ) are for the 'LS93 and '93A and pin numbers shown in [ ] are for the 54L93.

schematics of inputs and outputs

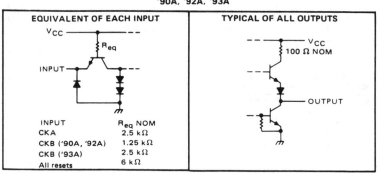

TEXAS
INSTRUMENTS

POST OFFICE BOX 655012 • DALLAS, TEXAS 75265

334

- **Package Options Include Plastic and Ceramic DIPs**

- **Dependable Texas Instruments Quality and Reliability**

description

The SN54111 and SN74111 are d-c coupled, variable-skew, J-K flip-flops which utilize TTL circuitry to obtain 25-MHz performance typically. They are termed "variable-skew" because they allow the maximum clock skew in a system to be a direct function of the clock pulse width. The J and K inputs are enabled to accept data only during a short period (30 nanoseconds maximum hold time) starting with, and immediately following the rising edge of the clock pulse. After this, inputs may be changed while the clock is at the high level without affecting the state of the master. At the threshold level of the falling edge of the clock pulse, the data stored in the master will be transferred to the output. The effective allowable clock skew then is minimum propagation delay time minus hold time, plus clock pulse width. This means that the system designer can set the maximum allowable clock skew needed by varying the clock pulse width. Thus system design is made easier and the requirements for sophisticated clock distribution systems are minimized or, in some cases, entirely eliminated. These flip-flops have an additional feature-the synchronous input has reduced sensitivity to data change while the clock is high because the data need be present for only a short period of time and the system's susceptibility to noise is thereby effectively reduced.

The SN54111 is characterized for operation over the full military temperature range of −55°C to 125°C; the SN74111 is characterized for operation from 0°C to 70°C.

SN54111 . . . J OR W PACKAGE
SN74111 . . . J OR N PACKAGE
(TOP VIEW)

```
    1K  [ 1   16 ]  VCC
  1PRE  [ 2   15 ]  2K
  1CLR  [ 3   14 ]  2PRE
    1J  [ 4   13 ]  2CLR
  1CLK  [ 5   12 ]  2J
    1Q  [ 6   11 ]  2CLK
    1Q  [ 7   10 ]  2Q
   GND  [ 8    9 ]  2Q
```

logic symbol

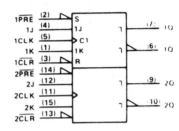

Pin numbers shown are for J and N packages

FUNCTION TABLE

INPUTS					OUTPUTS	
PRE	CLR	CLK	J	K	Q	Q̄
L	H	X	X	X	H	L
H	L	X	X	X	L	H
L	L	X	X	X	H†	H†
H	H	⊓	L	L	Q₀	Q̄₀
H	H	⊓	H	L	H	L
H	H	⊓	L	H	L	H
H	H	⊓	H	H	TOGGLE	

† This configuration is non-stable; that is, it will not persist when preset or clear return to their inactive (high) level.

TEXAS INSTRUMENTS
POST OFFICE BOX 225012 • DALLAS, TEXAS 75265

TTL DEVICES

TYPES SN54111, SN74111
DUAL J-K MASTER-SLAVE
FLIP-FLOPS WITH DATA LOCKOUT

logic diagram

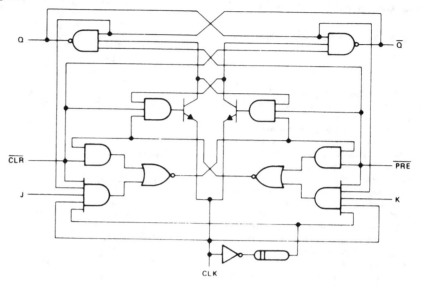

schematics of inputs and outputs

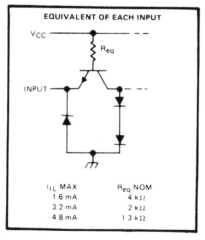

EQUIVALENT OF EACH INPUT

I_{IL} MAX	R_{eq} NOM
1.6 mA	4 kΩ
3.2 mA	2 kΩ
4.8 mA	1.3 kΩ

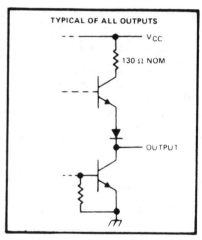

TYPICAL OF ALL OUTPUTS

130 Ω NOM

absolute maximum ratings over operating free-air temperature range (unless otherwise noted)

Supply voltage, V_{CC} (see Note 1)	7 V
Input voltage	5.5 V
Operating free-air temperature range SN54'	55°C to 125°C
SN74'	0°C to 70°C
Storage temperature range	−65°C to 150°C

NOTE 1   Voltage values are with respect to network ground terminal

TEXAS
INSTRUMENTS
POST OFFICE BOX 225012 • DALLAS TEXAS 75265

recommended operating conditions

			SN54111			SN74111			UNIT
			MIN	NOM	MAX	MIN	NOM	MAX	
V_{CC}	Supply voltage		4.5	5	5.5	4.75	5	5.25	V
V_{IH}	High-level input voltage		2			2			V
V_{IL}	Low-level input voltage				0.8			0.8	V
I_{OH}	High-level output current				−0.8			−0.8	mA
I_{OL}	Low-level output current				16			16	mA
t_w	Pulse duration	CLK high or low	25			25			ns
		$\overline{PRE}$ or $\overline{CLR}$ low	25			25			
t_{su}	Input setup time before CLK ↑		0			0			ns
t_h	Input hold time data after CLK ↑		30			30			ns
T_A	Operating free-air temperature		−55		125	0		70	°C

electrical characteristics over recommended operating free-air temperature range (unless otherwise noted)

PARAMETER		TEST CONDITIONS †	SN54111			SN74111			UNIT
			MIN	TYP‡	MAX	MIN	TYP‡	MAX	
V_{IK}		V_{CC} = MIN, I_I = −12 mA			−1.5			−1.5	V
V_{OH}		V_{CC} = MIN, V_{IH} = 2 V, V_{IL} = 0.8 V, I_{OH} = −0.8 mA	2.4	3.4		2.4	3.4		V
V_{OL}		V_{CC} = MIN, V_{IH} = 2 V, V_{IL} = 0.8 V, I_{OL} = 16 mA		0.2	0.4		0.2	0.4	V
I_I		V_{CC} = MAX, V_I = 5.5 V			1			1	mA
I_{IH}	J or K				40			40	
	$\overline{CLR}$ or $\overline{PRE}$	V_{CC} = MAX, V_I = 2.4 V			80			80	μA
	CLK				120			120	
I_{IL}	J or K				−1.6			−1.6	
	$\overline{CLR}$★	V_{CC} = MAX, V_I = 0.4 V			−3.2			−3.2	mA
	$\overline{PRE}$★				−3.2			−3.2	
	CLK				−4.8			−4.8	
I_{OS}§		V_{CC} = MAX	−20		−57	−18		−57	mA
I_{CC}		V_{CC} = MAX, See Note 2		14	20.5		14	20.5	mA

† For conditions shown as MIN or MAX, use the appropriate value specified under recommended operating conditions.
‡ All typical values are at V_{CC} = 5 V, T_A = 25°C.
§ Not more than one output should be shorted at a time.
★ Clear is tested with preset high and preset is tested with clear high.
NOTE 2: With all outputs open, I_{CC} is measured with the Q and $\overline{Q}$ outputs high in turn. At the time of measurement, the clock input is at 4.5 V.

switching characteristics, V_{CC} = 5 V, T_A = 25°C (see note 3)

PARAMETER	FROM (INPUT)	TO (OUTPUT)	TEST CONDITIONS	MIN	TYP	MAX	UNIT
f_{max}				20	25		MHz
t_{PLH}	$\overline{PRE}$ or $\overline{CLR}$	Q or $\overline{Q}$	R_L = 400 Ω, C_L = 15 pF		12	18	ns
t_{PHL}					21	30	ns
t_{PLH}	CLK	Q or $\overline{Q}$			12	17	ns
t_{PHL}					20	30	ns

NOTE 3: See General Information Section for load circuits and voltage waveforms.

TTL DEVICES

TEXAS
INSTRUMENTS
POST OFFICE BOX 225012 • DALLAS, TEXAS 75265

- **Programmable Output Pulse Width**
  With R_{int} . . . 35 ns Typ
  With R_{ext}/C_{ext} . . . 40 ns to 28 Seconds

- **Internal Compensation for Virtual Temperature Independence**

- **Jitter-Free Operation up to 90% Duty Cycle**

- **Inhibit Capability**

SN54121 . . . J OR W PACKAGE
SN54L121 . . . J PACKAGE
SN74121 . . . J OR N PACKAGE

(TOP VIEW)

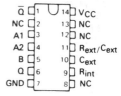

NC - No internal connection.

FUNCTION TABLE

INPUTS			OUTPUTS	
A1	A2	B	Q	$\overline{Q}$
L	X	H	L	H
X	L	H	L†	H†
X	X	L	L†	H†
H	H	X	L†	H†
H	↓	H	⊓	⊔
↓	H	H	⊓	⊔
↓	↓	H	⊓	⊔
L	X	↑	⊓	⊔
X	L	↑	⊓	⊔

For explanation of function table symbols, see page
† These lines of the function table assume that the indicated steady-state conditions at the A and B inputs have been setup long enough to complete any pulse started before the setup.

description

These multivibrators feature dual negative-transition-triggered inputs and a single positive-transition-triggered input which can be used as an inhibit input. Complementary output pulses are provided.

Pulse triggering occurs at a particular voltage level and is not directly related to the transition time of the input pulse. Schmitt-trigger input circuitry (TTL hysteresis) for the B input allows jitter-free triggering from inputs with transition rates as slow as 1 volt/second, providing the circuit with an excellent noise immunity of typically 1.2 volts. A high immunity to V_{CC} noise of typically 1.5 volts is also provided by internal latching circuitry.

Once fired, the outputs are independent of further transitions of the inputs and are a function only of the timing components. Input pulses may be of any duration relative to the output pulse. Output pulse length may be varied from 40 nanoseconds to 28 seconds by choosing appropriate timing components. With no external timing components (i.e., R_{int} connected to V_{CC}, C_{ext} and R_{ext}/C_{ext} open), an output pulse of typically 30 or 35 nanoseconds is achieved which may be used as a d-c triggered reset signal. Output rise and fall times are TTL compatible and independent of pulse length.

Pulse width stability is achieved through internal compensation and is virtually independent of V_{CC} and temperature. In most applications, pulse stability will only be limited by the accuracy of external timing components.

Jitter-free operation is maintained over the full temperature and V_{CC} ranges for more than six decades of timing capacitance (10 pF to 10 μF) and more than one decade of timing resistance (2 kΩ to 30 kΩ for the SN54121/SN54L121 and 2 kΩ to 40 kΩ for the SN74121). Throughout these ranges, pulse width is defined by the relationship $t_{w(out)} = C_{ext}R_T\ln2 \approx 0.7\ C_{ext}R_T$. In circuits where pulse cutoff is not critical, timing capacitance up to 1000 μF and timing resistance as low as 1.4 kΩ may be used. Also, the range of jitter-free output pulse widths is extended if V_{CC} is held to 5 volts and free-air temperature is 25°C. Duty cycles as high as 90% are achieved when using maximum recommended R_T'. Higher duty cycles are available if a certain amount of pulse-width jitter is allowed.

TEXAS
INSTRUMENTS

POST OFFICE BOX 225012 ● DALLAS, TEXAS 75265

3-471

3

TTL DEVICES

logic diagram (positive logic)

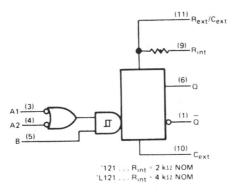

'121 . . . R_{int} = 2 kΩ NOM
'L121 . . . R_{int} = 4 kΩ NOM

Pin numbers shown on logic notation are for J or N packages

NOTES: 1. An external capacitor may be connected between C_{ext} (positive) and R_{ext} C_{ext}.
2. To use the internal timing resistor, connect R_{int} to V_{CC}. For improved pulse width accuracy and repeatability, connect an external resistor between R_{ext}/C_{ext} and V_{CC} with R_{int} open-circuited.

schematics of inputs and outputs

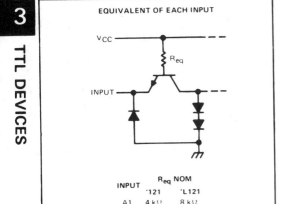

EQUIVALENT OF EACH INPUT

INPUT	R_{eq} NOM	
	'121	'L121
A1	4 kΩ	8 kΩ
A2	4 kΩ	8 kΩ
B	2 kΩ	4 kΩ

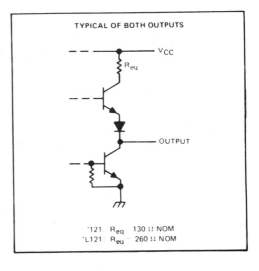

TYPICAL OF BOTH OUTPUTS

'121: R_{eq} 130 Ω NOM
'L121: R_{eq} 260 Ω NOM

TEXAS INSTRUMENTS
POST OFFICE BOX 225012 • DALLAS, TEXAS 75265

339

absolute maximum ratings over operating free-air temperature range (unless otherwise noted)

Supply voltage, V_{CC} (see Note 1) '121 . . . . 7 V

'L121 . . . . 8 V

Input voltage: . . . . 5.5 V

Operating free-air temperature range: SN54121, SN54L121 . . . . −55°C to 125°C

SN74121 . . . . 0°C to 70°C

Storage temperature range . . . . −65°C to 150°C

NOTE 1. Voltage values are with respect to network ground terminal.

recommended operating conditions

			SN54121 SN74121			SN54L121			UNIT
			MIN	NOM	MAX	MIN	NOM	MAX	
V_{CC}	Supply voltage	54 Family	4.5	5	5.5	4.5	5	5.5	V
		74 Family	4.75	5	5.25				
I_{OH}	High-level output current				−0.4			−0.2	mA
I_{OL}	Low-level output current				16			8	mA
dv/dt	Rate of rise or fall of input pulse	Schmitt input, B	1			1			V/s
		Logic inputs, A1, A2	1			1			V/µs
$t_{w(in)}$	Input pulse width		50			100			ns
R_{ext}	External timing capacitance	54 Family	1.4		30	1.4		30	kΩ
		74 Family	1.4		40				
C_{ext}	External timing capacitance		0		1000	0		1000	µF
	Duty cycle	$R_T = 2$ kΩ			67			67	%
		$R_T = $ MAX R_{ext}			90			90	
T_A	Operating free-air termperature	54 Family	−55		125	−55		125	°C
		74 Family	0		70				

3

TTL DEVICES

TEXAS
INSTRUMENTS
POST OFFICE BOX 225012 • DALLAS, TEXAS 75265

3-473

electrical characteristics over recommended operating free-air temperature range (unless otherwise noted)

PARAMETER		TEST CONDITIONS†		SN54121 SN74121 MIN	TYP‡	MAX	SN54L121 MIN	TYP‡	MAX	UNIT
V_{T+}	Positive-going threshold voltage at A input	V_{CC} = MIN			1.4	2		1.4	2	V
V_{T-}	Negative-going threshold voltage at A input	V_{CC} = MIN		0.8	1.4		0.8	1.4		V
V_{T+}	Positive-going threshold voltage at B input	V_{CC} = MIN			1.55	2		1.55	2	V
V_{T-}	Negative-going threshold voltage at B input	V_{CC} = MIN		0.8	1.35		0.8	1.35		V
V_{IK}	Input clamp voltage	V_{CC} = MIN,	I_I = −12 mA			−1.5			−1.5	V
V_{OH}	High-level output voltage	V_{CC} = MIN,	I_{OH} = MAX	2.4	3.4		2.4	3.4		V
V_{OL}	Low-level output voltage	V_{CC} = MIN,	I_{OL} = MAX		0.2	0.4		0.2	0.4	V
I_I	Input current at maximum input voltage	V_{CC} = MAX,	V_I = 5.5 V			1			1	mA
I_{IH}	High-level input current	V_{CC} = MAX, V_I = 2.4 V	A1 or A2			40			20	μA
			B			80			40	
I_{IL}	Low-level input current	V_{CC} = MAX, V_I = 0.4 V	A1 or A2			−1.6			−0.8	mA
			B			−3.2			−1.6	
I_{OS}	Short-circuit output current♦	V_{CC} = MAX	54 Family	−20		−55	−10		−27	mA
			74 Family	−18		−55				
I_{CC}	Supply current	V_{CC} = MAX	Quiescent		13	25		7	12	mA
			Triggered		23	40		9	20	

†For conditions shown as MIN or MAX, use the appropriate value specified under recommended operating conditions.
‡All typical values are at V_{CC} = 5 V, T_A = 25°C.
♦Not more than one output should be shorted at a time.

switching characteristics, V_{CC} = 5 V, T_A = 25°C

PARAMETER		TEST CONDITIONS		'121 MIN	TYP	MAX	'L121 MIN	TYP	MAX	UNIT
t_{PLH}	Propagation delay time, low-to-high-level Q output from either A input				45	70			140	ns
t_{PLH}	Propagation delay time, low-to-high-level Q output from B input	C_{ext} = 80 pF, R_{int} to V_{CC}			35	55			110	ns
t_{PHL}	Propagation delay time, high-to-low-level Q output from either A input				50	80			160	ns
t_{PHL}	Propagation delay time, high-to-low-level Q output from B input	C_L = 15 pF, R_L = 400 Ω for '121, R_L = 800 Ω for 'L121, See Note 2			40	65			130	ns
$t_{w(out)}$	Pulse width obtained using internal timing resistor		C_{ext} = 80 pF, R_{int} to V_{CC}	70	110	150	70	225	260	ns
$t_{w(out)}$	Pulse width obtained with zero timing capacitance		C_{ext} = 0, R_{int} to V_{CC}		30	50		35	70	ns
$t_{w(out)}$	Pulse width obtained using external timing resistor		C_{ext} = 100 pF, R_T = 10 kΩ	600	700	800	600	700	850	ns
			C_{ext} = 1 μF, R_T = 10 kΩ	6	7	8	6	7	8	ms

NOTE 2   See General Information Section for load circuits and voltage waveforms.

TEXAS
INSTRUMENTS
POST OFFICE BOX 225012 • DALLAS, TEXAS 75265

341

54/74125
54LS/74LS125A
QUAD BUS BUFFER GATE
(With 3-State Outputs)

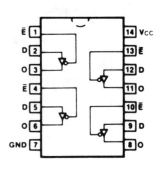

ORDERING CODE: See Section 9

PKGS	PIN OUT	COMMERCIAL GRADE $V_{CC} = +5.0$ V $\pm5\%$, $T_A = 0°$C to $+70°$C	MILITARY GRADE $V_{CC} = +5.0$ V $\pm10\%$, $T_A = -55°$C to $+125°$C	PKG TYPE
Plastic DIP (P)	A	74125PC, 74LS125APC		9A
Ceramic DIP (D)	A	74125DC, 74LS125ADC	54125DM, 54LS125ADM	6A
Flatpak (F)	A	74125FC, 74LS125AFC	54125FM, 54LS125AFM	3I

INPUT LOADING/FAN-OUT: See Section 3 for U.L. definitions

PINS	54/74 (U.L.) HIGH/LOW	54/74LS (U.L.) HIGH/LOW
Inputs	1.0/1.0	0.5/0.25
Outputs	130/10	65/15
	(50)	(25)/(7.5)

TRUTH TABLE

INPUTS		OUTPUT
$\bar{E}$	D	
L	L	L
L	H	H
H	X	Z

H = HIGH Voltage Level
L = LOW Voltage Level
X = Immaterial
Z = High Impedance

DC AND AC CHARACTERISTICS: See Seciton 3*

SYMBOL	PARAMETER		54/74 Min	54/74 Max	54/74LS Min	54/74LS Max	UNITS	CONDITIONS	
V_{OH}	Output HIGH Voltage	XM	2.4				V	$I_{OH} = -2.0$ mA	V_{CC} = Min, $V_{IN} = V_{IH}$ or V_{IL}
		XC	2.4					$I_{OH} = -5.2$ mA	
		XM			2.4			$I_{OH} = -1.0$ mA	
		XC			2.4			$I_{OH} = -2.6$ mA	
I_{OS}	Output Short Circuit Current	XM	-30	-70	-30	-130	mA	V_{CC} = Max	
		XC	-28	-70	-30	-130			
I_{CC}	Power Supply Current			54		20	mA	Outputs OFF, V_{IN} = Gnd $V_E = 4.5$ V, V_{CC} = Max	
t_{PLH} t_{PHL}	Propagation Delay Data to Output			13 18		15 18	ns	Figs. 3-3, 3-5	
t_{PZH} t_{PZL}	Output Enable Time			17 25		16 25	ns	Figs. 3-3, 3-11, 3-12	
t_{PLZ} t_{PHZ}	Output Disable Time			8.0 12		25 25	ns	Figs. 3-3, 3-11, 3-12	

*DC limits apply over operating temperature range; AC limits apply at $T_A = +25°$C and $V_{CC} = +5.0$ V

- **Designed Specifically for High-Speed: Memory Decoders Data Transmission Systems**

- **3 Enable Inputs to Simplify Cascading and/or Data Reception**

- **Schottky-Clamped for High Performance**

description

These Schottky-clamped TTL MSI circuits are designed to be used in high-performance memory decoding or data-routing applications requiring very short propagation delay times. In high-performance memory systems, these docoders can be used to minimize the effects of system decoding. When employed with high-speed memories utilizing a fast enable circuit, the delay times of these decoders and the enable time of the memory are usually less than the typical access time of the memory. This means that the effective system delay introduced by the Schottky-clamped system decoder is negligible.

The 'LS138, SN54S138, and SN74S138A decode one of eight lines dependent on the conditions at the three binary select inputs and the three enable inputs. Two active-low and one active-high enable inputs reduce the need for external gates or inverters when expanding. A 24-line decoder can be implemented without external inverters and a 32-line decoder requires only one inverter. An enable input can be used as a data input for demultiplexing applications.

All of these decoder/demultiplexers feature fully buffered inputs, each of which represents only one normalized load to its driving circuit. All inputs are clamped with high-performance Schottky diodes to suppress line-ringing and to simplify system design.

The SN54LS138 and SN54S138 are characterized for operation over the full military temperature range of −55°C to 125°C. The SN74LS138 and SN74S138A are characterized for operation from 0°C to 70°C.

SN54LS138, SN54S138 . . . J OR W PACKAGE
SN74LS138, SN74S138A . . . D OR N PACKAGE
(TOP VIEW)

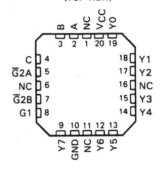

SN54LS138, SN54S138 . . . FK PACKAGE
(TOP VIEW)

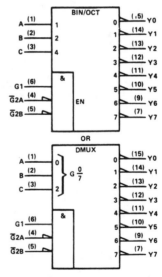

NC—No internal connection

logic symbols[†]

[†]These symbols are in accordance with ANSI/IEEE Std 91-1984 and IEC Publication 617-12.
Pin numbers shown are for D, J, N, and W packages.

Copyright © 1972, Texas Instruments Incorporated

TEXAS INSTRUMENTS
POST OFFICE BOX 655012 • DALLAS, TEXAS 75265

2-425

2

TTL Devices

SN54LS138, SN54S138, SN74LS138, SN74S138A
3-LINE-TO 8-LINE DECODERS/DEMULTIPLEXERS

logic diagram and function table

'LS138, SN54S138, SN74S138A

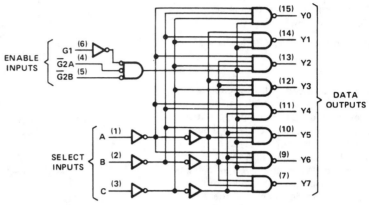

Pin numbers shown are for D, J, N, and W packages.

'LS138, SN54138, SN74S138A
FUNCTION TABLE

INPUTS					OUTPUTS							
ENABLE		SELECT										
G1	G̅2*	C	B	A	Y0	Y1	Y2	Y3	Y4	Y5	Y6	Y7
X	H	X	X	X	H	H	H	H	H	H	H	H
L	X	X	X	X	H	H	H	H	H	H	H	H
H	L	L	L	L	L	H	H	H	H	H	H	H
H	L	L	L	H	H	L	H	H	H	H	H	H
H	L	L	H	L	H	H	L	H	H	H	H	H
H	L	L	H	H	H	H	H	L	H	H	H	H
H	L	H	L	L	H	H	H	H	L	H	H	H
H	L	H	L	H	H	H	H	H	H	L	H	H
H	L	H	H	L	H	H	H	H	H	H	L	H
H	L	H	H	H	H	H	H	H	H	H	H	L

*$\overline{G2} = \overline{G2A} + \overline{G2B}$
H = high level, L = low level, X = irrelevant

TEXAS
INSTRUMENTS
POST OFFICE BOX 655012 • DALLAS, TEXAS 75265

344

54S/74S139
54LS/74LS139
DUAL 1-OF-4 DECODER

CONNECTION DIAGRAM
PINOUT A

$\bar{E}_a$	1		16	V_{CC}
A_{0a}	2		15	$\bar{E}_b$
A_{1a}	3		14	A_{0b}
$\bar{O}_{0a}$	4		13	A_{1b}
$\bar{O}_{1a}$	5		12	$\bar{O}_{0b}$
$\bar{O}_{2a}$	6		11	$\bar{O}_{1b}$
$\bar{O}_{3a}$	7		10	$\bar{O}_{2b}$
GND	8		9	$\bar{O}_{3b}$

DESCRIPTION — The '139 is a high speed dual 1-of-4 decoder/demultiplexer. The device has two independent decoders, each accepting two inputs and providing four mutually exclusive active LOW outputs. Each decoder has an active LOW Enable input which can be used as a data input for a 4-output demultiplexer. Each half of the '139 can be used as a function generator providing all four minterms of two variables. The '139 is fabricated with the Schottky barrier diode process for high speed.

- **SCHOTTKY PROCESS FOR HIGH SPEED**
- **MULTIFUNCTION CAPABILITY**
- **TWO COMPLETELY INDEPENDENT 1-OF-4 DECODERS**
- **ACTIVE LOW MUTUALLY EXCLUSIVE OUTPUTS**

LOGIC SYMBOL

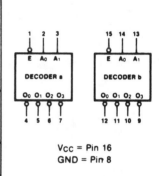

V_{CC} = Pin 16
GND = Pin 8

ORDERING CODE: See Section 9

PKGS	PIN OUT	COMMERCIAL GRADE V_{CC} = +5.0 V ±5%, T_A = 0°C to +70°C	MILITARY GRADE V_{CC} = +5.0 V ±10%, T_A = -55°C to +125°C	PKG TYPE
Plastic DIP (P)	A	74S139PC, 74LS139PC		9B
Ceramic DIP (D)	A	74S139DC, 74LS139DC	54S139DM, 54LS139DM	6B
Flatpak (F)	A	74S139FC, 74LS139FC	54S139FM, 54LS139FM	4L

INPUT LOADING/FAN-OUT: See Section 3 for U.L. definitions

PIN NAMES	DESCRIPTION	54/74S (U.L.) HIGH/LOW	54/74LS (U.L.) HIGH/LOW
A_0, A_1	Address Inputs	1.25/1.25	0.5/0.25
$\bar{E}$	Enable Input (Active LOW)	1.25/1.25	0.5/0.25
$\bar{O}_0 - \bar{O}_3$	Outputs (Active LOW)	25/12.5	10/5.0 (2.5)

FUNCTIONAL DESCRIPTION — The '139 is a high speed dual 1-of-4 decoder/demultiplexer fabricated with the Schottky barrier diode process. The device has two independent decoders, each of which accepts two binary weighted inputs (A_0, A_1) and provides four mutually exclusive active LOW outputs ($\overline{O}_0 - \overline{O}_3$). Each decoder has an active LOW enable ($\overline{E}$). When $\overline{E}$ is HIGH all outputs are forced HIGH. The enable can be used as the data input for a 4-output demultiplexer application. Each half of the '139 generates all four minterms of two variables. These four minterms are useful in some applications, replacing multiple gate functions as shown in *Figure a*, and thereby reducing the number of packages required in a logic network.

TRUTH TABLE

INPUTS			OUTPUTS			
$\overline{E}$	A_0	A_1	$\overline{O}_0$	$\overline{O}_1$	$\overline{O}_2$	$\overline{O}_3$
H	X	X	H	H	H	H
L	L	L	L	H	H	H
L	H	L	H	L	H	H
L	L	H	H	H	L	H
L	H	H	H	H	H	L

H = HIGH Voltage Level
L = LOW Voltage Level
X = Immaterial

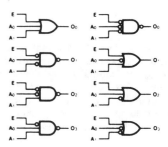

Fig. a

LOGIC DIAGRAM

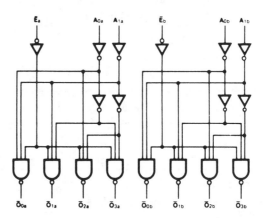

(Courtesy of Fairchild — A Schlumberger Company)

DC CHARACTERISTICS OVER OPERATING TEMPERATURE RANGE (unless otherwise specified)

SYMBOL	PARAMETER	54/74LS		54/74S		UNITS	CONDITIONS
		Min	Max	Min	Max		
I_{CC}	Power Supply Current		11		90	mA	V_{CC} = Max

AC CHARACTERISTICS: V_{CC} = +5.0 V, T_A = +25°C (See Section 3 for waveforms and load configurations)

SYMBOL	PARAMETER	54/74LS		54/74S		UNITS	CONDITIONS
		C_L = 15 pF		C_L = 15 pF R_L = 280 Ω			
		Min	Max	Min	Max		
t_{PLH} t_{PHL}	Propagation Delay A_0 or A_1 to $\overline{O}_n$		18 27		12 12	ns	Figs. 3-1, 3-4, 3-5
t_{PLH} t_{PHL}	Propagation Delay $\overline{E}$ to $\overline{O}_n$		15 24		8.0 10	ns	Figs. 3-1, 3-5

'147, 'LS147

- Encodes 10-Line Decimal to 4-Line BCD

- Applications Include:

    Keyboard Encoding
    Range Selection: '148, 'LS148

- Encodes 8 Data Lines to 3-Line Binary (Octal)

- Applications Include:

    N-Bit Encoding
    Code Converters and Generators

TYPE	TYPICAL DATA DELAY	TYPICAL POWER DISSIPATION
'147	10 ns	225 mW
'148	10 ns	190 mW
'LS147	15 ns	60 mW
'LS148	15 ns	60 mW

description

These TTL encoders feature priority decoding of the inputs to ensure that only the highest-order data line is encoded. The '147 and 'LS147 encode nine data lines to four-line (8-4-2-1) BCD. The implied decimal zero condition requires no input condition as zero is encoded when all nine data lines are at a high logic level. The '148 and 'LS148 encode eight data lines to three-line (4-2-1) binary (octal). Cascading circuitry (enable input EI and enable output EO) has been provided to allow octal expansion without the need for external circuitry. For all types, data inputs and outputs are active at the low logic level. All inputs are buffered to represent one normalized Series 54/74 or 54LS/74LS load, respectively.

SN54147, SN54LS147,
SN54148, SN54LS148 . . . J OR W PACKAGE
SN74147, SN74148 . . . N PACKAGE
SN74LS147, SN74LS148 . . . D OR N PACKAGE
(TOP VIEW)

SN54LS147, SN54LS148 . . . FK PACKAGE
(TOP VIEW)

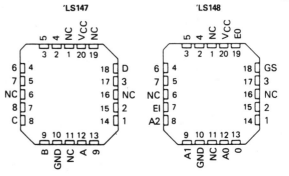

NC - No internal connection

'147, 'LS147 FUNCTION TABLE

INPUTS									OUTPUTS			
1	2	3	4	5	6	7	8	9	D	C	B	A
H	H	H	H	H	H	H	H	H	H	H	H	H
X	X	X	X	X	X	X	X	L	L	H	H	H
X	X	X	X	X	X	X	L	H	L	H	H	H
X	X	X	X	X	X	L	H	H	H	L	L	L
X	X	X	X	X	L	H	H	H	H	L	L	H
X	X	X	X	L	H	H	H	H	H	L	H	L
X	X	X	L	H	H	H	H	H	H	L	H	H
X	X	L	H	H	H	H	H	H	H	H	L	L
X	L	H	H	H	H	H	H	H	H	H	L	H
L	H	H	H	H	H	H	H	H	H	H	H	L

'148, 'LS148 FUNCTION TABLE

INPUTS									OUTPUTS				
EI	0	1	2	3	4	5	6	7	A2	A1	A0	GS	EO
H	X	X	X	X	X	X	X	X	H	H	H	H	H
L	H	H	H	H	H	H	H	H	H	H	H	H	L
L	X	X	X	X	X	X	X	L	L	L	L	L	H
L	X	X	X	X	X	X	L	H	L	L	H	L	H
L	X	X	X	X	X	L	H	H	L	H	L	L	H
L	X	X	X	X	L	H	H	H	L	H	H	L	H
L	X	X	X	L	H	H	H	H	H	L	L	L	H
L	X	X	L	H	H	H	H	H	H	L	H	L	H
L	X	L	H	H	H	H	H	H	H	H	L	L	H
L	L	H	H	H	H	H	H	H	H	H	H	L	H

H = high logic level, L = low logic level, X = irrelevant

TEXAS
INSTRUMENTS

POST OFFICE BOX 655012 • DALLAS, TEXAS 75265

2-451

2

TTL Devices

SN54147, SN54148, SN54LS147, SN54LS148, SN74147, SN74148 (TIM9907), SN74LS147, SN74LS148
10-LINE TO 4-LINE AND 8-LINE TO 3-LINE PRIORITY ENCODERS

logic symbols†

'147, 'LS147   '148, 'LS148

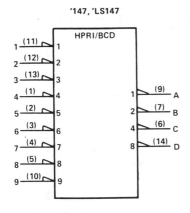
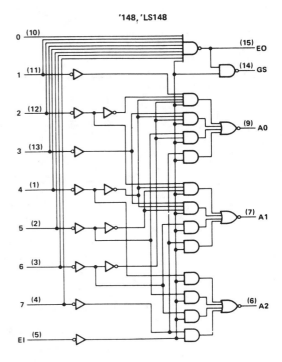

†These symbols are in accordance with ANSI/IEEE Std. 91-1984 and
IEC Publication 617-12.
Pin numbers shown are for D, J, N, and W packages.

logic diagrams

'147, 'LS147   '148, 'LS148

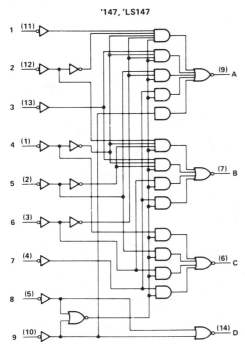

Pin numbers shown are for D, J, N, and W packages.

TEXAS
INSTRUMENTS
POST OFFICE BOX 655012 • DALLAS, TEXAS 75265

SN54147, SN54148 (TIM9907), SN54LS147, SN54LS148, SN74147, SN74148, SN74LS147, SN74LS148
10-LINE TO 4-LINE AND 8-LINE TO 3-LINE PRIORITY ENCODERS

TYPICAL APPLICATION DATA

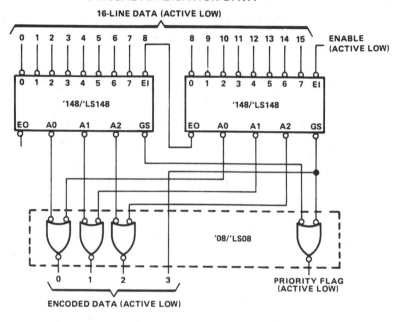

ENCODED DATA (ACTIVE LOW)

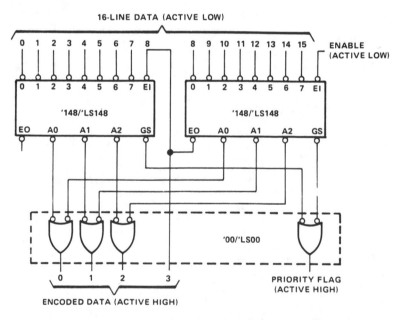

ENCODED DATA (ACTIVE HIGH)

Since the '147/'LS147 and '148/'LS148 are combinational logic circuits, wrong addresses can appear during input transients. Moreover, for the '148/'LS148 a change from high to low at input EI can cause a transient low on the GS output when all inputs are high. This must be considered when strobing the outputs.

TEXAS
INSTRUMENTS

POST OFFICE BOX 655012 • DALLAS, TEXAS 75265

54/74151A
54S/74S151
54LS/74LS151

8-INPUT MULTIPLEXER

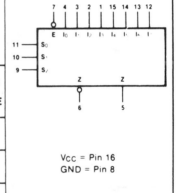

DESCRIPTION — The '151 is a high speed 8-input digital multiplexer. It provides in one package, the ability to select one line of data from up to eight sources. The '151 can be used as a universal function generator to generate any logic function of four variables. Both assertion and negation outputs are provided.

LOGIC SYMBOL

V_{CC} = Pin 16
GND = Pin 8

ORDERING CODE: See Section 9

PKGS	PIN OUT	COMMERCIAL GRADE V_{CC} = +5.0 V ±5%, T_A = 0°C to +70°C	MILITARY GRADE V_{CC} = +5.0 V ±10%, T_A = -55°C to +125°C	PKG TYPE
Plastic DIP (P)	A	74151APC, 74S151PC 74LS151PC		9B
Ceramic DIP (D)	A	74151ADC, 74S151DC 74LS151DC	54151ADM, 54S151DM 54LS151DM	6B
Flatpak (F)	A	74151AFC, 74S151FC 74LS151FC	54151AFM, 54S151FM 54LS151FM	4L

INPUT LOADING/FAN-OUT: See Section 3 for U.L. definitions

PIN NAMES	DESCRIPTION	54/74 (U.L.) HIGH/LOW	54/74S (U.L.) HIGH/LOW	54/74LS (U.L.) HIGH/LOW
$I_0 - I_7$	Data Inputs	1.0/1.0	1.25/1.25	0.5/0.25
$S_0 - S_2$	Select Inputs	1.0/1.0	1.25/1.25	0.5/0.25
$\overline{E}$	Enable Input (Active LOW)	1.0/1.0	1.25/1.25	0.5/0.25
Z	Data Output	20/10	25/12.5	10/5.0 (2.5)
$\overline{Z}$	Inverted Data Output	20/10	25/12.5	10/5.0 (2.5)

(Courtesy of Fairchild – A Schlumberger Company)

FUNCTIONAL DESCRIPTION — The '151 is a logical implementation of a single pole, 8-position switch with the switch position controlled by the state of three Select inputs, S_0, S_1, S_2. Both assertion and negation outputs are provided. The Enable input ($\overline{E}$) is active LOW. When it is not activated, the negation output is HIGH and the assertion output is LOW regardless of all other inputs. The logic function provided at the output is:

$$Z = \overline{E} \bullet (I_0 \bullet \overline{S}_0 \bullet \overline{S}_1 \bullet \overline{S}_2 + I_1 \bullet S_0 \bullet \overline{S}_1 \bullet \overline{S}_2 + I_2 \bullet \overline{S}_0 \bullet S_1 \bullet \overline{S}_2 + I_3 \bullet S_0 \bullet S_1 \bullet \overline{S}_2 +$$
$$I_4 \bullet \overline{S}_0 \bullet \overline{S}_1 \bullet S_2 + I_5 \bullet S_0 \bullet \overline{S}_1 \bullet S_2 + I_6 \bullet \overline{S}_0 \bullet S_1 \bullet S_2 + I_7 \bullet S_0 \bullet S_1 \bullet S_2).$$

The '151 provides the ability, in one package, to select from eight sources of data or control information. By proper manipulation of the inputs, the '151 can provide any logic function of four variables and its negation.

TRUTH TABLE

INPUTS				OUTPUTS	
$\overline{E}$	S_2	S_1	S_0	$\overline{Z}$	Z
H	X	X	X	H	L
L	L	L	L	$\overline{I}_0$	I_0
L	L	L	H	$\overline{I}_1$	I_1
L	L	H	L	$\overline{I}_2$	I_2
L	L	H	H	$\overline{I}_3$	I_3
L	H	L	L	$\overline{I}_4$	I_4
L	H	L	H	$\overline{I}_5$	I_5
L	H	H	L	$\overline{I}_6$	I_6
L	H	H	H	$\overline{I}_7$	I_7

H = HIGH Voltage Level
L = LOW Voltage Level

LOGIC DIAGRAM

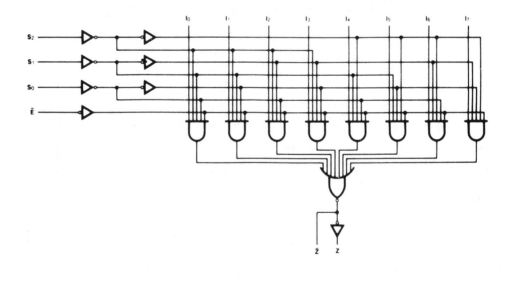

54/74173
54LS/74LS173

4-BIT D-TYPE REGISTER
(With 3-State Outputs)

CONNECTION DIAGRAM
PINOUT A

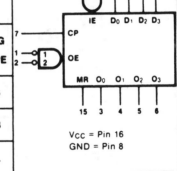

DESCRIPTION — The '173 is a high speed 4-bit register featuring 3-state outputs for use in bus-organized systems. The clock is fully edge-triggered allowing either a load from the D inputs or a hold (retain register contents) depending on the state of the Input Enable lines ($\overline{IE}_1$, $\overline{IE}_2$). A HIGH on either Output Enable line ($\overline{OE}_1$, $\overline{OE}_2$) brings the output to a high impedence state without affecting the actual register contents. A HIGH on the Master Reset (MR) input resets the register regardless of the state of the Clock (CP), the Output Enable ($\overline{OE}_1$, $\overline{OE}_2$) or the Input Enable ($\overline{IE}_1$, $\overline{IE}_2$) lines.

- **FULLY EDGE-TRIGGERED**
- **3-STATE OUTPUTS**
- **GATED INPUT AND OUTPUT ENABLES**

LOGIC SYMBOL

ORDERING CODE: See Section 9

PKGS	PIN OUT	COMMERCIAL GRADE Vcc = +5.0 V ±5%, TA = 0°C to +70°C	MILITARY GRADE Vcc = +5.0 V ±10%, TA = -55°C to +125°C	PKG TYPE
Plastic DIP (P)	A	74173PC, 74LS173PC		9B
Ceramic DIP (D)	A	74173DC, 74LS173DC	54173DM, 54LS173DM	7B
Flatpak (F)	A	74173FC, 74LS173FC	54173FM, 54LS173FM	4L

Vcc = Pin 16
GND = Pin 8

INPUT LOADING/FAN-OUT: See Section 3 for U.L. definitions

PIN NAMES	DESCRIPTION	54/74 (U.L.) HIGH/LOW	54/74LS (U.L.) HIGH/LOW
$D_0 — D_3$	Data Inputs	1.0/1.0	0.5/0.25
$\overline{IE}_1$, $\overline{IE}_2$	Input Enable Inputs (Active LOW)	1.0/1.0	0.5/0.25
$\overline{OE}_1$, $\overline{OE}_2$	3-State Output Enable Inputs (Active LOW)	1.0/1.0	0.5/0.25
CP	Clock Pulse Input (Active Rising Edge)	1.0/1.0	0.5/0.25
MR	Asynchronous Master Reset Input (Active HIGH)	1.0/1.0	0.5/0.25
$O_0 — O_3$	3-State Outputs	130/10 (50)	65/5.0 (25)/(2.5)

(Courtesy of Fairchild — A Schlumberger Company)

TRUTH TABLE

INPUTS					OUTPUT
MR	CP	$\overline{IE}_1$	$\overline{IE}_2$	D_n	Q_n
H	X	X	X	X	L
L	L	X	X	X	Q_n
L	⌐	H	X	X	Q_n
L	⌐	X	H	X	Q_n
L	⌐	L	L	L	L
L	⌐	L	L	H	H

When either $\overline{OE}_1$ or $\overline{OE}_2$ are HIGH, the output
is in the OFF state (high impedenace), however
this does not affect the contents or sequential
operating of the register

H = HIGH Voltage Level
L = LOW Voltage Level
X = Immaterial

LOGIC DIAGRAM

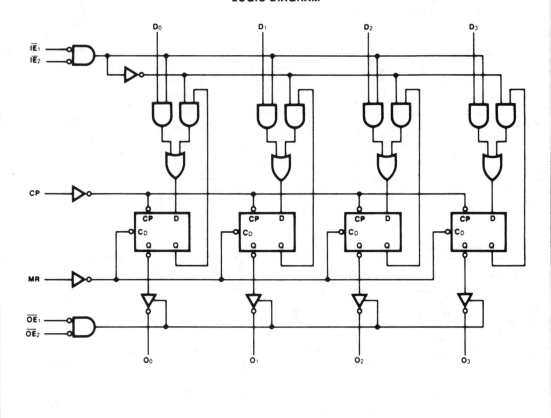

DC CHARACTERISTICS OVER OPERATING TEMPERATURE RANGE (unless otherwise specified)

SYMBOL	PARAMETER	54/74		54/74LS		UNITS	CONDITIONS
		Min	Max	Min	Max		
Ios	Output Short Circuit Current	-30	-70	-20	-100	mA	Vcc = Max
Icc	Power Supply Current		72		28	mA	Vcc = Max, MR = ⌐_ CP, $\overline{OE}_1$ = 4.5 V $\overline{OE}_2$, $\overline{IE}_1$, $\overline{IE}_2$, D_n = Gnd

AC CHARACTERISTICS: Vcc = +5.0 V, T_A = +25°C (See Section 3 for waveforms and load configurations)

SYMBOL	PARAMETER	54/74		54/74LS		UNITS	CONDITIONS
		C_L = 50 pF R_L = 400 Ω		C_L = 15 pF			
		Min	Max	Min	Max		
f_{max}	Maximum Clock Frequency	25		30		MHz	Figs. 3-1, 3-8
t_{PLH} t_{PHL}	Propagation Delay CP to O_n		43 31		40 25	ns	
t_{PHL}	Propagation Delay, MR to O_n		27		25	ns	Figs. 3-1, 3-16
t_{PZH} t_{PZL}	Output Enable Time		30 30		20 20	ns	Figs. 3-3, 3-11, 3-12 R_L = 2 kΩ ('LS173)
t_{PHZ} t_{PLZ}	Output Disable Time		14 20		16 16	ns	Figs. 3-3, 3-11, 3-12 R_L = 2 kΩ ('LS173) C_L = 5 pF

AC OPERATING REQUIREMENTS: Vcc = +5.0 V, T_A = +25°C

SYMBOL	PARAMETER	54/74		54/74LS		UNITS	CONDITIONS
		Min	Max	Min	Max		
t_s (H) t_s (L)	Setup Time HIGH or LOW D_n to CP	10 10		10 10		ns	
t_h (H) t_h (L)	Hold Time HIGH or LOW D_n to CP	10 10		10 10		ns	Fig. 3-6
t_s (H) t_s (L)	Setup Time HIGH or LOW $\overline{IE}$ to CP	17 17		17 17		ns	
t_h (H) t_h (L)	Hold Time HIGH or LOW $\overline{IE}$ to CP	2.0 2.0		2.0 2.0		ns	
t_w (L)	CP Pulse Width LOW	20		17		ns	Fig. 3-8
t_w (H)	MR Pulse Width HIGH	20		17		ns	Fig. 3-16
t_{rec}	Recovery Time, MR to CP	10		15		ns	

(Courtesy of Fairchild – A Schlumberger Company)

54/74174
54S/74S174
54LS/74LS174

HEX D FLIP-FLOP

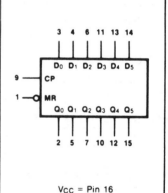

Pin		Pin	
$\overline{MR}$	1	16	V_{CC}
Q_0	2	15	Q_5
D_0	3	14	D_5
D_1	4	13	D_4
Q_1	5	12	Q_4
D_2	6	11	D_3
Q_2	7	10	Q_3
GND	8	9	CP

DESCRIPTION — The '174 is a high speed hex D flip-flop. The device is used primarily as a 6-bit edge-triggered storage register. The information on the D inputs is transferred to storage during the LOW-to-HIGH clock transition. The device has a Master Reset to simultaneously clear all flip-flops.

- **EDGE-TRIGGERED D-TYPE INPUTS**
- **BUFFERED POSITIVE EDGE-TRIGGERED CLOCK**
- **ASYNCHRONOUS COMMON RESET**

ORDERING CODE: See Section 9

PKGS	PIN OUT	COMMERCIAL GRADE $V_{CC} = +5.0 V \pm5\%$, $T_A = 0°C$ to $+70°C$	MILITARY GRADE $V_{CC} = +5.0 V \pm10\%$, $T_A = -55°C$ to $+125°C$	PKG TYPE
Plastic DIP (P)	A	74174PC, 74S174PC, 74LS174PC		9B
Ceramic DIP (D)	A	74174DC, 74S174DC, 74LS174DC	54174DM, 54S174DM, 54LS174DM	6B
Flatpak (F)	A	74174FC, 74S174FC, 74LS174FC	54174FM, 54S174FM, 54LS174FM	4L

LOGIC SYMBOL

```
      3  4  6  11 13 14
      |  |  |  |  |  |
    ┌──────────────────┐
    │ D0 D1 D2 D3 D4 D5 │
9 ──│ CP               │
1 ─○│ MR               │
    │ Q0 Q1 Q2 Q3 Q4 Q5 │
    └──────────────────┘
      |  |  |  |  |  |
      2  5  7  10 12 15
```

V_{CC} = Pin 16
GND = Pin 8

INPUT LOADING/FAN-OUT: See Section 3 for U.L. definitions

PIN NAMES	DESCRIPTION	54/74 (U.L.) HIGH/LOW	54/74S (U.L.) HIGH/LOW	54/74LS (U.L.) HIGH/LOW
$D_0 - D_5$	Data Inputs	1.0/1.0	1.25/1.25	0.5/0.25
CP	Clock Pulse Input (Active Rising Edge)	1.0/1.0	1.25/1.25	0.5/0.25
$\overline{MR}$	Master Reset Input (Active LOW)	1.0/1.0	1.25/1.25	0.5/0.25
$Q_0 - Q_5$	Flip-Flop Outputs	20/10	25/12.5	10/5.0 (2.5)

FUNCTIONAL DESCRIPTION — The '174 consists of six edge-triggered D flip-flops with individual D inputs and Q outputs. The Clock (CP) and Master Reset ($\overline{MR}$) are common to all flip-flops. Each D input's state is transferred to the corresponding flip-flop's output following the LOW-to-HIGH Clock (CP) transition. A LOW input to the Master Reset ($\overline{MR}$) will force all outputs LOW independent of Clock or Data inputs. The '174 is useful for applications where the true output only is required and the Clock and Master Reset are common to all storage elements.

TRUTH TABLE

INPUTS	OUTPUTS
@ t_n, $\overline{MR}$ = H	@ t_{n+1}
D_n	Q_n
H	H
L	L

t_n = Bit time before positive-going clock transition
t_{n+1} = Bit time after positive-going clock transition
H = HIGH Voltage Level
L = LOW Voltage Level

LOGIC DIAGRAM

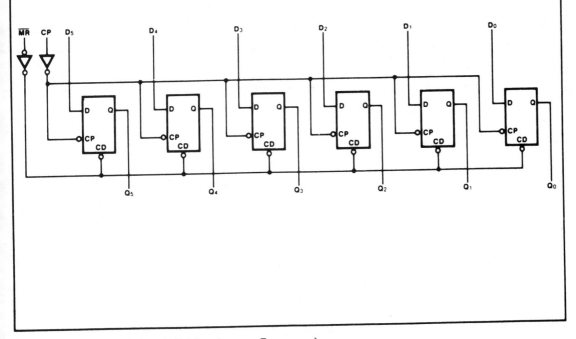

(Courtesy of Fairchild – A Schlumberger Company)

DC CHARACTERISTICS OVER OPERATING TEMPERATURE RANGE (unless otherwise specified)

SYMBOL	PARAMETER	54/74		54/74S		54/74LS		UNITS	CONDITIONS
		Min	Max	Min	Max	Min	Max		
I_{CC}	Power Supply Current		65		144		26	mA	V_{CC} = Max $D_n = \overline{MR}$ = 4.5 V CP = ⌐

AC CHARACTERISTICS: V_{CC} = +5.0 V, T_A = +25°C (See Section 3 for waveforms and load configurations)

SYMBOL	PARAMETER	54/74 C_L = 15 pF R_L = 400 Ω		54/74S C_L = 15 pF R_L = 280 Ω		54/74LS C_L = 15 pF		UNITS	CONDITIONS
		Min	Max	Min	Max	Min	Max		
f_{max}	Maximum Clock Frequency	25		75		30		MHz	Figs. 3-1, 3-8
t_{PLH} t_{PHL}	Propagation Delay CP to Q_n		30 35		12 17		25 22	ns	Figs. 3-1, 3-8
t_{PHL}	Propagation Delay $\overline{MR}$ to Q_n		35		22		35	ns	Figs. 3-1, 3-16

AC OPERATING REQUIREMENTS: V_{CC} = +5.0 V, T_A = +25°C

SYMBOL	PARAMETER	54/74		54/74S		54/74LS		UNITS	CONDITIONS
		Min	Max	Min	Max	Min	Max		
t_s (H) t_s (L)	Setup Time HIGH or LOW D_n to CP	20 20		5.0 5.0		10 10		ns	Fig. 3-6
t_h (H) t_h (L)	Hold Time HIGH or LOW D_n to CP	5.0 5.0		3.0 3.0		5.0 5.0		ns	
t_w (H)	CP Pulse Width HIGH	20		7.0		18		ns	Fig. 3-8
t_w (L)	$\overline{MR}$ Pulse Width LOW	20		7.0		18		ns	Fig. 3-16
t_{rec}	Recovery Time $\overline{MR}$ to CP	25		5.0		12		ns	

54/74178
4-BIT SHIFT REGISTER

CONNECTION DIAGRAM
PINOUT A

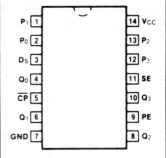

P₁	1	14	V$_{CC}$
P₀	2	13	P₂
D$_S$	3	12	P₃
Q₀	4	11	SE
$\overline{CP}$	5	10	Q₃
Q₁	6	9	PE
GND	7	8	Q₂

LOGIC SYMBOL

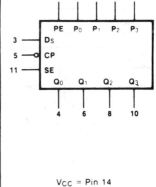

V_{CC} = Pin 14
GND = Pin 7

DESCRIPTION — The '178 features synchronous parallel or serial entry and parallel outputs. The flip-flops are fully edge-triggered, with state changes initiated by a HIGH-to-LOW transition of the clock. Parallel Enable and Serial Enable inputs are used to select Load, Shift and Hold modes of operation. The '178 is the 14-pin version of the '179. For detail specifications, please refer to the '179 data sheet.

ORDERING CODE: See Section 9

PKGS	PIN OUT	COMMERCIAL GRADE V_{CC} = +5.0 V ±5%, T_A = 0°C to +70°C	MILITARY GRADE V_{CC} = +5.0 V ±10%, T_A = -55°C to +125°C	PKG TYPE
Plastic DIP (P)	A	74178PC		9A
Ceramic DIP (D)	A	74178DC	54178DM	6A
Flatpak (F)	A	74178FC	54178FM	3I

INPUT LOADING/FAN-OUT: See Section 3 for U.L. definitions

PIN NAMES	DESCRIPTION	54/74 (U.L.) HIGH/LOW
PE	Parallel Enable Input	1.0/1.0
P₀ — P₃	Parallel Data Inputs	1.0/1.0
D$_S$	Serial Data Input	1.0/1.0
SE	Shift Enable Input	1.0/1.0
$\overline{CP}$	Clock Pulse Input (Active Falling Edge)	1.0/1.0
Q₀ — Q₃	Flip-flop Outputs	20/10

(Courtesy of Fairchild — A Schlumberger Company)

FUNCTIONAL DESCRIPTION — The '178 contains four D-type edge-triggered flip-flops and sufficient inter-stage logic to perform parallel load, shift right or hold operations. All state changes are initiated by a HIGH-to-LOW transition of the clock. A HIGH signal on the Shift Enable (SE) input prevents parallel loading and permits a right shift each time the clock makes a negative transition. When the SE input is LOW, the signal applied to the Parallel Enable (PE) input determines whether the circuit is in a parallel load or a hold mode, as shown in the Mode Select Table. The SE, PE, D_S and P_n inputs can change when the clock is in either state, provided only that the recommended setup and hold times are observed.

MODE SELECT TABLE

INPUTS			RESPONSE
SE	PE	$\overline{CP}$	
H	X	⌐_	Right Shift. $D_S \rightarrow Q_0$; $Q_0 \rightarrow Q_1$, etc.
L	H	⌐_	Parallel load $P_n \rightarrow Q_n$.
L	L	X	Hold

H = HIGH Voltage Level
L = LOW Voltage Level
X = Immaterial.

LOGIC DIAGRAM

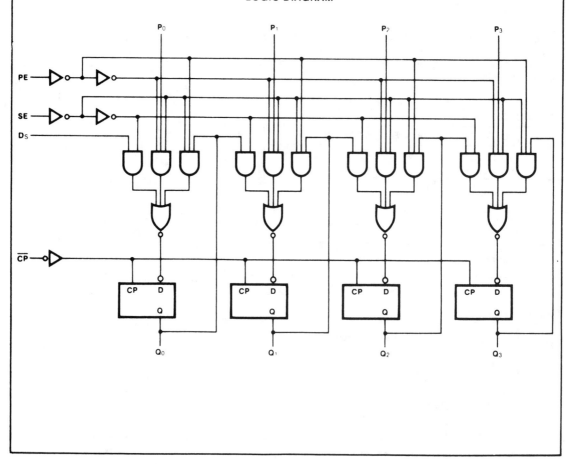

- **Cascading Circuitry Provided Internally**
- **Synchronous Operation**
- **Individual Preset to Each Flip-Flop**
- **Fully Independent Clear Input**

TYPES	TYPICAL MAXIMUM COUNT FREQUENCY	TYPICAL POWER DISSIPATION
'192,'193	32 MHz	325 mW
'LS192,'LS193	32 MHz	95 mW

SN54192, SN54193, SN54LS192,
SN54LS193 . . . J OR W PACKAGE
SN74192, SN74193 . . . N PACKAGE
SN74LS192, SN74LS193 . . . D OR N PACKAGE
(TOP VIEW)

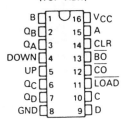

SN54LS192, SN54LS193 . . . FK PACKAGE
(TOP VIEW)

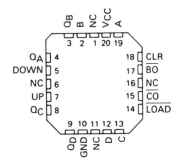

NC - No internal connection

description

These monolithic circuits are synchronous reversible (up/down) counters having a complexity of 55 equivalent gates. The '192 and 'LS192 circuits are BCD counters and the '193 and 'LS193 are 4-bit binary counters. Synchronous operation is provided by having all flip-flops clocked simultaneously so that the outputs change coincidently with each other when so instructed by the steering logic. This mode of operation eliminates the output counting spikes which are normally associated with asynchronous (ripple-clock) counters.

The outputs of the four master-slave flip-flops are triggered by a low-to-high-level transition of either count (clock) input. The direction of counting is determined by which count input is pulsed while the other count input is high.

All four counters are fully programmable; that is, each output may be preset to either level by entering the desired data at the data inputs while the load input is low. The output will change to agree with the data inputs independently of the count pulses. This feature allows the counters to be used as modulo-N dividers by simply modifying the count length with the preset inputs.

A clear input has been provided which forces all outputs to the low level when a high level is applied. The clear function is independent of the count and load inputs. The clear, count, and load inputs are buffered to lower the drive requirements. This reduces the number of clock drivers, etc., required for long words.

These counters were designed to be cascaded without the need for external circuitry. Both borrow and carry outputs are available to cascade both the up- and down-counting functions. The borrow output produces a pulse equal in width to the count-down input when the counter underflows. Similarly, the carry output produces a pulse equal in width to the count-up input when an overflow condition exists. The counters can then be easily cascaded by feeding the borrow and carry outputs to the count-down and count-up inputs respectively of the succeeding counter.

absolute maximum ratings over operating free-air temperature range (unless otherwise noted)

	SN54'	SN54LS'	SN74'	SN74LS'	UNIT
Supply voltage, V_{CC} (see Note 1)	7	7	7	7	V
Input voltage	5.5	7	5.5	7	V
Operating free-air temperature range	– 55 to 125		0 to 70		°C
Storage temperature range	– 65 to 150		– 65 to 150		°C

NOTE 1: Voltage values are with respect to network ground terminal.

TEXAS
INSTRUMENTS

POST OFFICE BOX 655012 • DALLAS, TEXAS 75265

2

TTL Devices

'193, 'LS193 BINARY COUNTERS

typical clear, load, and count sequences

Illustrated below is the following sequence:

1. Clear outputs to zero.
2. Load (preset) to binary thirteen.
3. Count up to fourteen, fifteen, carry, zero, one, and two.
4. Count down to one, zero, borrow, fifteen, fourteen, and thirteen.

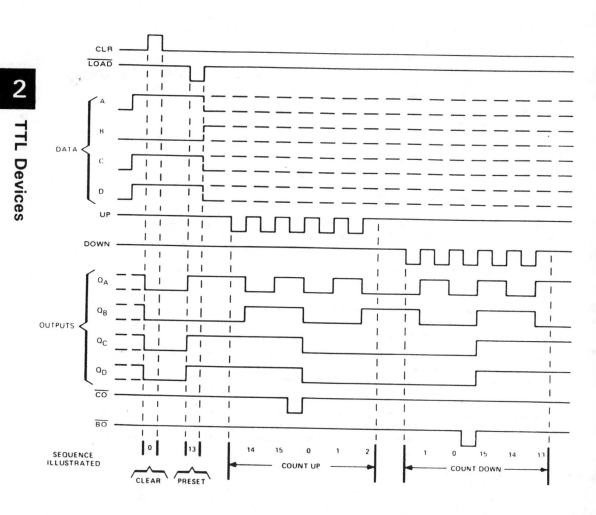

NOTES: A. Clear overrides load, data, and count inputs.

B. When counting up, count-down input must be high; when counting down, count-up input must be high.

TEXAS
INSTRUMENTS
POST OFFICE BOX 655012 • DALLAS, TEXAS 75265

362

- **Parallel Inputs and Outputs**
- **Four Operating Modes:**

  Synchronous Parallel Load
  Right Shift
  Left Shift
  Do Nothing

- **Positive Edge-Triggered Clocking**
- **Direct Overriding Clear**

TYPE	TYPICAL MAXIMUM CLOCK FREQUENCY	TYPICAL POWER DISSIPATION
'194	36 MHz	195 mW
'LS194A	36 MHz	75 mW
'S194	105 MHz	425 mW

SN54194, SN54LS194A, SN54S194 . . . J OR W PACKAGE
SN74194 . . . J OR N PACKAGE
SN74LS194A, SN74S194 . . . D, J OR N PACKAGE

(TOP VIEW)

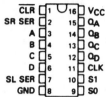

```
         ___
  CLR [ 1   U  16 ] VCC
SR SER [ 2      15 ] QA
     A [ 3      14 ] QB
     B [ 4      13 ] QC
     C [ 5      12 ] QD
     D [ 6      11 ] CLK
SL SER [ 7      10 ] S1
   GND [ 8       9 ] S0
```

SN54LS194A, SN54S194 . . . FK PACKAGE
SN74LS194A, SN74S194 . . . FN PACKAGE

(TOP VIEW)

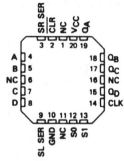

NC – No internal connection

description

These bidirectional shift registers are designed to incorporate virtually all of the features a system designer may want in a shift register. The circuit contains 46 equivalent gates and features parallel inputs, parallel outputs, right-shift and left-shift serial inputs, operating-mode-control inputs, and a direct overriding clear line. The register has four distinct modes of operation, namely:

Inhibit clock (do nothing)
Shift right (in the direction Q_A toward Q_D)
Shift left (in the direction Q_D toward Q_A)
Parallel (broadside) load

Synchronous parallel loading is accomplished by applying the four bits of data and taking both mode control inputs, S0 and S1, high. The data are loaded into the associated flip-flops and appear at the outputs after the positive transition of the clock input. During loading, serial data flow is inhibited.

Shift right is accomplished synchronously with the rising edge of the clock pulse when S0 is high and S1 is low. Serial data for this mode is entered at the shift-right data input. When S0 is low and S1 is high, data shifts left synchronously and new data is entered at the shift-left serial input.

Clocking of the shift register is inhibited when both mode control inputs are low. The mode controls of the SN54194/SN74194 should be changed only while the clock input is high.

TEXAS
INSTRUMENTS
POST OFFICE BOX 225012 • DALLAS, TEXAS 75265

3

TTL DEVICES

FUNCTION TABLE

CLEAR	MODE		CLOCK	SERIAL		PARALLEL				OUTPUTS			
	S1	S0		LEFT	RIGHT	A	B	C	D	Q_A	Q_B	Q_C	Q_D
L	X	X	X	X	X	X	X	X	X	L	L	L	L
H	X	X	L	X	X	X	X	X	X	Q_{A0}	Q_{B0}	Q_{C0}	Q_{D0}
H	H	H	↑	X	X	a	b	c	d	a	b	c	d
H	L	H	↑	X	H	X	X	X	X	H	Q_{An}	Q_{Bn}	Q_{Cn}
H	L	H	↑	X	L	X	X	X	X	L	Q_{An}	Q_{Bn}	Q_{Cn}
H	H	L	↑	H	X	X	X	X	X	Q_{Bn}	Q_{Cn}	Q_{Dn}	H
H	H	L	↑	L	X	X	X	X	X	Q_{Bn}	Q_{Cn}	Q_{Dn}	L
H	L	L	X	X	X	X	X	X	X	Q_{A0}	Q_{B0}	Q_{C0}	Q_{D0}

H = high level (steady state)
L = low level (steady state)
X = irrelevant (any input, including transitions)
↑ = transition from low to high level
a, b, c, d = the level of steady-state input at inputs A, B, C, or D, respectively.
Q_{A0}, Q_{B0}, Q_{C0}, Q_{D0} = the level of Q_A, Q_B, Q_C, or Q_D, respectively, before the indicated steady-state input conditions were established.
Q_{An}, Q_{Bn}, Q_{Cn}, Q_{Dn} = the level of Q_A, Q_B, Q_C, respectively, before the most-recent ↑ transition of the clock.

schematics of inputs and outputs

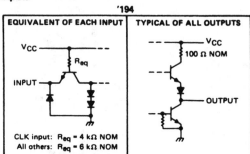

'194

EQUIVALENT OF EACH INPUT / TYPICAL OF ALL OUTPUTS

CLK input: R_{eq} = 4 kΩ NOM
All others: R_{eq} = 6 kΩ NOM

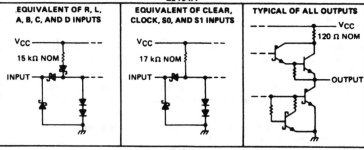

'LS194A

EQUIVALENT OF R, L, A, B, C, AND D INPUTS / EQUIVALENT OF CLEAR, CLOCK, S0, AND S1 INPUTS / TYPICAL OF ALL OUTPUTS

15 kΩ NOM   17 kΩ NOM   120 Ω NOM

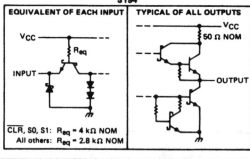

'S194

EQUIVALENT OF EACH INPUT / TYPICAL OF ALL OUTPUTS

$\overline{CLR}$, S0, S1: R_{eq} = 4 kΩ NOM
All others: R_{eq} = 2.8 kΩ NOM

TEXAS INSTRUMENTS
POST OFFICE BOX 225012 • DALLAS, TEXAS 75265

logic diagrams (continued)

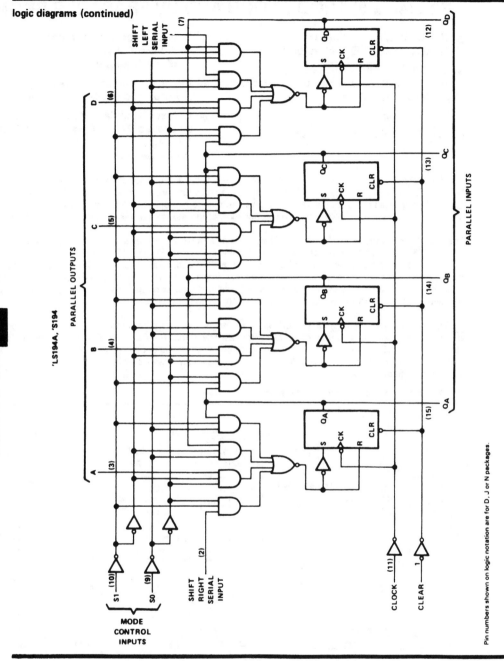

TEXAS
INSTRUMENTS
POST OFFICE BOX 225012 • DALLAS, TEXAS 75265

365

2732A
32K (4K x 8) PRODUCTION AND UV ERASABLE PROMS

- **200 ns (2732A-2) Maximum Access Time ... HMOS*-E Technology**
- **Compatible with High-Speed Microcontrollers and Microprocessors ... Zero WAIT State**
- **Two Line Control**
- **10% V_{CC} Tolerance Available**

- **Low Current Requirement**
  −100 mA Active
  −35 mA Standby
- **int$_e$ligent Identifier™ Mode −Automatic Programming Operation**
- **Industry Standard Pinout ... JEDEC Approved 24 Pin Ceramic and Plastic Package**
  (See Packaging Spec. Order # 221369)

The Intel 2732A is a 5V-only, 32,768-bit ultraviolet erasable (cerdip) Electrically Programmable Read-Only Memory (EPROM). The standard 2732A access time is 250 ns with speed selection (2732A-2) available at 200 ns. The access time is compatible with high performance microprocessors such as the 8 MHz iAPX 186. In these systems, the 2732A allows the microprocessor to operate without the addition of WAIT states.

The 2732A is currently available in two different package types. Cerdip packages provide flexibility in prototyping and R & D environments where reprogrammability is required. Plastic DIP EPROMs provide optimum cost effectiveness in production environments. Inventoried in the unprogrammed state, the P2732A is programmed quickly and efficiently when the need to change code arises. Costs incurred for new ROM masks or obsoleted ROM inventories are avoided. The tight package dimensional controls, inherent non-erasability, and high reliability of the P2732A make it the ideal component for these production applications.

An important 2732A feature is Output Enable ($\overline{OE}$) which is separate from the Chip Enable ($\overline{CE}$) control. The $\overline{OE}$ control eliminates bus contention in microprocessor systems. The $\overline{CE}$ is used by the 2732A to place it in a standby mode ($\overline{CE} = V_{IH}$) which reduces power consumption without increasing access time. The standby mode reduces the current requirement by 65%; the maximum active current is reduced from 100 mA to a standby current of 35 mA.

*HMOS is a patented process of Intel Corporation.

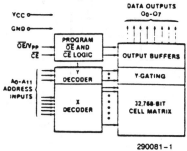

Figure 1. Block Diagram

290081–1

Pin Names

A_0–A_{11}	Addresses
$\overline{CE}$	Chip Enable
$\overline{OE}/V_{PP}$	Output Enable/V_{PP}
O_0–O_7	Outputs

NOTE:
Intel "Universal Site" compatible EPROM configurations are shown in the blocks adjacent to the 2732A pins.

290081–2

Figure 2. Cerdip/Plastic DIP Pin Configuration

Order Number: 290081-002

EXTENDED TEMPERATURE (EXPRESS) EPROMs

The Intel EXPRESS EPROM family is a series of electrically programmable read only memories which have received additional processing to enhance product characteristics. EXPRESS processing is available for several densities of EPROM, allowing the choice of appropriate memory size to match system applications. EXPRESS EPROM products are available with 168 ±8 hour, 125°C dynamic burn-in using Intel's standard bias configuration. This process exceeds or meets most industry specifications of burn-in. The standard EXPRESS EPROM operating temperature range is 0°C to 70°C. Extended operating temperature range (−40°C to +85°C) EXPRESS products are available. Like all Intel EPROMs, the EXPRESS EPROM family is inspected to 0.1% electrical AQL. This may allow the user to reduce or eliminate incoming inspection testing.

READ OPERATION

D.C. CHARACTERISTICS

Electrical Parameters of EXPRESS EPROM products are identical to standard EPROM parameters except for:

Symbol	Parameter	TD2732A LD2732A Min	TD2732A LD2732A Max	Test Conditions
I_{SB}	V_{CC} Standby Current (mA)		45	$\overline{CE} = V_{IH}$, $\overline{OE} = V_{IL}$
I_{CC_1}[1]	V_{CC} Active Current (mA)		150	$\overline{OE} = \overline{CE} = V_{IL}$
	V_{CC} Active Current at High Temperature (mA)		125	$\overline{OE} = \overline{CE} = V_{IL}$, $V_{PP} = V_{CC}$, $T_{Ambient} = 85°C$

NOTE:
1. Maximum current value is with outputs O_0 to O_7 unloaded.

EXPRESS EPROM PRODUCT FAMILY

PRODUCT DEFINITONS

Type	Operating Temperature	Burn-in 125°C (hr)
Q	0°C to +70°C	168 ±8
T	−40°C to −85°C	None
L	−40°C to −85°C	168 ±8

EXPRESS OPTIONS

2732A Versions

Packaging Options		
Speed Versions	Cerdip	Plastic
−2	Q	
STD	Q, T, L	
−3	Q	
−4	Q, T, L	
−20	Q	
−25	Q, T, L	
−30	Q	
−45	Q, T, L	

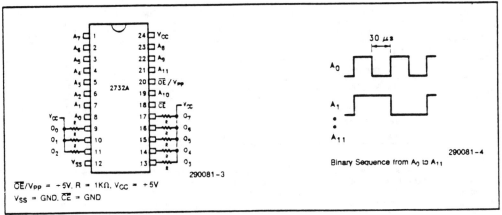

$\overline{OE}/V_{PP} = -5V$. R = 1KΩ. $V_{CC} = +5V$
V_{SS} = GND. $\overline{CE}$ = GND

Binary Sequence from A_0 to A_{11}

290081-3   290081-4

Burn-in Bias and Timing Diagrams

4-2

ABSOLUTE MAXIMUM RATINGS*

Operating Temp. During Read .... 0°C to +70°C
Temperature Under Bias .... −10°C to +80°C
Storage Temperature .... −65°C to +125°C
All Input or Output Voltages with
  Respect to Ground .... −0.3V to +6V
Voltage on A9 with Respect
  to Ground .... −0.3V to +13.5V
Vpp Supply Voltage with Respect to Ground
  During Programming .... −0.3V to +22V
Vcc Supply Voltage with
  Respect to Ground .... −0.3V to +7.0V

*Notice: Stresses above those listed under "Absolute Maximum Ratings" may cause permanent damage to the device. This is a stress rating only and functional operation of the device at these or any other conditions above those indicated in the operational sections of this specification is not implied. Exposure to absolute maximum rating conditions for extended periods may affect device reliability.

READ OPERATION

D.C. CHARACTERISTICS $0°C \leq T_A \leq +70°C$

Symbol	Parameter	Limits			Units	Conditions
		Min	Typ[3]	Max		
I_{LI}	Input Load Current			10	μA	$V_{IN} = 5.5V$
I_{LO}	Output Leakage Current			10	μA	$V_{OUT} = 5.5V$
I_{SB}[2]	V_{CC} Current (Standby)			35	mA	$\overline{CE} = V_{IH}, \overline{OE} = V_{IL}$
I_{CC1}[2]	V_{CC} Current (Active)			100	mA	$\overline{OE} = \overline{CE} = V_{IL}$
V_{IL}	Input Low Voltage	−0.1		0.8	V	
V_{IH}	Input High Voltage	2.0		$V_{CC} + 1$	V	
V_{OL}	Output Low Voltage			0.45	V	$I_{OL} = 2.1$ mA
V_{OH}	Output High Voltage	2.4			V	$I_{OH} = -400$ μA

A.C. CHARACTERISTICS $0°C \leq T_A \leq 70°C$

Versions	$V_{CC} \pm 5\%$	2732A-2 P2732A-2		2732A P2732A		2732A-3 P2732A-3		2732A-4 P2732A-4		Units	Test Conditions
	$V_{CC} \pm 10\%$	2732A-20		2732A-25		2732A-30		2732A-45			
Symbol	Parameter	Min	Max	Min	Max	Min	Max	Min	Max		
t_{ACC}	Address to Output Delay		200		250		300		450	ns	$\overline{CE} = \overline{OE} = V_{IL}$
t_{CE}	$\overline{CE}$ to Output Delay		200		250		300		450	ns	$\overline{OE} = V_{IL}$
t_{OE}	$\overline{OE}/V_{PP}$ to Output Delay		70		100		150		150	ns	$\overline{CE} = V_{IL}$
t_{DF}[4]	$\overline{OE}/V_{PP}$ High to Output Float	0	60	0	60	0	130	0	130	ns	$\overline{CE} = V_{IL}$
t_{OH}	Output Hold from Addresses, $\overline{CE}$ or $\overline{OE}/V_{PP}$, Whichever Occurred First	0		0		0		0		ns	$\overline{CE} = \overline{OE} = V_{IL}$

NOTES:
1. V_{CC} must be applied simultaneously or before $\overline{OE}/V_{PP}$ and removed simultaneously or after $\overline{OE}/V_{PP}$.
2. The maximum current value is with outputs O_0 to O_7 unloaded.
3. Typical values are for $T_A = 25°C$ and nominal supply voltages.
4. This parameter is only sampled and is not 100% tested. Output Float is defined as the point where data is no longer driven—see timing diagram.

CAPACITANCE (2) $T_A = 25°C, f = 1$ MHz

Symbol	Parameter	Typ	Max	Unit	Conditions
C_{IN1}	Input Capacitance Except $\overline{OE}$/Vpp	4	6	pF	$V_{IN} = 0V$
C_{IN2}	$\overline{OE}$/Vpp Input Capacitance		20	pF	$V_{IN} = 0V$
C_{OUT}	Output Capacitance	8	12	pF	$V_{OUT} = 0V$

A.C. TESTING INPUT/OUTPUT WAVEFORM

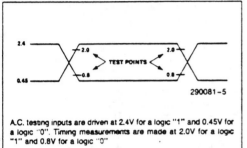

A.C. testing inputs are driven at 2.4V for a logic "1" and 0.45V for a logic "0". Timing measurements are made at 2.0V for a logic "1" and 0.8V for a logic "0"

A.C. TESTING LOAD CIRCUIT

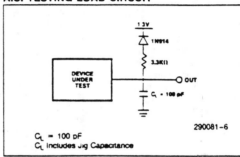

$C_L = 100$ pF
C_L Includes Jig Capacitance

A.C. WAVEFORMS

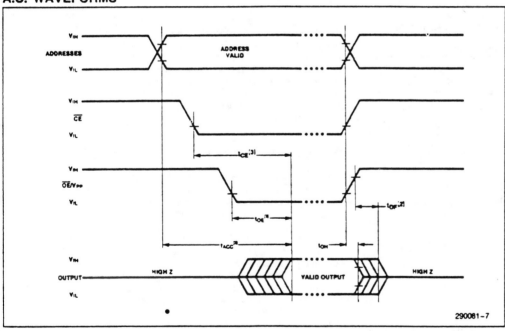

NOTES:
1. Typical values are for $T_A = 25°C$ and nominal supply voltages.
2. This parameter is only sampled and is not 100% tested. Output float is defined as the point where data is no longer driven—see timing diagram.
3. $\overline{OE}$/Vpp may be delayed up to $t_{ACC} - t_{OE}$ after the falling edge of $\overline{CE}$ without impacting t_{CE}.

4-4

PLASTIC EPROM APPLICATIONS

Intel's P2732A is the result of a multi-year effort to make EPROMs more cost effective for production applications. The benefits of a plastic package enable the P2732A to be used for high volume production with lower profile boards and easier production assembly (no cover over UV transparent windows).

The reliability of plastic EPROMs is equivalent to traditional CERDIP packaging. The plastic is rugged and durable making it optimal for auto insertion and auto handling equipment. Design and testing ensures device programmability, data integrity, and impermeability to moisture.

Intel's Plastic EPROMs are designed for total compatibility with their CERDIP packaged predecessors. This encompasses quality, reliability, and programming. All Intel Plastic EPROMs have passed Intel's strict process and product reliability qualifications.

DEVICE OPERATION

The modes of operation of the 2732A are listed in Table 1. A single 5V power supply is required in the read mode. All inputs are TTL levels except for $\overline{OE}/V_{PP}$ during programming and 12V on A_9 for the int$_e$ligent Identifier™ mode. In the program mode the $\overline{OE}/V_{PP}$ input is pulsed from a TTL level to 21V.

Table 1. Mode Selection

Mode \ Pins	$\overline{CE}$	$\overline{OE}/V_{PP}$	A_9	A_0	V_{CC}	Outputs
Read/Program Verify	V_{IL}	V_{IL}	X	X	V_{CC}	D_{OUT}
Output Disable	V_{IL}	V_{IH}	X	X	V_{CC}	High Z
Standby	V_{IH}	X	X	X	V_{CC}	High Z
Program	V_{IL}	V_{PP}	X	X	V_{CC}	D_{IN}
Program Inhibit	V_{IH}	V_{PP}	X	X	V_{CC}	High Z
Int$_e$ligent Identifier[3]						
—Manufacturer	V_{IL}	V_{IL}	V_H	V_{IL}	V_{CC}	89H
—Device	V_{IL}	V_{IL}	V_H	V_{IH}	V_{CC}	01H

NOTES:
1. X can be V_{IH} or V_{IL}.
2. $V_H = 12V \pm 0.5V$.
3. $A_1 - A_8$, A_{10}, $A_{11} = V_{IL}$.

Read Mode

The 2732A has two control functions, both of which must be logically active in order to obtain data at the outputs. Chip Enable ($\overline{CE}$) is the power control and should be used for device selection. Output Enable ($\overline{OE}/V_{PP}$) is the output control and should be used to gate data from the output pins, independent of device selection. Assuming that addresses are stable, address access time (t_{ACC}) is equal to the delay from $\overline{CE}$ to output (t_{CE}). Data is available at the outputs after the falling edge of $\overline{OE}/V_{PP}$, assuming that $\overline{CE}$ has been low and addresses have been stable for at least $t_{ACC} - t_{OE}$.

Standby Mode

EPROMs can be placed in a standby mode which reduces the maximum active current of the device by applying a TTL-high signal to the $\overline{CE}$ input. When in standby mode, the outputs are in a high impedance state, independent of the $\overline{OE}/V_{PP}$ input.

Two Line Output Control

Because EPROMs are usually used in larger memory arrays, Intel has provided two control lines which accommodate this multiple memory connection. The two control lines allow for:

a) The lowest possible memory power dissipation, and

b) complete assurance that output bus contention will not occur.

To use these two control lines most efficiently, $\overline{CE}$ should be decoded and used as the primary device selecting function, while $\overline{OE}/V_{PP}$ should be made a common connection to all devices in the array and connected to the $\overline{READ}$ line from the system control bus. This assures that all deselected memory devices are in their low power standby mode and that the output pins are active only when data is desired from a particular memory device.

SYSTEM CONSIDERATION

The power switching characteristics of EPROMs require careful decoupling of the devices. The supply current, I_{CC}, has three segments that are of interest to the system designer—the standby current level, the active current level, and the transient current peaks that are produced by the falling and rising edges of Chip Enable. The magnitude of these transient current peaks is dependent on the output capacitive and inductive loading of the device. The associated transient voltage peaks can be suppressed by complying with Intel's two-line control and by use of properly selected decoupling capacitors. It is recommended that a 0.1 µF ceramic capacitor be used on every device between V_{CC} and GND. This should be a high frequency capacitor of low inherent inductance and should be placed as close to the device as possible. In addition, a 4.7 µF bulk electrolytic capacitor should be used between V_{CC} and GND for every eight devices. The bulk capacitor should be located near where the power supply is connected to the array. The purpose of the bulk capacitor is to overcome the voltage droop caused by the inductive effects of PC board traces.

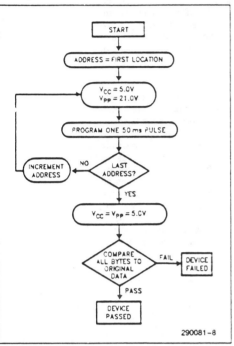

Figure 3. Standard Programming Flowchart

PROGRAMMING MODES

CAUTION: Exceeding 22V on $\overline{OE}/V_{PP}$ will permanently damage the device.

Initially, and after each erasure (cerdip EPROMs), all bits of the EPROM are in the "1" state. Data is introduced by selectively programming "0s" into the bit locations. Although only "0s" will be programmed, both "1s" and "0s" can be present in the data word. The only way to change a "0" to a "1" in cerdip EPROMs is by ultraviolet light erasure.

The device is in the programming mode when the $\overline{OE}/V_{PP}$ input is at 21V. It is required that a 0.1 μF capacitor be placed across $\overline{OE}/V_{PP}$ and ground to suppress spurious voltage transients which may damage the device. The data to be programmed is applied 8 bits in parallel to the data output pins. The levels required for the address and data inputs are TTL.

When the address and data are stable, a 20 ms (50 ms typical) active low, TTL program pulse is ap-

plied to the $\overline{CE}$ input. A program pulse must be applied at each address location to be programmed (see Figure 3). Any location can be programmed at any time—either individually, sequentially, or at random. The program pulse has a maximum width of 55 ms. The EPROM must not be programmed with a DC signal applied to the $\overline{CE}$ input.

Programming of multiple 2732As in parallel with the same data can be easily accomplished due to the simplicity of the programming requirements. Like inputs of the paralleled 2732As may be connected together when they are programmed with the same data. A low level TTL pulse applied to the $\overline{CE}$ input programs the paralleled 2732As.

Program Inhibit

Programming of multiple EPROMs in parallel with different data is easily accomplished by using the Program Inhibit mode. A high level $\overline{CE}$ input inhibits the other EPROMs from being programmed. Except for $\overline{CE}$, all like inputs (including $\overline{OE}/V_{PP}$) of the parallel EPROMs may be common. A TTL low level pulse applied to the $\overline{CE}$ input with $\overline{OE}/V_{PP}$ at 21V will program that selected device.

Program Verify

A verify (Read) should be performed on the programmed bits to determine that they have been correctly programmed. The verify is performed with $\overline{OE}/V_{PP}$ and $\overline{CE}$ at V_{IL}. Data should be verified t_{DV} after the falling edge of $\overline{CE}$.

int_eligent Identifier™ Mode

The int_eligent Identifier Mode allows the reading out of a binary code from an EPROM that will identify its manufacturer and type. This mode is intended for use by programming equipment for the purpose of automatically matching the device to be programmed with its corresponding programming algorithm. This mode is functional in the 25°C ±5°C ambient temperature range that is required when programming the device.

To activate this mode, the programming equipment must force 11.5V to 12.5V on address line A9 of the EPROM. Two identifier bytes may then be sequenced from the device outputs by toggling address line A0 from V_{IL} to V_{IH}. All other address lines must be held at V_{IL} during the int_eligent Identifier Mode.

Byte 0 (A0 = V_{IL}) represents the manufacturer code and byte 1 (A0 = V_{IH}) the device identifier code. These two identifier bytes are given in Table 1.

INTEL EPROM PROGRAMMING SUPPORT TOOLS

Intel offers a full line of EPROM Programmers providing state-of-the-art programming for all Intel programmable devices. The modular architecture of Intel's EPROM programmers allows you to add new support as it becomes available, with very low cost add-ons. For example, even the earliest users of the iUP-FAST 27/K module may take advantage of Intel's new Quick-Pulse Programming™ Algorithm, the fastest in the industry.

Intel EPROM programmers may be controlled from a host computer using Intel's PROM Programming software (iPPS). iPPS makes programming easy for a growing list of industry standard hosts, including the IBM PC, XT, AT; and PCDOS compatibles, Intellec Development Systems, Intel's iPDS Personal Development System, and the Intel Network Development System (iNDS-II). Stand-alone operation is also available, including device previewing, editing, programming, and download of programming data from any source over an RS232C port.

For further details consult the EPROM Programming section of the Development Systems Handbook.

ERASURE CHARACTERISTICS (FOR CERDIP EPROMS)

The erasure characteristics are such that erasure begins to occur upon exposure to light with wave-lengths shorter than aproximately 4000 Angstroms (Å). It should be noted that sunlight and certain types of fluorescent lamps have wavelengths in the 3000–4000Å range. Data shows that constant exposure to room level fluorescent lighting could erase the EPROM in approximately 3 years. while it would take approximately 1 week to cause erasure when exposed to direct sunlight. If the device is to be exposed to these types of lighting conditions for extended periods of time, opaque labels should be placed over the window to prevent unintentional erasure.

The recommended erasure procedure is exposure to shortwave ultraviolet light which has a wavelength of 2537 Angstroms (Å). The integrated dose (i.e., UV intensity × exposure time) for erasure should be a minimum of 15 Wsec/cm^2. The erasure time with this dosage is approximately 15 to 20 minutes using an ultraviolet lamp with a 12000 μW/cm^2 power rating. The EPROM should be placed within 1 inch of the lamp tubes during erasure. The maximum integrated dose an EPROM can be exposed to without damage is 7258 Wsec/cm^2 (1 week @ 12000 μW/cm^2). Exposure of the device to high intensity UV light for longer periods may cause permanent damage.

PROGRAMMING

D.C. PROGRAMMING CHARACTERISTICS

$T_A = 25°C \pm 5°C$, $V_{CC} = 5V \pm 5\%$, $V_{PP} = 21V \pm 0.5V$

Symbol	Parameter	Limits			Units	Test Conditions (Note 1)
		Min	Typ[3]	Max		
I_{LI}	Input Current (All Inputs)			10	μA	$V_{IN} = V_{IL}$ or V_{IH}
V_{IL}	Input Low Level (All Inputs)	−0.1		0.8	V	
V_{IH}	Input High Level (All Inputs Except $\overline{OE}/V_{PP}$)	2.0		$V_{CC} + 1$	V	
V_{OL}	Output Low Voltage During Verify			0.45	V	$I_{OL} = 2.1$ mA
V_{OH}	Output High Voltage During Verify	2.4			V	$I_{OH} = -400$ μA
I_{CC_2}[4]	V_{CC} Supply Current (Program and Verify)		85	100	mA	
I_{PP_2}[4]	V_{PP} Supply Current (Program)			30	mA	$\overline{CE} = V_{IL}$, $\overline{OE}/V_{PP} = V_{PP}$
V_{ID}	A_9 intelligent Identifier Voltage	11.5		12.5	V	

4-7

A.C. PROGRAMMING CHARACTERISTICS

$T_A = 25°C \pm 5°C$, $V_{CC} = 5V \pm 5\%$, $V_{PP} = 21V \pm 0.5V$

Symbol	Parameter	Limits			Units	Test Conditions* (Note 1)
		Min	Typ(3)	Max		
t_{AS}	Address Setup Time	2			μs	
t_{OES}	$\overline{OE}$/V_{PP} Setup Time	2			μs	
t_{DS}	Data Setup Time	2			μs	
t_{AH}	Address Hold Time	0			μs	
t_{DH}	Data Hold Time	2			μs	
t_{DFP}	$\overline{OE}$/V_{PP} High to Output Not Driven	0		130	ns	(Note 2)
t_{PW}	$\overline{CE}$ Pulse Width During Programming	20	50	55	ms	
t_{OEH}	$\overline{OE}$/V_{PP} Hold Time	2			μs	
t_{DV}	Data Valid from $\overline{CE}$			1	μs	$\overline{CE} = V_{IL}$, $\overline{OE}$/$V_{PP} = V_{IL}$
t_{VR}	V_{PP} Recovery Time	2			μs	
t_{PRT}	$\overline{OE}$/V_{PP} Pulse Rise Time During Programming	50			ns	

NOTES:

1. V_{CC} must be applied simultaneously or before $\overline{OE}$/V_{PP} and removed simultaneously or after $\overline{OE}$/V_{PP}.
2. This parameter is only sampled and is not 100% tested. Output Float is defined as the point where data is no longer driven—see timing diagram.
3. Typical values are for $T_A = 25°C$ and nominal supply voltages.
4. The maximum current value is with outputs 0_0 to 0_7 unloaded.

*A.C. TEST CONDITIONS

Input Rise and Fall Time (10% to 90%) . . . . . ≤20 ns

Input Pulse Levels . . . . 0.45V to 2.4V

Input Timing Reference Level . . . . 0.8V and 2.0V

Output Timing Reference Level . . . . . . 0.8V and 2.0V

PROGRAMMING WAVEFORMS

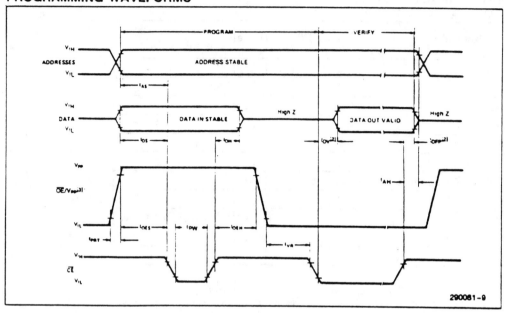

290081-9

NOTES:

1. The input timing reference level is 0.8V for a V_{IL} and 2V for a V_{IH}.
2. t_{OV} and t_{DFP} are characteristics of the device but must be accommodated by the programmer.
3. When programming the 2732A, a 0.1μF capacitor is required across $\overline{OE}$/V$_{PP}$ and ground to suppress spurious voltage transients which can damage the device.

4-9

374

LOGIC CIRCUIT TESTER

An inexpensive digital testing system having many of the capabilities of a commercially available system can be constructed with parts listed in the equipment list. The basic logic circuit tester described here may be either temporarily breadboarded as needed or mounted more permanently on some type of circuit board.

Lamp Monitor

A light emitting diode (LED) can be easily used as a lamp monitor for digital signals. A driver circuit (see Fig. A-1) using an inverter from a 74LS04 can be used to turn on the LED without loading down the monitored gate's output.

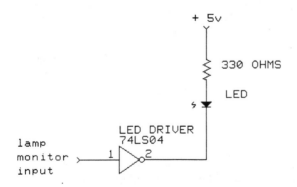

Fig. A-1 LED lamp monitor circuit

Logic Switches

An SPST toggle switch can be conveniently used for logic inputs in digital circuit testing. Fig. A-2 shows how to wire a simple logic switch.

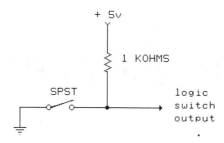

Fig. A-2 Logic switch circuit

Pushbutton

A pushbutton or momentary switch can be easily debounced, thereby making it suitable for use in digital circuits, using a simple NAND latch as shown in Fig. A-3.

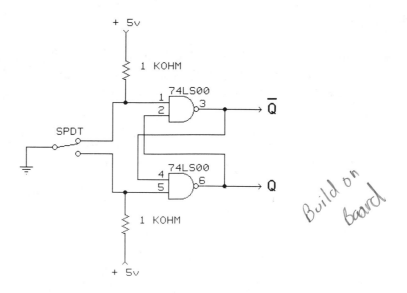

Fig. A-3 Debounced switch circuit

Clock

A 555 timer chip can be conveniently used to produce a TTL compatible square wave for clocking digital circuits. The frequency may be varied by changing the timing components R_A, R_B, and C. Fig. A-4 shows the clock circuit schematic and equations for determining the frequency and duty cycle of the output waveform.

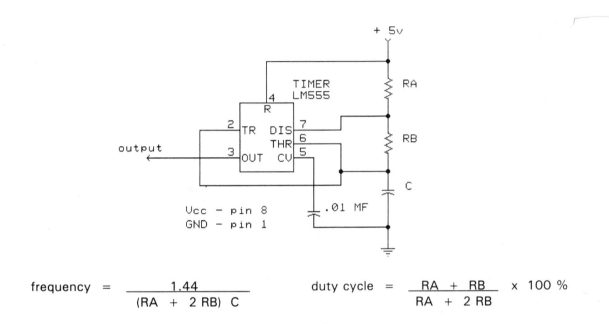

$$\text{frequency} = \frac{1.44}{(RA + 2\,RB)\,C} \qquad \text{duty cycle} = \frac{RA + RB}{RA + 2\,RB} \times 100\,\%$$

Fig. A-4 Clock circuit using a 555 timer

PLD DESIGN VERIFICATION USING CSIM

CSIM is a program from Logical Devices that can be used with the PLD compiler, CUPL. There are two principal applications for CSIM. It can be used to perform a functional simulation on the logic of a PLD design to determine if the design has been defined correctly. It can also be used to create test vectors that can be downloaded to many PLD programmers to perform a functional test on the actual PLD device after it has been programmed with the design.

An input file (filename.SI) that contains the desired test specifications is created using a text editor. This file contains a sequential list of test vectors that includes the input pin stimuli and the expected output pin results. For logic simulation of the design, these test vectors are compared with the actual results as determined by the logic definition given in the CUPL source file. The calculated output values for the design are contained in a file called an absolute file (filename.ABS). The absolute file must be created before you can run CSIM for the design. The absolute file is generated by CUPL when the design is compiled. This is accomplished by specifying the Absolute file option flag for the compiler operation.

Two output files can be generated by CSIM: a simulation output listing file (filename.SO) and an extension to the JEDEC programming file (filename.JED), which contains the test vectors to test the programmed device. The simulation output listing file contains the results of the simulation. The test vectors are numbered and the inputs and outputs are listed in a tabular form in the order specified by the CSIM input file. Any output tests that failed in the simulation are flagged and the actual output value for the design is listed. Each output that fails is marked and the user-expected result is listed along with an appropriate error message.

After the PLD design has been compiled (with the Absolute option) and if the simulation input file has already been created, you can choose to "Simulate the CUPL file" from the MCUPL menu. You will then be asked to select the file and press ENTER. The CSIM option flags will be listed for your selection. These options include generating the simulation output listing file <L> and appending the test vectors onto the JEDEC download file <J>. Additional options may also be selected, such as translating the tabular functional simulation output results into a waveform format <W> that can be viewed on the computer screen or to display automatically the tabular simulation results on the computer screen after the simulation is complete <V>. After selecting the desired options, press F5. The MCUPL menu also allows the user to view the simulation output results at any time.

```
                    Test Vector Values
     Input
    Values              Description
      0         drive input low
      1         drive input high
      X         input high or low
      C         drive clock input  (low-high-low)
      K         drive clock input  (high-low-high)
      P         preload internal registers

    Output
    Values              Description
      L         test output for low
      H         test output for high
      X         output high or low
      Z         test output for high impedance
      N         output not tested
      *         simulator determines output value
```

Table B-1 Test vector values in CSIM

The CSIM test specification file (filename.SI) normally contains the same header information as the CUPL logic description file (filename.PLD). If any header information is different, a warning message will suggest that the status of the logic equations could be inconsistent with the current test vectors in the test specification file. The easiest way to create the test specification file is to copy the logic description file to the "filename.SI" file and then delete everything except the header information from the test specification file. Comments (/* · · · */) may be placed anywhere within the test specification file. The CSIM keyword **ORDER** is used to list the variables to be used in the simulation table and to define how you wish them to be displayed. In the order statement, a colon is placed after the word ORDER, then each input/output variable (separated by commas) is listed, and the list is terminated by a semicolon. Column spaces can be inserted in the simulation table with the order statement by using the percent symbol (%) followed by the number of (decimal) spaces desired. The test vector table is prefixed by the CSIM keyword **VECTORS**, which is followed by a colon. Each sequential test vector must be specified on a single line. The possible input and output values for each test vector are shown in Table B-1.

Example B-1

Create a test specification file and simulate the design in example 7-2.

The simulation input file is shown in Fig. B-1. The desired order for the inputs and outputs is specified in the ORDER statement. Two blank spaces are specified between the last input bit (I0) and the first output bit (N7). Also a single blank space is specified between the upper 4 bits and the lower 4 bits of the output. The spacing was done to improve the readability of the vector table. The VECTORS statement is followed by three lines of documentation messages for the simulator output file. **$msg** is called a simulator directive. All simulator directives begin with a "$". The desired text string in the message is placed in double quotes and the directive ends with a semicolon. There are <u>exactly 6 leading spaces</u> in the message string because the simulator output file (see Fig. B-2) numbers each of the vector lines (4-digit number + colon + space = 6 character spaces). The vector table lists the input values and the expected output results. The results of this simulation are shown in Fig. B-2. No errors were detected in the simulation (since there were no error messages).

```
Name        SQUARE;
Partno      L105-2;
Date        02/04/91;
Revision    03;
Designer    Greg Moss;
Company     Digi-Lab, Inc.;
Assembly    SQUARE NUMBER GENERATOR;
Location    U210;
Device      G16V8A;
Format      j;
/**********************************************/
/* Simulation of design example 7-2           */
/* Generates the square of an input value      */
/**********************************************/

ORDER:    I3,I2,I1,I0,%2,N7,N6,N5,N4,%1,N3,N2,N1,N0;

VECTORS:

$msg"        IIII  NNNN NNNN";
$msg"        3210  7654 3210";
$msg"";
             0000  LLLL LLLL
             0001  LLLL LLLH
             0010  LLLL LHLL
             0011  LLLL HLLH
             0100  LLLH LLLL
             0101  LLLH HLLH
             0110  LLHL LHLL
             0111  LLHH LLLH
             1000  LHLL LLLL
             1001  LHLH LLLH
             1010  LHHL LHLL
             1011  LHHH HLLH
             1100  HLLH LLLL
             1101  HLHL HLLH
             1110  HHLL LHLL
             1111  HHHL LLLH
```

Fig. B-1 Computer listing of SQUARE.SI for example B-1

```
CSIM: CUPLPLD Simulation Program
Version 4.2a Serial# SK-59999991
Copyright (c) 1983, 1991 Logical Devices, Inc.
CREATED Mon Mar 07 14:14:44 1994

LISTING FOR SIMULATION FILE: A:\SQUARE.si

    1: Name          SQUARE;
    2: Partno        L105-2;
    3: Date          02/04/91;
    4: Revision      03;
    5: Designer      Greg Moss;
    6: Company       Digi-Lab, Inc.;
    7: Assembly      SQUARE NUMBER GENERATOR;
    8: Location      U210;
    9: Device        G16V8A;
   10: Format        j;
   11:
   12: /*********************************************/
   13: /* Simulation of design example 7-2          */
   14: /* Generates the square of an input value    */
   15: /*********************************************/
   16:
   17: ORDER:    I3,I2,I1,I0,%2,N7,N6,N5,N4,%1,N3,N2,N1,N0;
   18:
===============================================================
                    Simulation Results
===============================================================
      IIII  NNNN NNNN
      3210  7654 3210

0001: 0000  LLLL LLLL
0002: 0001  LLLL LLLH
0003: 0010  LLLL LHLL
0004: 0011  LLLL HLLH
0005: 0100  LLLH LLLL
0006: 0101  LLLH HLLH
0007: 0110  LLHL LHLL
0008: 0111  LLHH LLLH
0009: 1000  LHLL LLLL
0010: 1001  LHLH LLLH
0011: 1010  LHHL LHLL
0012: 1011  LHHH HLLH
0013: 1100  HLLH LLLL
0014: 1101  HLHL HLLH
0015: 1110  HHLL LHLL
0016: 1111  HHHL LLLH
```

Fig. B-2 Computer listing of SQUARE.SO for example B-1

Example B-2

Modify the alternate design for example 7-1 (see Fig. 7-6) so that the effect of errors in logic equations may be investigated. The same logic functions are desired but the

equations are incorrectly defined. Determine the effect on the simulation results.
Change the equations for GT9 and LT4 to the following:

$$\text{GT9 = INPUTS:[9..F];}$$
$$\text{LT4 = INPUTS:[0,1,2,3,4];}$$

```
Name       LAB-ERR;
Partno     L105-1;
Date       03/08/94;
Revision   01;
Designer   Greg Moss;
Company    Digi-Lab, Inc.;
Assembly   Example Board;
Location   U101;
Device     G16V8A;
Format     j;

   /**********************************************/
   /*   ERROR in circuit design for example 7-1   */
   /**********************************************/

ORDER:  D,C,B,A,%3,GT9,%1,!LT4,%1,RNG,%1,!TEN;

VECTORS:

$msg"                   !    !";
$msg"               G  L  R  T";
$msg"               T  T  N  E";
$msg"      DCBA     9  4  G  N";
$msg"";
          0000     L  L  L  H
          0001     L  L  L  H
          0010     L  L  L  H
          0011     L  L  L  H
          0100     L  H  L  H
          0101     L  H  L  H
          0110     L  H  L  H
          0111     L  H  H  H
          1000     L  H  H  H
          1001     L  H  H  H
          1010     H  H  H  L
          1011     H  H  L  H
          1100     H  H  L  H
          1101     H  H  L  H
          1110     H  H  L  H
          1111     H  H  L  H
```

Fig. B-3 Computer listing of simulation input file for example B-2

The correct simulation input file is shown in Fig. B-3. Simulating the design with the errors in the logic equations produced the results shown in Fig. B-4.

```
CSIM: CUPLPLD Simulation Program
Version 4.2a Serial# SK-59999991
Copyright (c) 1983, 1991 Logical Devices, Inc.
CREATED Tue Mar 08 10:32:09 1994

LISTING FOR SIMULATION FILE: A:\LAB-ERR.si

    1: Name        LAB-ERR;
    2: Partno      L105-1;
    3: Date        03/08/94;
    4: Revision    01;
    5: Designer    Greg Moss;
    6: Company     Digi-Lab, Inc.;
    7: Assembly    Example Board;
    8: Location    U101;
    9: Device      G16V8A;
   10: Format      j;
   11:
   12:    /**********************************************/
   13:    /*    ERROR in circuit design for example 7-1   */
   14:    /**********************************************/
   15:
   16: ORDER:  D,C,B,A,%3,GT9,%1,!LT4,%1,RNG,%1,!TEN;
   17:


===============================================================
                    Simulation Results
===============================================================
                   !   !
                 G L R T
                 T T N E
       DCBA      9 4 G N

0001: 0000      L L L H
0002: 0001      L L L H
0003: 0010      L L L H
0004: 0011      L L L H
0005: 0100      L L L H
                  ^

[0019sa] user expected (H) for LT4

0006: 0101      L H L H
0007: 0110      L H L H
0008: 0111      L H H H
0009: 1000      L H H H
0010: 1001      H H H H
                ^

[0019sa] user expected (L) for GT9

0011: 1010      H H H L
0012: 1011      H H L H
0013: 1100      H H L H
0014: 1101      H H L H
0015: 1110      H H L H
0016: 1111      H H L H
```

Fig. B-4 Computer listing of simulation output file for example B-2

Example B-3

Create a test specification file and simulate the design in example 14-5.

The simulation input file is shown in Fig. B-5. The test vectors for this simulation were arbitrarily chosen, but an attempt was made to test all functions of this circuit design. List notation was used for appropriate variables in the ORDER statement. Each test vector is commented to assist in interpretation of the simulation. The input variable "C" was used to provide a positive pulse to clock the sequential PLD circuit. The input value "X" was used several times when the input logic did not matter in the test vector. The CSIM directive "$repeat" causes the vector immediately following to be repeated a specified (in decimal) number of times. The output test values during the repeat directive are not specified (an asterisk causes CSIM to supply the output test value) since they will be different values as the counter is clocked repeatedly. The resultant simulation output file is shown in Fig. B-6.

```
Name       LOADCNTR;           Partno    L155-17E;
Date       07/20/93;           Revision  01;
Designer   G. Moss;            Company   Digi-Lab;
Assembly   Controller;         Location  U922;
Device     G16V8A;             Format    j;

/*****************************************************/
/*  Mod-16 binary up/down counter with parallel load    */
/*****************************************************/

ORDER:  clk, %2, M2..0, %2, D3..0, %4, Q3..0;

VECTORS:
$msg"       c                   ";
$msg"       1   MMM   DDDD   QQQQ";
$msg"       k   210   3210   3210";
$msg"                          ";
            C   11X   XXXX   LLLL        /* reset counter */
            C   00X   XXXX   LLLL        /* hold count */
            0   XXX   XXXX   LLLL        /* no clock */
            C   100   XXXX   LLLH        /* count up */
            C   100   XXXX   LLHL        /* count up */
            C   100   XXXX   LLHH        /* count up */
            C   100   XXXX   LHLL        /* count up */
$repeat 4;
            C   100   XXXX   ****        /* count up 4 cycles */
            0   100   XXXX   HLLL        /* no clock */
            C   100   XXXX   HLLH        /* count up */
            C   000   XXXX   HLLH        /* hold count */
            C   100   XXXX   HLHL        /* disable output */
            C   001   XXXX   HLHL        /* hold count */
$repeat 4;
            C   100   XXXX   ****        /* count up 4 cycles */
            C   00X   XXXX   HHHL        /* hold count */
            C   100   XXXX   HHHH        /* count up */
            C   100   XXXX   LLLL        /* count up - recycled */
            C   101   XXXX   HHHH        /* count down */
            C   101   XXXX   HHHL        /* count down */
```

```
$repeat 8;
        C   101   XXXX    ****        /* count down 8 cycles */
        0   101   XXXX    LHHL        /* no clock */
        C   000   XXXX    LHHL        /* hold count */
        C   010   1010    HLHL        /* load 1010 into counter */
        C   101   XXXX    HLLH        /* count down */
        C   100   XXXX    HLHL        /* count up */
$repeat 16;
        C   100   XXXX    ****        /* count up 16 cycles */
        C   00X   XXXX    HLHL        /* hold count */
        C   011   0101    LHLH        /* load 0101 into counter */
        C   01X   0000    LLLL        /* load 0000 into counter */
$repeat 10;
        C   100   0000    ****        /* count up 10 cycles */
$repeat 12;
        C   101   0000    ****        /* count down 12 cycles */
        0   101   0000    HHHL        /* no clock */
        0   01X   1111    HHHL        /* no clock */
        0   11X   1111    HHHL        /* no clock */
        C   11X   1111    LLLL        /* reset counter */
$repeat 16;
        C   101   XXXX    ****        /* count down 16 cycles */
        C   101   XXXX    HHHH        /* count down */
```

Fig. B-5 Computer listing of simulation input file for example B-3

```
CSIM: CUPLPLD Simulation Program
Version 4.2a Serial# SK-59999991
Copyright (c) 1983, 1991 Logical Devices, Inc.
CREATED Thu Mar 10 12:20:11 1994

LISTING FOR SIMULATION FILE: A:\LOADCNTR.si

  1: Name       LOADCNTR;           Partno    L155-17E;
  2: Date       07/20/93;           Revision  01;
  3: Designer   G. Moss;            Company   Digi-Lab;
  4: Assembly   Controller;         Location  U922;
  5: Device     G16V8A;             Format    j;
  6:
  7: /*****************************************************/
  8: /*  Mod-16 binary up/down counter with parallel load  */
  9: /*****************************************************/
 10:
 11: ORDER:  clk,  %2, M2..0, %2, D3..0, %4, Q3..0;
 12:


=====================================================================
                      Simulation Results
=====================================================================
       c
       l  MMM  DDDD    QQQQ
       k  210  3210    3210

0001:  C   11X  XXXX    LLLL
0002:  C   00X  XXXX    LLLL
0003:  0   XXX  XXXX    LLLL
0004:  C   100  XXXX    LLLH
0005:  C   100  XXXX    LLHL
0006:  C   100  XXXX    LLHH
0007:  C   100  XXXX    LHLL
0008:  C   100  XXXX    LHLH
0009:  C   100  XXXX    LHHL
0010:  C   100  XXXX    LHHH
0011:  C   100  XXXX    HLLL
0012:  0   100  XXXX    HLLL
0013:  C   100  XXXX    HLLH
0014:  C   000  XXXX    HLLH
0015:  C   100  XXXX    HLHL
0016:  C   001  XXXX    HLHL
0017:  C   100  XXXX    HLHH
0018:  C   100  XXXX    HHLL
0019:  C   100  XXXX    HHLH
0020:  C   100  XXXX    HHHL
0021:  C   00X  XXXX    HHHL
0022:  C   100  XXXX    HHHH
0023:  C   100  XXXX    LLLL
0024:  C   101  XXXX    HHHH
0025:  C   101  XXXX    HHHL
0026:  C   101  XXXX    HHLH
0027:  C   101  XXXX    HHLL
0028:  C   101  XXXX    HLHH
0029:  C   101  XXXX    HLHL
0030:  C   101  XXXX    HLLH
0031:  C   101  XXXX    HLLL
```

```
0032:  C   101   XXXX   LHHH
0033:  C   101   XXXX   LHHL
0034:  0   101   XXXX   LHHL
0035:  C   000   XXXX   LHHL
0036:  C   010   1010   HLHL
0037:  C   101   XXXX   HLLH
0038:  C   100   XXXX   HLHL
0039:  C   100   XXXX   HLHH
0040:  C   100   XXXX   HHLL
0041:  C   100   XXXX   HHLH
0042:  C   100   XXXX   HHHL
0043:  C   100   XXXX   HHHH
0044:  C   100   XXXX   LLLL
0045:  C   100   XXXX   LLLH
0046:  C   100   XXXX   LLHL
0047:  C   100   XXXX   LLHH
0048:  C   100   XXXX   LHLL
0049:  C   100   XXXX   LHLH
0050:  C   100   XXXX   LHHL
0051:  C   100   XXXX   LHHH
0052:  C   100   XXXX   HLLL
0053:  C   100   XXXX   HLLH
0054:  C   100   XXXX   HLHL
0055:  C   00X   XXXX   HLHL
0056:  C   011   0101   LHLH
0057:  C   01X   0000   LLLL
0058:  C   100   0000   LLLH
0059:  C   100   0000   LLHL
0060:  C   100   0000   LLHH
0061:  C   100   0000   LHLL
0062:  C   100   0000   LHLH
0063:  C   100   0000   LHHL
0064:  C   100   0000   LHHH
0065:  C   100   0000   HLLL
0066:  C   100   0000   HLLH
0067:  C   100   0000   HLHL
0068:  C   101   0000   HLLH
0069:  C   101   0000   HLLL
0070:  C   101   0000   LHHH
0071:  C   101   0000   LHHL
0072:  C   101   0000   LHLH
0073:  C   101   0000   LHLL
0074:  C   101   0000   LLHH
0075:  C   101   0000   LLHL
0076:  C   101   0000   LLLH
0077:  C   101   0000   LLLL
0078:  C   101   0000   HHHH
0079:  C   101   0000   HHHL
0080:  0   101   0000   HHHL
0081:  0   01X   1111   HHHL
0082:  0   11X   1111   HHHL
0083:  C   11X   1111   LLLL
0084:  C   101   XXXX   HHHH
0085:  C   101   XXXX   HHHL
0086:  C   101   XXXX   HHLH
0087:  C   101   XXXX   HHLL
0088:  C   101   XXXX   HLHH
0089:  C   101   XXXX   HLHL
```

```
0090: C  101  XXXX    HLLH
0091: C  101  XXXX    HLLL
0092: C  101  XXXX    LHHH
0093: C  101  XXXX    LHHL
0094: C  101  XXXX    LHLH
0095: C  101  XXXX    LHLL
0096: C  101  XXXX    LLHH
0097: C  101  XXXX    LLHL
0098: C  101  XXXX    LLLH
0099: C  101  XXXX    LLLL
0100: C  101  XXXX    HHHH
```

Fig. B-6 Computer listing of simulation output file for example B-3